VOLUME I

SMITHSONIAN
TREASURY
OF SCIENCE

Edited by Webster P. True

FORMERLY CHIEF OF THE EDITORIAL

AND PUBLICATIONS DIVISION,

SMITHSONIAN INSTITUTION

PUBLISHED BY SIMON AND SCHUSTER, INC., NEW YORK,

IN CO-OPERATION WITH

THE SMITHSONIAN INSTITUTION, WASHINGTON, D. C.

LIBRARY OF CONGRESS CATALOG CARD NUMBER: 60-12579
MANUFACTURED IN THE UNITED STATES OF AMERICA
BY RAND McNALLY COMPANY, CONKEY DIVISION
CHICAGO, ILLINOIS

ACKNOWLEDGMENTS

Grateful acknowledgment is expressed to the original publishers for permission to use the articles listed below:

"The Structure of the Universe," by Claude W. Heaps. From the *Rice Institute Pamphlet*. Reprinted by permission of the Rice Institute.

"The Time Scale of Our Universe," by E. J. Öpik. From the *Irish Astronomical Journal*.

"The Origin of the Earth," by Thornton Page. From *Physics Today*.

"The Development of Radio Astronomy," by Gerald S. Hawkins. From the *American Scientist*. Copyright by the Society of the Sigma Xi.

"The Mystery of Mars," by H. P. Wilkins. From the book *Mysteries of Time and Space*, published by Frederick Muller Ltd., London.

"Meteors," by Fred L. Whipple. From *Publications of the Astronomical Society of the Pacific*. Published by permission of the Society.

"The Scientific Importance of X-rays," by L. Henry Garland. From *Electrical Engineering*.

"The Story of Cosmic Rays," by W. F. G. Swann. From *Sky and Telescope*. Published by permission of Sky Publishing Corporation, Harvard College Observatory, Cambridge, Mass.

"Nuclear Fission," by Karl K. Darrow. From *Science*.

"Isaac Newton," by Albert Einstein. From the *Manchester Guardian* (England). Copyright by the *Manchester Guardian* in the U.S.A.

"Wireless Telegraphy," by G. Marconi. From *Proceedings of the Royal Institution of Great Britain*.

"Physical Science in the Crime-Detection Laboratory," by J. Edgar Hoover. From the *Review of Scientific Instruments*.

"The Abundance of the Chemical Elements," by Hans E. Suess. From *Foote Prints*, published by Foote Mineral Company, Philadelphia, Pa.

"Earthquakes in North America," by B. Gutenberg. From *Science*.

"The Biography of an Ancient American Lake," by Wilmot H. Bradley. From the *Scientific Monthly*.

"The Mystery of Life," by F. G. Donnan. From an evening discourse before the British Association for the Advancement of Science. Published by permission of the Association.

"The Mechanism of Organic Evolution," by Charles B. Davenport. From the *Journal of the Washington Academy of Sciences*.

"Enzymes: Machine Tools of the Cellular Factory," by B. A. Kilby. From *Discovery*, London.

"The Vampire Bat," by Raymond L. Ditmars and Arthur M. Greenhall. From *Zoologica*.

"The Coelacanth Fishes," by Errol White. From *Discovery*, London.

"The Electron Microscope in Biology," by Ralph W. G. Wyckoff. From *Nature,* London.

"The Nature of Viruses, Cancer, Genes, and Life— A Declaration of Dependence," by Wendell M. Stanley. From *Proceedings of the American Philosophical Society.*

"Easter Island," by Alfred Métraux. From *The Yale Review.* Copyright Yale University Press.

"The Wright Brothers as Aeronautical Engineers," by M. P. Baker. Published by permission of the Society of Automotive Engineers.

"Fifty Years of Flying Progress," by Grover Loening. From the *Journal of the Franklin Institute.*

"At the North Pole," by Lincoln Ellsworth. From *The Yale Review.* Copyright Yale University Press.

"The First Crossing of Antarctica," by Lincoln Ellsworth. From the *Geographical Journal,* London. Published by permission of the Royal Geographical Society.

"The Discovery of the Future," by H. G. Wells. From *Nature,* London.

TABLE OF CONTENTS

VOLUME **II**

VOLUME III

PREFACE

THE SMITHSONIAN INSTITUTION has been in existence for more than a century— years that have witnessed the greatest advance of all time in science. This is particularly true of America, where up to the middle of the last century science had been very poorly supported. It was then that the Smithsonian came into being through the bequest of James Smithson, an English scientist, who left his entire fortune to the United States to found an establishment "for the increase and diffusion of knowledge among men." This event in itself focused public attention on science, but even more importantly it made available through the aid and encouragement that the Smithsonian could give the means and incentives for other organizations and individuals to expand their scientific work. The founding of the Smithsonian indeed marked the beginning of a new era in American science, and the Institution can justly feel pride in the part it played in this new growth.

Today the Smithsonian has grown into a complex organization known and respected throughout the world. Besides a number of scientific bureaus, it operates three distinct museums, three art galleries, and one of the most popular zoological parks in the world.

A potent means of fulfilling its program for the "diffusion of knowledge" has always been its series of scientific publications, for the most part technical in character, but also to a limited extent directed toward the general public. From the first, it has been the Smithsonian's policy to distribute these publications to libraries, scientific organizations, and specialists. This compendium of Smithsonian Report articles is published in co-operation with Simon and Schuster, Inc., for the purpose of making some of the outstanding Report articles in many branches of science available to a wider audience.

The introduction which follows will explain that the Smithsonian Reports have for more than a century aimed at a wide dissemination of the progress of science, and that this present Smithsonian *Treasury of Science* is intended to further the same purpose. It will also show the plan of the volumes and point out how the sciences overlap today to an extent that makes it difficult at times to distinguish the chemist from the physiologist, or the botanist from the anthropologist. It is our hope that readers may derive profit and pleasure from this body of authentic writings that underline the importance to mankind of the specialized world of science.

LEONARD CARMICHAEL
Secretary, Smithsonian Institution

INTRODUCTION

FROM ITS ESTABLISHMENT in 1846 the Smithsonian Institution has each year published an Annual Report covering the affairs of the year, and enriched from the beginning by the addition of selected articles by recognized authorities to highlight the status of the several branches of scientific study. Many of the articles are written specially for the Smithsonian Report; others are selected by the chief of the editorial and publications division, with the assistance of the scientific staff, from the hundreds of scientific journals published in this country and abroad. While in no sense a formal annual summary of science progress, the Report nevertheless provides each year an anthology of many of the important happenings in the world of science, for the general reader.

For this Smithsonian Institution Treasury of Science, the editor has scanned the entire series of Smithsonian Reports from 1846 to 1958 and has selected from some three thousand articles fifty which, in his opinion, will symbolize in a general way the development and present state of many branches of science. In this number of articles it is of course impossible to cover all science. Furthermore, many specialized types of research are so highly technical in character that it would be very difficult to present them to the layman. The aim has been, rather, to strike a rough balance between the so-called physical sciences and the natural sciences. In the first group we include astronomy, physics, and chemistry; in the second, geology, biology, and anthropology.

Under these very broad headings the articles themselves will be seen to reach out into the vastness of the cosmos in the attempt to understand the make-up and duration in time of our universe. Next they dip into the mysteries of matter itself, reaching down farther and farther into the basic components of the atoms themselves, which seem in some ways to repeat the pattern of our solar system with its spinning satellite planets. Passing through the strange world *of radioactivity and other forms of radiation, the articles then emerge into the more familiar atmosphere of our own particular planet, earth. On this scene experts in geology and related sciences write of earth happenings some of which are fairly well understood, others admittedly still in the realm of mystery.*

On the surface of our planet is found the phenomenon we know as life. Its infinitely varied manifestations include, among many others, mammals, fishes, mollusks, insects, and plants, all of which come under consideration in the selected Report articles. Also under the heading of biology in its broadest sense come discussions of the nature of life itself; how new forms have evolved, flourished, and disappeared; and how new optical inventions now enable man to see the cells of which his own body is composed and even watch them divide before his very eyes.

At the apex of all life forms stands man, set apart from all the rest by many special human qualities. For the study of this present ruler of the earth, anthropologists take us far back into the mists of long past ages to see man's clumsy progenitors contriving with only bone and stone tools and perhaps without spoken language. Of much later date, but still long before recorded history, we will read of cities forgotten and buried thousands of years before the birth of Christ, yet well advanced on the road toward civilization. Lastly, we will look at some of the achievements of modern man, in the form of engineering feats and the exploration of little-known regions of the earth.

No set division into fixed compartments will be found in these volumes, although the articles falling under the broad classifications mentioned are more or less grouped together. Actually the classical subdivisions of science have been more and more closely interwoven until it has become increasingly difficult to determine where one ends and another begins. Thus we have astrophysics, geophysics, biochemistry, ethnobotany, and many other blended branches of study, showing clearly that all science is interrelated and all has the same basic purpose— to learn the truth about all creation, from the simplest form of living thing to the great drama of the universe itself.

The older articles are presented with the more recent for their great historical interest. Some of them record the actual break-

through into knowledge of entirely new phenomena on which much of our present marvelous development has been based. In this category of historically valuable articles fall Roentgen's account of the discovery of X-rays and of his subsequent experiments on them. Curie writes of the isolation of radium as an element by himself and Madame Curie. Marconi gives in his own words the story of the very first uses of wireless telegraphy, including the first instances of the saving of lives at sea through the new means of instantaneous communication. Eugène Dubois' article on the Java "ape-man," Pithecanthropus erectus, aroused a world-wide controversy as the time of its discovery more than half a century ago. Samuel P. Langley, a former Secretary of the Smithsonian Institution, pictures the struggles and disappointments involved in his efforts to build a model "flying machine" that would fly.

In several of the branches of science under discussion, certain articles form natural pairs or, in one instance, a group of three. Thus, the first two articles, on "The Structure of the Universe" and "The Time Scale of Our Universe," obviously complement each other. Roentgen's pioneering account of "The X-rays" is followed by a résumé of present-day X-ray uses as presented by a leading radiologist, Dr. L. H. Garland, in "The Scientific Importance of X-rays." Ralph W. G. Wyckoff's account of "The Electron Microscope in Biology" is appropriately followed by a stimulating discussion of viruses— first observed directly through the use of the electron microscope— and their relation to cancer, genes, and life itself. The author, Wendell M. Stanley, is a leader in American virus research.

In the field of anthropology, Dubois' article on the primitive man-like skull of Pithecanthropus erectus *is supplemented by Raymond A. Dart's account of the more recently discovered South African man-apes, now generally accepted as very early progenitors of mankind. In aeronautics, a group of three related articles include Langley's "Story of Experiments in Mechanical Flight," written in 1897, M. P. Baker's illuminating description of "The Wright Brothers as Aeronautical Engineers," and, as a sequel, Grover Loening's study in retrospect of "Fifty Years of Flying Progress."*

For the more recent articles, authors have been asked to make such minor revisions as seemed desirable to indicate current changes in thought. Where this has been done, the fact is indicated in a footnote on the first page of the article. In the case of authors no longer living, it will be understood that had the opportunity been available, they would doubtless likewise have wished to do some revising. Most of the articles presented under such circumstances, however, have been chosen for their more or less timeless character, and lack of modernization does not detract from their value.

A number of the articles originally concluded with long lists of bibliographical references, chiefly to technical journals. In the belief that such lists would be of little usefulness to the average reader, they have here been omitted, and that fact is indicated in a footnote on the first page of the article to which it applies. Any reader desiring to pursue a particular subject further, however, will find these bibliographies in the appropriate Smithsonian Reports, which are available in nearly all large libraries.

Webster P. True

EDITOR

SMITHSONIAN
TREASURY
OF SCIENCE

VOLUME I

CLAUDE W. HEAPS

The Structure of the Universe

[FROM THE SMITHSONIAN REPORT FOR 1944]

FEW TOPICS *could envision as great a range of investigations as the subject of this article. Starting with the particles that compose atoms, far too small for the eye ever to see, such investigations must deal with objects of ever-increasing magnitude up to the super-galaxies — assemblages of galaxies like our own system of some hundred billion stars.*

The late Claude W. Heaps, formerly professor of physics at Rice Institute and associated with the Federal Office of Research and Development during World War II, pictures some of the immense difficulties inherent in the study of the infinitesimally small and of the inconceivably large. He also gives us a glimpse of the many intricate laws of nature that operate equally in the tiny world of the atom and in the grandeur of our solar system. Although admittedly opinions often differ among authorities on the various phases of the structure of the universe, nevertheless a misty picture is emerging that undoubtedly bears some resemblance to actuality, and year by year the focus becomes a little sharper.

In this field of endeavor, as in all other phases of the search for new knowledge, each problem solved opens up a whole series of new problems. Yet the astronomers and physicists are never dis-

1

couraged, for they see clearly that over the years and the centuries our understanding of the universe we live in has been advancing slowly but surely.

Had Dr. Heaps lived to see this later publication of his 1944 article, he would doubtless have wished to make minor revisions to cover recent findings. Nevertheless, the article is basically as sound today as when it was written.

It MAY SEEM, at first sight, presumptuous to attempt the discussion, in one hour or less, of such a comprehensive topic as the structure of the universe. Actually the subject is not as big as it sounds. There are, in one sense, as many universes as there are individuals; but the universe in this personal sense will be ruled out of the present discussion. A tremendous simplification is at once achieved when we limit our topic to the physical universe. We now inquire, what is the physical universe?

Eddington has defined it as the "theme of a specified body of knowledge, just as Mr. Pickwick might be defined as the hero of a specified novel." Such a definition emphasizes the epistemological point of view and therefore it suffers from lack of definiteness and simplicity. There is beautiful directness and decisiveness in the attitude of the mathematician who wrote an equation on one line in one of his published papers and said, "This equation contains everything we know about the physical universe." The conciseness of the language of mathematics is probably nowhere better exemplified than in this equation. On the other hand, the universe, if it can be described in terms of mathematical symbols and with one equation, may not seem like such a big subject after all.

To the physicist, matter, space, and time exist outside the human mind. The physical universe is an objective, dynamic arrangement of all matter, space, and time. In discussing the structure of the universe we merely attempt to describe some of the features of this arrangement.

Before beginning such a description it seems necessary to indicate just how it is related to human welfare — since the general title of this series of lectures is "Science and Human Welfare." I am venturing to interpret the phrase "human welfare" in the broadest possible sense. There are many types of scientific investigation which do not appear to have any direct bearing on the pleasures or pains of the human race. The discovery of the planet Pluto cannot be said to have done very much toward raising the sum total of human welfare, in the ordinary sense. But in the broadest sense, it may be said that the welfare of a nation is closely tied up with the capacity of that nation for untiring search after truth. Intellectual unrest, intellectual curiosity is, we like to think, essential to the true growth and development of a people. A dairy company advertises that its milk comes from contented cows. A rival company is perhaps more progressive in its views when it advertises that its cows are not contented — they are always trying to do better.

The thesis is, then, that the pursuit of pure knowledge is indicative of a healthy national mind; that full development of intellectual activity, whether it be in the matter of investigating the stars or in building a better radio, is essential to the true welfare of a nation. The Russians asked a captured Nazi why he came to their country. He replied, "I am just a little man, I do what the Führer says." A nation is facing tragedy when free speculation is discouraged, when science is devoted solely to control of men and machines and to the production of a workable mass of "little men."

To begin this discussion of matter, space, and time we will try first to systematize our ideas of space, or size, in relation to matter. Imagine a long, horizontal line drawn so as to represent the "x-axis." Let all objects in the universe be placed along this line in the order of their sizes. The smallest objects will be placed near the beginning of the line, at its left end. Larger and larger objects will be placed farther and farther to the right. We next divide the line

	MICROSCOPIC REGION					MACROSCOPIC REGION			
Zero size	Electron							Solar	Spiral
	Positron		Neutron		Stone	Mountain	Earth	system	nebula
	Neutrino	Mesotron	Proton	Atom					

ILLUS. 1

into two parts by a vertical line. All objects to the left of this vertical line are too small to be seen with the naked eye, so this region is called the *microscopic region*. In it are placed different kinds of particles such as molecules, atoms, the proton, the neutron, the mesotron, the electron, positron, and neutrino. These particles are placed nearer and nearer to the origin of the line as they become smaller and smaller. It is worth noting that nature seems not to have given us anything smaller than the electron, in spite of the fact that there is plenty of room for particles between the electron and the origin of the line.

To the right of the vertical dividing line we place all objects large enough to be seen with the naked eye. This region is called the *macroscopic region*. We might put in here, stones, mountain, earth, solar system, spiral nebulae. The farther end of the macroscopic region may be given a special subtitle, the *astronomical region*.

We have arranged here various matter elements in a certain spatial relationship. The time concept is involved because this is an arrangement which may be correct only at one instant of time. It is possible that the position of some of these entities on the line is constantly changing. When an electron gets into rapid motion its mass is changed a little and it shortens one of its dimensions. It thus shifts its position on the line slightly to the left whenever it has a high velocity. The solar system may be slowly running down so that the planets gradually approach the sun. If this is the case the position of the solar system on the line is slowly shifting to the left.

Certain segments of this line have occupied the attention of various specialists. Astronomers deal with everything listed to the right of earth. Thousands of specialists work on the section from earth to atom. Physicists in recent years have concentrated intensively on the segment from atom to zero. The discovery of the positron, the neutron, and the mesotron within the last decade, has opened up a most fruitful field of research in physics. In this region, forever beyond the reach of the human eye, is probably contained most of the mystery of the entire universe. As K. K. Darrow has expressed it, "This field is unique in modern physics for the minuteness of the phenomena, the delicacy of the observations, the adventurous excursions of the observers, the subtlety of the analysis, and the grandeur of the inferences."

It is not too much to say that if some American physicist could only make the right kind of discovery in this domain our entire oil and coal industries would become more or less obsolete and World War II would be won in a matter of days. It should also be said that such a discovery is possible but not probable.*

Returning now to our linear lay-out for the universe we may note that everything to the right of proton is constructed out of the material included in the range from proton to zero. All matter in the universe exists in the form of bunches or aggregates of smaller parts. Protons, neutrons, electrons bunch to form atoms; atoms group into molecules; molecules group into stones and mountains; stones and mountains form the earth. In the astronomical field, planets group about the sun to form the solar system — a solar system which in the astronomical field is remarkably like the atom in the microscopic field.

The important unit of structure in the astronomical field is a sun. Practically all the stars which we can see on a clear night are distant suns, much like our own, although it is thought that only an extremely small fraction of these suns have planets around them like our own.

All these suns which can be recognized distinctly are grouped in a sort of flattened, disklike bunch which is whirling in empty space. Our own sun and planetary system is a member of this group, being located about 30,000 light-years† distant from the center, or hub, of this gigantic disk. When we look into space along the plane of the disk the stars seem to be distributed very densely. We see the milky way. This bunch of suns is called a spiral nebula. It is sometimes called a galaxy, or an island universe. The word "universe" in this sense has a restricted meaning because our island universe is not the only one in existence. There are millions of others distributed throughout space as far as our most powerful telescopes have been able to penetrate.

The nebulae are by no means recent discoveries. Sir William Herschel, 150 years ago, suspected that they were distant groups of stars. The philosopher Kant believed that they were "systems of

---

* This article was written just before the first atomic bomb was perfected. — ED.

† A light-year is the distance which light travels in one year. It is approximately 6,000,000,000,000 miles.

many stars, whose distance presents them in such a narrow space that the light which is individually imperceptible from each of them, reaches us, on account of their immense multitude, in a uniform pale glimmer." They have been described as looking like candlelight seen through horn." A rough diagram, not drawn to scale, is given in Illustration 2 to indicate the total extent of the entire universe which has been observed, up to the present (1944), with our most powerful telescopes.

We might now indicate on the linear lay-out Illustration 1 the approximate size of the largest bunch of matter, the spiral nebula, as 100,000 light-years. Also we might speculate as to the possibility of nebulae themselves forming still larger groups. Extensive surveys have been made by the astronomers at Harvard and Mount Wilson, of the distribution in space of the nebulae, and there is, indeed, evidence of grouping of nebulae. It is legitimate to add another bunch of matter to the line lay-out — the supernebula, or supergalaxy.

The supergalaxy is the largest known aggregation of matter in the universe. Its diameter may be of the order of a million light-years. At least that is the estimate made by Harlow Shapley of the diameter of the group of nebulae in which our own is located. Our local group contains perhaps 15 or 20 nebulae, but in some supergalaxies there are hundreds of members.

So far, then, our picture of the universe reveals a granular, or atomic structure. We start near the zero point of size, with a particle of definite size. A fundamental law of attraction operates to cause the small particles to group together to form larger particles, these larger particles again group to form still larger particles, and so on until we reach the limit of observation, the enormous supergalaxy. We are unable to put a stop at the right-hand end of our line, as we have done at the left end. Space may go on into infinity — possibly matter may go on bunching up into larger and larger aggregates with no limit as to the ultimate size of any final bunch, because there may never be any final bunch. Speculations of this kind may be interesting but they are not of much significance otherwise, because they take us outside the realm of possible human experience.

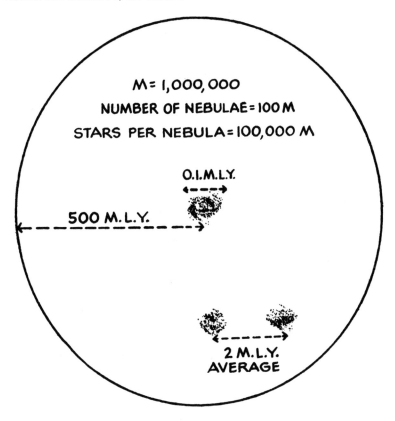

ILLUS. 2—*Sphere of view of the 100-inch telescope. Distances are in light-years, L. Y., and the diagram is not to scale. Our earth is about 30,000 L. Y. away from the center of the central nebula above.*

It seems probable that in detecting the supergalaxy man has reached the limits of observation in his probing of the depths of space. The new 200-inch telescope will be doing a fine job in helping to chart and analyze these enormous groups of matter.

The line diagram of the universe, limited at one end by the electron, at the other by the supergalaxy, has given a rather simple picture in terms of two variables, space and matter. The third variable, time, must now be considered. We have to consider the relationship between the various units of our structure as this relationship may change from time to time. Newton's Law of Universal Gravitation says that every particle of matter in the universe attracts every other particle. If forces of attraction cause matter to bunch up into aggregates of various sizes, why may not the various bunches themselves start coming together until eventually there results just one large, static bunch of matter floating quietly in an infinity of space? Such an end result seems logical, but it cannot happen until the kinetic energy of matter, the energy of motion, has been converted into radiation and transferred to infinity. Such a transfer of energy appears, in fact, to be going on.

A study of the motions of the various aggregates many be expected to throw some light on this question. We start with the smallest particles, electrons, for example. In addition to random motions caused by collisions with other particles, all electrons are supposed to spin. They may be thought of as being like tops which never run down. When an electron helps to form an atom, in addition to spinning it also revolves about the nucleus, just as the earth revolves about the sun. The aggregations of matter between atom and earth on the diagram of Illustration 1 may have various kinds of motion but when earth is reached we again have the spin about an axis and the revolution about the sun. Our sun, together with all the other suns in its group, forms a nebula which spins with high speed about a central axis. The spin velocity is very high, but the size of our nebula is so great that it takes about 2 million centuries for it to make one revolution. As Shapley puts it, this is the time required to "click off one cosmic year."

The motion of the supernebula is not known in accurate detail. It is possible that some sort of gigantic spin is present here also, but so far such a spin has not been detected. Instead, a very surprising sort of motion has been discovered, a motion which is just contrary to what we expect if matter is to agglomerate into one big bunch. The supernebulae appear to be receding from us. The supernebula to which our galaxy belongs maintains its fixed dimensions, and behaves more or less as a unit, but all the other supernebulae appear to be flying away from ours with high speeds. The farther away from us they are, the faster they seem to recede. There seems to be no good way of explaining such a phenomenon. One might assume that a primeval explosion started all matter out in all directions from an original concentration, but there are serious difficulties involved in such a theory.

The whole question of the expanding universe is definitely controversial. The consequences of accepting or rejecting the theory are so great that it will be worth while to review briefly the evidence.

Suppose the lights of a very distant city are observed at night through a telescope. The various spots of light all look much alike. However, they are not all the same in character. Some may be caused by incandescent lamps, some by neon signs, some, perhaps, may be due to the newer type of yellow sodium lamp used for illuminating highways.

We now put a glass prism in front of the telescope objective. The telescope must be deviated sideways, if we are to see the city through the prism and the telescope. When we do see it, each spot of light appears to be smeared out into a band of color. The colors present in each spot of light are separated and spread out and we can see just what colors are present in the light from each source. The neon signs are characterized by definite colors in the orange and red; the sodium lamps can be recognized by the fact that only one color, yellow, is visible.

If we were to photograph the lights of an enormous city from an enormous distance the whole city would appear as a small, luminous spot. The prism would smear out the separate lights of which the spot is composed, but they would all be superposed in a single smeared spot for the whole city. However, if there were a large number of sodium lamps one point in the smear would be brighter than the rest because there would be an excess of the yellow sodium light.

A nebula, consisting of millions of suns a long distance away, behaves like our hypothetical city except for one small difference. Light from a sun has *dark* absorption lines or bands from which color is missing as a result of absorption in the sun's atmosphere. There is a dark line in the spectrum of our own sun, corresponding to absorption of hydrogen in the sun's atmosphere. This dark line always appears at the same place in the spectrum no matter what kind of a source, and always means that hydrogen is present. Dark lines appear in the nearer nebulae about where they should be in the spectrum. For the more distant nebulae, however, they are shifted toward the red end of the spectrum.

There is only one known explanation for such a shift of a spectral line. If the source is moving away from an observer the light received appears redder than when the source is stationary. This phenomenon is called the Doppler effect. It is a matter of common experience in the field of sound. The pitch of an automobile horn is lowered as the horn passes rapidly by an observer and recedes from him.

The photographs of the nebulae show that the hydrogen absorption line is shifted farther and farther away from the normal position as the pictures go to more and more distant nebulae. The amount of the shift gives the velocity of recession. Many nebulae have been observed and the conclusion is reached that for every million light-years' distance from the earth the velocity of recession is increased by about 100 miles per second. The farthest nebulae observed are flying away from us with a speed of about 25,000 miles per second.

It is well to weigh critically the evidence for results like these. As regards estimates of nebular distances, the methods used by astronomers seem entirely adequate. In the nearest nebula individual stars can be seen. Some of these stars fluctuate in brightness with a period of 5⅓ days. Similar stars, known as Cepheid variables, are found in our own nebula, and the distances of a few of them have been determined by ordinary engineering methods. It is found that these stars are all of about the same size, so that if one Cepheid variable is much fainter than another its faintness may be attributed solely to its greater distance. The distance of the nearest nebula can thus be determined with considerable accuracy by comparing the brightness of one of its Cepheid variables with the brightness of a similar star in our own galaxy — a star whose distance has been measured by reliable methods. Having a good estimate of the distance of one nebula it is legitimate to infer that other nebulae of the same type are fainter and smaller only because they are farther away. It is thus possible to estimate their distances. The results of these estimates might give occasional large errors, but when a great number of observations are made the individual errors must average out fairly well.

As regards the shift of the absorption line toward the red, a good many attempts have been made to explain it in some other way than by the Doppler effect. So far, all these attempts have failed or encountered logical difficulties. During the last few years, however, certain evidence has accumulated which has brought about a paradoxical situation in the theory of the expanding universe. There are some very serious objections to the theory. First, let us suppose that our explosion hypothesis is more or less in accord with the facts. After all, if the nebulae are now observed to be scattering they must at some previous time have been more closely bunched. It is not difficult to calculate how long ago it was when the nebulae were all together and touching each other. We know how far away they are now, we know how fast they are receding, and how their velocity of recession varies with the distance from us. These data enable us to calculate the time when they must have started. According to Hubble, after all corrections have been made this starting time was about 1,000 million years ago. Unfortunately this is only a fraction of the age of the earth — indeed there is evidence that life actually existed on earth that long ago. It is difficult to see how our earth could exist in its present form at a time when all matter in the universe was assembled and ready for a cosmic blowout of such tremendous proportions.

So much for objection number one. The second objection arises as follows. When a source of light moves away from an observer there are two effects produced. The first, the Doppler effect, has been mentioned as a change of color, a reddening of the light. A second effect is a decrease of brightness, known as the "dimming factor." It is easy to see why a light should appear to be dimmer when the source moves away from the observer. Suppose a stationary machine gun is firing bullets at a fixed target at the rate of five per second. Then every second five bullets hit the target. However, if the gun is moving away from the target, still firing five shots a second, there will not be five bullets hitting every second. The bullet discharged from the gun at the end of a given second will have had to traverse a greater distance than the bullet which was fired at the beginning of the second, so it will take a longer time to reach the target. Perhaps only four bullets will hit the target in one second. The extra bullet has gone to fill the extra space in the bullet stream — the extra space created by the recession of the gun. The case of a light source is exactly analogous.

Now in estimating the distance of a nebula its brightness is taken as a criterion of the distance. The question arises as to whether the dimming factor should be applied when making the distance estimates. If the nebulae are actually moving away from us then the factor must certainly be applied. If the reddening of the light is not caused by a velocity of recession then the dimming factor must not be applied. With such tremendous speeds of recession this factor makes quite a big difference in results.

The following discussion is very largely taken from the annual Sigma Xi lecture delivered in December 1941 at Dallas by E. P. Hubble of the Mount Wilson Observatory. Dr. Hubble is one of the world's foremost authorities on the subject of nebulae.

Let us first suppose that the reddening of the light is *not* caused by a velocity of recession. It may be due to some hitherto undiscovered and unknown phenomenon. We can then estimate distances without any dimming factor and a survey can be made to find out how the nebulae are distributed throughout the region of space within our present range of view. Such surveys have been made at Mount Wilson and Mount Hamilton, out to a distance of 420 million light-years. Data have also been obtained and analyzed at Harvard, and the net result indicates a fairly uniform distribution of nebulae throughout the observable regions of space. There are, on the average, just as many per unit volume at great distances as in the immediate neighborhood of our own group.

This result is intellectually very satisfactory. In fact, it agrees with a fundamental principle of cosmological theory, a principle which has been postulated by theorists for no other reason than its appeal to our sense of order and the fitness of things. This principle states that the universe, on a grand scale, will appear much the same from whatever position in space it may be viewed or explored. This principle of cosmology is satisfied, therefore, if the nebulae are not assumed to be receding.

We next investigate the consequences of assuming the red shift to be due to a real velocity of recession of the nebulae. The dimming factor must now be applied in estimating distances, with the result that the most distant cluster is actually about 13 percent fainter than it would be if it were stationary. The scale of distances is thus altered, so that when we make our space survey to find out how the nebulae are distributed it turns out that they are no longer scattered uniformly. The number per unit volume increases steadily with their distance away from us. Here is a result which is intellectually very disquieting. The cosmological principle of no favored position is violated. We might be willing to accept this violation if it went the other way, that is, if the density of nebulae decreased with distance. Then we would conclude, very happily, that we had discovered another super-supergalaxy, another big matter bunch to put on the right-hand end of our linear lay-out. No such interpretation can be given when the nebulae are found not to thin out at big distances, but actually to become more dense in numbers.

It may seem obvious to the layman that we ought to discard the idea of an expanding universe. It makes us worry about the short time which has elapsed since the original cosmic explosion occurred; it bothers us with an increasing density of matter as we proceed farther and farther into the depths of space; and the only evidence we have to go on is a series of pictures, rather hazy, smeary pictures, in fact, with a light patch shifted too far to one side.

The physicist and the astronomer, unfortunately, cannot treat these fuzzy pictures in such a cavalier manner. There is no denying the existence of the shifted light patch in the pictures, hazy though it may be. There is no denying the fact that all such similar shifts of color have been explained satisfactorily by the Doppler effect and by the Doppler effect alone. One is reminded of the saying of the old colored man, whose years of experience had developed a certain ripe philosophy of life. "It ain't so much what you don't know that gets you into trouble, it's what you do know and ain't so!"

There are several ways, more or less unsatisfactory, of escaping from the dilemma of the expanding universe. The first way is not a good way, but like other escapist philosophies it must be considered and estimated for what it is worth. It involves spatial curvature.

The idea of curved space is now quite a familiar idea to most people. Eddington, Jeans, Einstein, and others have written books for popular consumption and the sales have been very gratifying. Even the pulp magazines do not hesitate to invoke the fourth dimension as a mode of escape for the hero or the villain. A simple way of approaching the concept of spatial curvature is as follows. Think of a straight line along one dimension. Given a second dimension at right angles to the first, then we have the possibility of curving the line into the second dimension. Think of a plane surface, like a sheet of paper flat on a desk. Given a third dimension, at right angles to the desk, we have the possibility of curving the paper sheet into this third dimension. Think of a solid filling three dimensions. Give a fourth dimension at right angles to the other three, we then have a possibility of curving the solid into the fourth dimension. It is only because we have three-dimensional minds that we cannot see this fourth dimension.

A mathematician may speak of space itself as being curved without reference to any solid matter in it. For example, consider the earth to be perfectly smooth. If we were two-dimensional creatures instead of being three-dimensional, we might draw a big circle on the earth's surface, measure its diameter and its circumference, and then find that the circumference was not equal to π times the diameter. We would not know that the circle was not flat (since we are assumed to be two-dimensional), but we could certainly infer a curvature of our flat space and even determine its radius if we knew enough about ordinary Euclidean geometry, which would work pretty well for small circles on the earth's surface.

The mathematical description of the universe to which allusion was made at the beginning of the lecture involved curving of three-dimensional space in somewhat the same fashion as described above for the two-dimensional space. If space actually is curved in this way our ordinary solid geometry, Euclidean geometry, would not be quite correct. In order to find out whether it is correct, measurements of certain kinds must be made. For example, if a negative parallax could ever be observed for a single star, a spherically curved space would be implied. The mathematician Schwarzschild, a good many years ago, attempted to find what curvature of space would be possible according to certain types of non-Euclidean geometry. In dealing with these geometries he said, "One there finds oneself, if one but will, in a geometrical fairyland, but the beauty of this fairy tale is that one does not know but that it may come true."

Schwarzschild's results need not be considered here because his data were limited and because we have at present more detailed modes of procedure than he used. There are at least two mathematicians who have achieved the unique distinction of having a universe named after them. They are Einstein, and a Dutchman named de Sitter. Both universes are non-Euclidean and the Einstein universe appears to be the more popular. The curvature of the Einstein universe is determined by the amount of matter in it, and if it is not a static universe, by certain other factors. A chunk of matter produces quite a large local curvature, which is evidenced to us by what we call gravitational attraction.

This universe is not infinite in extent. It is a closed universe with a finite volume but having no boundaries, just as the surface of a sphere is a closed surface of finite area yet has no bounding edges. In this universe one might expect to see a star in two directions, first by looking directly at it, second, by looking in the exactly opposite direction at light rays which have gone completely around the circuit of the universe in the opposite direction. Star images have not been seen in this way, possibly because their light is too faint after the long trip around the universe. There is also the possibility that the theory is wrong. It has, however, been seriously suggested that two very faint nebulae, observed in a certain direction, may actually be the backs of two of our nearest neighbors, as seen the long way around.

The theory of a finite, closed universe is very attractive in many respects. We may again use the term "intellectually satisfactory" in this connection, largely because this universe can be given a concise mathematical description and in terms that explain the gravitational effects of matter. There is also, in many individuals, a definite repugnance to the idea of infinite space. In discussing the stars Kant, in 1755, says, "There is here no end, but an abyss of real immensity in presence of which all the capability of human conception sinks exhausted." The finite mind likes to set up a blank wall somewhere, in order to end it all. It is probably intellectually satisfactory to know that one can start out in imagination and not have to get farther away forever and ever, but will eventually get back to the good old familiar region of the starting point.

With this picture of a finite, closed universe in mind we may now return to the question regarding the nebulae. Why should they appear to be crowded together at great distances from us? The answer might be that the curvature of space appears to make them crowd into smaller and smaller volumes as their distance increases. If this is true it is possible to calculate what radius of curvature of the universe would give the observed apparent crowding of the nebulae at great distances. Such calculations have been made and the universe turns out to be remarkably small. In fact, it is so small that our largest telescopes would allow us to see about one-sixth of the way around it. This small universe is required in order to explain the apparent nonuniform distribution of the nebulae. However, if we calculate the radius of the universe in this way we are obliged to have only a certain amount of matter in it, since, according to Einstein, the radius is determined by this total amount of matter. Hubble has made surveys to find out whether the observed amount of matter will fit in with the radius as determined above. He estimates that if all observable stars and nebulae were smeared out uniformly there would be a maximum of about one hydrogen atom per cubic meter. This density of matter is far too small. In other words, there is not enough matter in the universe to give it a curvature great enough to spread out the nebulae uniformly. The theory of curvature of space has, therefore, failed to resolve the problem.

Another way out of the dilemma is to suppose that the observations of the astronomers are in error. Here is what Hubble has to say.

> These questions have been carefully reexamined during the past few years. Various minor revisions have been made, but the end results remain substantially unchanged. By the usual criteria of probable errors the data seem to be sufficiently consistent for their purpose. Nevertheless, the operations are delicate, and the most significant data are found near the limits of the greatest telescopes. Under such conditions it is always possible that results may be affected by hidden systematic errors. Although no suggestion of such errors has been found, the possibility will persist until investigations can be repeated with improved techniques and more powerful telescopes. Ultimately the problem should be settled beyond question by the 200-inch reflector destined for Palomar.

The last way which may be suggested for escaping from the dilemma is to suppose that in the region of astronomical magnitudes some new principle of nature is operative — some principle which we have not yet discovered in the ordinary macroscopic field. Such a principle would have to free us from the necessity of using the Doppler effect, and we would no longer have to say that experimental observation shows the universe to be expanding. This new principle would, therefore, have to explain why the light from nebulae gets redder and redder as it travels greater and greater distances. Perhaps light which has been traveling for 100 million years in a straight line exhibits its senility by a decrease in the frequency of its vibrations. We do not know of any possible reason such as this why old light should be different in any way from new light. The only place from which we can get really old light is from the distant nebulae, so our chances of establishing by experiment a new principle of physics like this seems at present to be involved in a vicious circle from which there is no escape.

It appears, therefore, that our knowledge of the structure of the universe at the limits of the astronomical range is unsatisfactory. We have to recognize that there are discrepancies between theory and experimental observations. Hubble says that "a choice is presented, as once before in the days of Copernicus, between a strangely small, finite universe, and a sensibly infinite universe plus a new principle of nature."

We may now go back once more for a comprehensive view of what we have called the linear lay-out of the universe in Illustration 1. The three components, or variables, were assumed quite simply to be space, matter, and time. At the right-hand end of the scale we have become embroiled in some rather questionable speculations regarding the nature of space and the behavior of light. In this region, where a light-year is the unit of distance and a nebula the unit of mass, we have good reason for suspecting that the mechanics of the universe cannot be described or explained in such a simple way as in the region of miles and mountains.

Peculiarly enough, if we go from the enormously great region to the extremely small region, the region of the electron and the positron, we encounter similar difficulties. You will remember that Darrow characterized the microscopic region as unique because "of the adventurous excursions of the observers," and "the grandeur of the inferences." One or two of these inferences and excursions may be cited here, and it will appear that the simple concepts of space and matter have suffered in the microscopic field in much the same way that they have suffered in the astronomical field. As the result of investigations in the field of the small particles it has become necessary to broaden our ideas as to the nature of matter. Cloud-chamber pictures have allowed us practically to see two particles of matter created in space from the energy contained in radiation.

The thing that happens is that a photon, an atom of radiant energy traveling with the speed of light, somehow gets itself into a peculiar situation in a microscopic field of some kind. The result is that the photon changes into two particles with electric charges, a positron and an electron.

In the macroscopic size range an equivalent phenomenon would be for a quantity of sunshine, passing by an iron ball, to change suddenly into a couple of buckshot.

Needless to say, no one has ever seen anything like this happen. It is only when sizes become so small as to prevent direct observation that the event occurs. We may well say that something peculiar is going on in the microscopic field. Something is happening which is foreign to our ordinary experience.

Technically this phenomenon is known as pair production by a photon. The reverse process, conversion of matter into radiation, can occur when an electron and a positron come together under proper conditions. They disappear and two photons of radiation are shot out with the speed of light in opposite directions.

Matter and energy can now be thought of as practically synonymous. It thus becomes possible to make certain grand inferences with the object of saving the universe from running down. Millions of suns are slowly but surely converting their matter and their energy into radiation and this radiation is constantly escaping into infinity. Perhaps somewhere in space radiation may be changed back into matter. Perhaps the universe is engaged in a reversible cycle, instead of an irreversible one, as is commonly supposed.

As an illustration of what Darrow calls an "adventurous excursion" of an observer we may take the Dirac theory of the positron. Dirac is a brilliant young Englishman, a mathematician who has demonstrated a high degree of daring and originality in his handling of theoretical physics.

His theory of the positron starts out with two peculiar assumptions. First, a particle may have a negative kinetic energy. Second, all space is filled with particles of negative kinetic energy. There is a distribution of electrons of infinite density everywhere in the world. A perfect vacuum is a region where all the states of positive energy are unoccupied and all those of negative energy are occupied.

When an electron, by some means or other, gets knocked out of this state of negative energy into a state of positive energy, it is observed as an ordinary electron; the hole which was left is a positron. This hole may wander around for a short time, but there are so many more electrons in the universe than holes that it is not long before some electron drops into the hole and both hole and electron disappear from the view of normal people. The very short life of the positron is thus explained, as is also the phenomenon of pair production and the conversion of matter into radiation.

I have given this hasty outline of the theory, not that I expect anyone to understand it — it is hardly to be expected that negative energy can be understood — but because it illustrates the lengths to which a theorist has to go in creating physical explanation in this field. In the microscopic range of sizes a quite perfect explanation of things is given by a specialized type of mathematics called wave mechanics. It is only when this mathematical symbolism is explained in terms of physical symbolism that we call it an adventurous excursion. Dirac showed great courage in even trying to give a physical picture of his mathematical theory. The fact is that in the microscopic field things may behave in a way entirely foreign to the way in which we have always seen large objects behave, hence they cannot be explained in the old familiar ways.

There is in most people a strong tendency to label as "bunk" that which is not understood. This tendency is, on the whole, a healthy one. Skepticism is preferable to credulity if one is thinking in terms of the struggle for existence. The radio listeners who believe all the remarkable statements about cough syrups, breakfast foods, cigarettes, etc., must certainly be struggling very hard for existence. However, skepticism based upon a lack of understanding is a dangerous attitude of mind. Prof. P. W. Bridgman of Harvard has this to say in his book, *The Logic of Modern Physics:*

It is difficult to conceive anything more scientifically bigoted than to postulate that all possible experience conforms to the same type as that with which we are already familiar, and therefore to demand that explanations use only elements familiar in everyday experience. Such an attitude bespeaks an unimaginativeness, a mental obtuseness and obstinacy which might be expected to have exhausted their pragmatic justification at a lower plane of mental activity.

The explanation of microscopic phenomena, then, utilizes concepts which are not familiar to everyday experience. For that reason the microscopic tends to undermine any smug complacency we may have regarding our knowledge of nature and the universe. Take, for example, the Heisenberg uncertainty principle. This principle states that we can never know accurately both the position and the velocity of a small particle. It is easy to see why this is true. We can see the small particle because light has bounced off of it into our eye. We see it in the direction from which the light bounced.

But the light, in bouncing from the particle, must have given it a push so that either its position or its velocity will have been changed by the mere fact that light must be used to observe it. By the time the light photon gets to the eye of the observer the particle will not be at exactly the spot from which the photon appeared to bounce.

This uncertainty principle has been given an exact mathematical formulation. It turns out that if the position of an electron is known to within 0.004 inch then the speed of its motion is uncertain to within about 3 feet per second — the speed of a slow walk.

The tendency, at first, is to consider this as rather a superficial principle. I can easily imagine a particle to have both position and momentum simultaneously; why bother so much about a mechanism for determining them? However, a thorough study of the situation, with an analysis of every conceivable means afforded by nature for making determinations, impresses one with a feeling that here is a conspiracy of nature to prevent man from acquiring too much detailed information. A conspiracy of nature is a law of nature; we cannot pass it over as being of no importance. It is as if nature had erected a wall of impenetrability around the smallest particles and forced us to see them only partially, as if through the cracks in the wall.

It appears, therefore, that we are asking a meaningless question when we ask just where an electron is when it has a certain definite momentum. No possible operation can be thought of by which an answer to this question can be obtained without violating a law of nature. The conclusion is that the electron cannot have an exact velocity and an exact momentum simultaneously. There is an essential fuzziness in the very foundations of nature herself. Time and space are a little peculiar in the microscopic region, most certainly.

Someone has said that "the infinite, whether the infinitely large, or the infinitely small, seems to carry disaster in its wake." I do not think the word disaster is happily chosen in this connection. It is true that the two infinities at either end of our linear lay-out have shattered the beautiful, crystal-clear mechanical system which described the universe during most of the nineteenth century — when the luminiferous ether was as definitely material as a piece of iron, and when a scientist could say that practically all pioneer research in physics was over and nothing remained except to measure things with increasing accuracy. This complacent attitude is fortunately gone forever, and the two infinities have had a great deal to do with its disappearance. The new problems presented, the paradoxes, the uncertainties, all combine to give us a picture of modern science once more struggling, once more growing. It seems better to change the quotation to read, "The infinite, whether the infinitely large or the infinitely small, seems to have carried renaissance in its wake."

In summing up the subject we may say that the small part of the universe open to everyday experience has given us a simple conception of nature, a simple body of laws, which seem unable to cope with problems either in the region of the supernebulae or in the region of the extremely small particles.

In the latter field we have found that, properly speaking, descriptions of phenomena must be mainly mathematical. Such descriptions are quite adequate at present, and we feel that the main problems of explanation are well in hand. But we must be careful not to expect the same type of explanation that is used for objects of ordinary size, and we must remember that here there is a certain indefiniteness of behavior. We do not say that a small particle can *never* get over a high hill when it does not have enough energy to carry it to the top. We say that the probability of its getting over is small. It actually has a small probability of doing the job with an insufficient amount of energy!

In the region of the supernebulae we are at present up against a paradox. We are at liberty to suppose that space is of a peculiarly curved character, or that it goes on to infinity; that the supernebulae are flying away with enormous velocities, or that some unknown principle of nature is deceiving us. We may be affected by a feeling of futility because of this state of affairs, and even have as sympathetic feeling for St. Ambrose, who in A.D. 389 wrote:

> To discuss the nature of the earth does not help us in our hope of the life to come. It is enough to know that Scripture states that He hung up the earth on nothing. Why argue whether He hung it up in air or on water? The majesty of God constrains it by the law of His will.

The spirit of modern science is not in agreement with St. Ambrose, and is not to be discouraged by apparent contradictions. This spirit demands continual arguing and speculating as to how the universe is hung up. Certainly we will always see as through a glass darkly, but just as certainly we will always keep on trying to polish the glass.

E. J. ÖPIK

The Time Scale of Our Universe

[FROM THE SMITHSONIAN REPORT FOR 1955*]

JUST AS *fascinating as the structure of the universe is the many-faceted problem of its origin and age, with its corollaries, the age of our galaxy and of our own particular planet. The author, Dr. Öpik, an astronomer of world-wide reputation, is at present Director of the Armagh Observatory of Northern Ireland and also Visiting Professor at the University of Maryland. Here he sets forth the various methods of estimating the age of the earth, the stars, and the universe as a whole. With commendable candor, he points out the inevitable discrepancies and disagreements arising from different methods of attack on the problem. Nevertheless, the most gennerally acceptable lines of evidence point to a remarkably similar series of age estimates, derived from diverse lines of investigation.*

A by-product of the age question is the uncertain decision between an eternally expanding universe and one that expands through a finite, although enormous, period of time, and then as a result of gravitational forces contracts again to the primordial atom or nebula of matter from which it originally expanded. Such cyclical expansions and contractions would imply infinite time — neither beginning nor end.

* Supplementary note added December 1959. List of references to literature omitted.

INTRODUCTION AND HISTORY

T HE AVERAGE SCIENTIST of half a century ago did not ponder much the question of the beginning and age of the universe. For lack of observational approach this problem remained outside the realm of exact science. It was generally felt that the universe should have neither beginning nor end, a viewpoint which was more influenced by opposition to former mythological or religious ideas of creation than by impartial reasoning.

Indeed, the second law of thermodynamics was well established at that time. According to this law, the universe is steadily running down toward equalization of the energy content of its parts. The ultimate state is that of universally constant temperature, "Wärmetod" or thermal death, where, in the absence of temperature differences, no exchange of energy, no relative motion except that of molecules could take place. Organic life, the metabolism of which consists in exchange of energy, could not exist then, even were the temperature favorable for life — which, in all probability, it would not be. The mere fact that temperature differences exist, that suns shine and planets carry life in the face of immensities of cold space (into which heat energy is lost in the form of radiation), would point to the youthfulness of our world, to a beginning a finite interval of time ago.

Scientists of the beginning of this century preferred to ignore this writing on the wall. There were some reasons or, rather, pretexts which seemed to justify this eluding of the fundamental problem. The second law of thermodynamics, or that of increasing "entropy," determines only the direction, not the speed with which equalization is approached. The speed, depending on a number of unknown processes, being itself unknown, no definite calculations of the time intervals involved could be made.

When going back in time, the second law leads to ever-increasing energy concentrations in the past; an unlimited past would lead to infinite energy concentrations, a concept which is physically unacceptable. Certainly some uneasiness was felt in this respect by those who did not want to draw the logical conclusion of a finite age for the present universe. But, then, there was Maxwell's demon, an imaginary intelligent being who could, at will, regulate molecular processes and thus do away with the law of entropy. This sufficed to show that the law is not absolute. The law is only of a statistical nature, exceptions being always possible although more or less improbable. Further, its validity for unlimited intervals of space and time was questioned. A perhaps not very justifiable complacency about the beginnings and ends of the world was thus sustained.

During the second quarter of this century a great change in the scientific outlook in this respect took place. The recession of the extragalactic nebulae, coupled with the finite age of the radioactive elements, suggested that there was a beginning a few thousand million years ago, the same for the galaxies and for the atomic material of which our planet is built. Following the above-mentioned phenomena back in time, moments could be reached beyond which the recession of nebulae and the decay of radioactive isotopes could not continue in the same manner as they do now. The two time limits were not found to be equal although they were of the same order of magnitude; but, within the uncertainties of theory and observation, they could be adjusted to each other. The idea of a finite age for the universe emerged. A stage, some 3,000 million years ago, was visualized at which the universe was closely packed together, when the temperature and density were high enough to invert the radioactive processes and to cause the building up of the heavy unstable isotopes at a rate equal to, or faster than, their total rate of decay (spontaneous + induced) in these conditions.

One view considered this stage merely the remotest phase of evolution of our world, beyond which extrapolation from the present state is not possible. It was not meant to be necessarily an absolute beginning — more likely it was not. The concept of age is thus reduced to that of a time scale, or a time interval during which the properties of the universe have radically changed. This definition appears to be somewhat vague; but it would imply nothing short of a complete absence, at the early stage, of all the classes of celestial bodies which are familiar to us now. In such a form the definition is stringent enough. Therefore, even if we could assign an upper limit of age to all existing stars, this would be only a subordinate time scale — that of stellar evolution — unless we could prove the total absence of any stars before that date, and not only of those existing at present.

A more drastic view preferred the concept of an absolute beginning, perhaps identifiable with an act of creation. The definition of the time scale remained the same as before, but additional meaning was attached to it as that of the absolute age of the universe. The initial stage, a singularity from which the universe started expanding, was the limit of extrapolation not only from the present, but from any state of the universe, however close to the initial stage.

The difference between the two viewpoints is a matter of principle, and not of how the initial state of the universe is pictured. Although Eddington's primeval nebula, assumed to have preceded the present expanding state of the universe, could have existed indefinitely, it could equally well have been the first created object, called into being in a peculiar state of almost exact equilibrium between gravitational attraction and the hypothetical force of cosmic repulsion. On the other hand, Lemaître's primeval atom, "the egg from which the universe hatched," is most simply interpreted as the result of an act of creation; yet it could also have been the final outcome of collapse of a previous universe, oscillating indefinitely in alternating expansion and contraction. The choice between the two, continuous existence or creation, will remain a matter for esthetic judgment, not for positive science defined as theory verified by observation.

There is no proof in purely esthetic matters. This does not mean that esthetic methods of approach to scientific problems are worthless. On the contrary, scientific theories are created by intuition, or by an essentially esthetic process. However, without the flesh and bone of experiment such theories remain mere shadows of possibilities.

To remain on solid ground, in the following we will pay little attention to esthetic considerations, however important these might appear from the standpoint of philosophy or religion. We will, further, be guided by the principle of minimum hypothesis, or economy of thought, which requires that new laws of nature must not be used for the explanation of phenomena which can be accounted for by known laws. This is a safeguard against becoming lost in the blind alleys of guesswork. The chances are small that a theory not supported by facts would prove to be correct.

As already mentioned, the fundamental fact requiring a short time scale was, and remains, the red shift of the extragalactic nebulae. With the existing laws of nature this phenomenon is explained in the most straightforward way as recession. There are yet no facts known which would contradict this explanation. The Hubble-Humason law (1928) of proportionality of the red shift, or velocity of recession to distance, led to a time scale for the universe equal to a few thousand million years. The uncertainty of the estimate depended upon how the rate of expansion of the universe, as revealed by recession, was assumed to vary with time. Nevertheless, various models of the expanding universe, based on different assumptions (de Sitter, Einstein, Friedmann, Lemaître, Eddington), gave figures within the same order of magnitude for the time of rapid change.

The new "short" time scale of some 3,000 million years was like a bombshell amidst the complacent "permanentists." At that time the pundits as well as the rank and file accepted a thousand times longer time scale for the stellar content of our galaxy alone, no mention being made of the universe as a whole. This "long" time scale, a multiple of a million million years, was mainly the outcome of mathematical investigations by Jeans into the statistics of stellar motions and the distribution of the orbits of double stars. Jeans assumed a state of "statistical equilibrium," or that the present motions of the stars are essentially influenced by their mutual gravitational action in past close encounters. A close encounter would mean the passage of another star through our planetary system at a distance — say, between Mercury and Neptune. Such a passage would leave both suns physically intact (although its effect on planetary orbits might be disastrous), yet their motions would be changed in much the same manner as those of two gas molecules after an elastic collision. Jeans actually applied the kinetic theory of gases to the stellar universe. Because of the great distances separating individual stars, close encounters can happen only about once in several million million years, a figure which can be arrived at by elementary calculation if the average velocity and distance between the stars is known. The "long" time scale was thus not a result of Jeans' elaborate mathematical theories, which were undoubtedly correct, but follow merely from his basic assumption of statistical equilibrium, implying that each star during its lifetime had a fair chance of undergoing several close encounters with other stars. In trying to prove his basic assumption, Jeans selected only certain statistical data which, superficially, seemed to agree with it, and, strangely enough, overlooked numerous more important criteria which contradicted his assumption. Thus, while carefully considering the effects of encounters on close binary stars, he disregarded the wide pairs and star clusters upon which the effects, according to his own theory, should have been thousands of times stronger. Indeed, with the long time scale these objects should have ceased to exist long ago, in contradiction to observation which reveals numberless wide double stars and loosely bound clusters in the sky. The evidence against statistical, "gas-kinetic" equilibrium is overwhelming, and there is no foundation whatever for the "long" time scale in our stellar universe. The battle of "short" versus "long" time scale is definitely won by the former, although the latter did not yield without a struggle.

In the course of the controversy, arguments based on subordinate time scales were produced. These subordinate time scales — of the earth, the radioactive elements, stellar evolution, stability of binaries and star clusters — all fell below a not too large multiple of one thousand million years; as, moreover, some were obvious overestimates, they were considered as supporting the short time scale of the universe itself. An early, apparently the first, synoptic account of the evidence relating to the age of the universe concludes as follows (Öpik, 1933): "the combined evidence presented by meteorites, by statistical data relating to wide double stars, by the distribution of stellar luminosities in globular clusters . . ., and by the observed recession of spiral nebulae . . . points to an age of the stellar universe of the same order of magnitude as the currently accepted age of the solar system: not much more than 3,000 million years." In this account stress was laid on radioactive age determinations of meteorites by Paneth (whose results were later greatly changed), and on the abundance of lead isotopes in the earth's crust as testifying to the age of the radioactive elements (results which have been corroborated since). Subsequent synoptic reviews invariably arrived at practically similar conclusions, formulated sometimes more, sometimes less cautiously, although, with the changing aspect of our knowledge and different personal approach, the emphasis was on different phenomena: radioactivity and the age of the earth, and stellar evolution with a hydrogen-helium source of energy (Russell, 1940); galactic dynamics (Bok, 1936); the stability of star clusters and binaries (Chandrasekhar, 1944; Bok, 1946); the red shift of nebulae and the radioactive age of the earth's crust (Shapley, 1945).

The survival of the idea of the short time scale over two decades of intense astronomical and physical research is in itself a measure of its worth; it serves now as a generally accepted working basis in widely different fields of study.

In the following an attempt is made to draw an up-to-date balance for the problem of the time scale or age of the universe.

THE AGE OF THE EARTH

The continental shields of northeastern Europe, Canada, South and Central Africa, and others, where mountain building ceased at an early age of our planet's history, represent the oldest undisturbed portions of the earth's crust. All these regions are lowlands or plateaus devoid of mountain chains, and are free from earthquakes which are the sign of continuing upheavals. The age of these old formations is expected to come nearest to that of the earth's crust or the earth itself.

The most suitable method of age determination of rocks consists in a comparison of the abundance of radioactive isotopes, such as those of uranium, with the abundance of their end products, e.g., lead isotopes. Pure minerals in the form of crystals are chosen for samples; there must be a guaranty that no exchange of substance between the sample and its surroundings has taken place, in which respect only individual crystals can be considered as reliable. Knowing the rate of decay of the radioactive substance, the time during which decay has been going on can be calculated from the amount of end product accumulated. The determinations are accurate to within 8 to 10 percent, much more accurate than the other astrophysical age estimates referred to below.

Radioactive age determinations yielded, indeed, high values for some mineral samples from the shields. Pegmatites from northern Karelia, in the so-called Baltic shield, gave an average age of 1,950 million years according to the lead method, but without isotope analysis (Ahrens, 1947). In the Canadian shield, lead isotope determinations for pegmatites from southeastern Manitoba resulted in an average age of 2,100 million years (Nier, 1941); for the same an average of 2,240 million years was derived by the radioactive rubidium-strontium method (Ahrens), in good agreement with the former value. At that remote epoch, unlike the present conditions, volcanic activity was prominent in the Canadian shield. The Manitoba pegmatites are associated with granitic intrusions into older rocks which reveal traces of a long previous geological history, and whose age can be estimated at 2,550 million years (Rankama, 1954; Holmes, 1948). Recent very consistent lead-isotope age determinations (Allan, Farquhar, and Russell, 1953) have yielded still higher values of age for some samples from the continental shields:

LOCALITY OF SAMPLE

	AGE Millions of years
Ivigtut, Greenland	1,830
Yellowknife Area, N. W. T., Canada	2,140
Horseshoe Island, Great Slave Lake, Canada	2,180
Phoenix Mine, Norseman, W. Australia	2,190
Borderline Mine, Busia, E. Province, Uganda	2,220
Risks Mine, Kenya	2,220
Copperhead Mine, W. Australia	2,300
Inguladhal, Mysore, India	2,300
Sioux Lookout, Ontario	2,310
Steel Rock Lake, Ontario	2,360
Rosetta Mine, South Africa	2,860
Sierra Leone, Br. W. Africa	2,930

Pegmatites from the Rhodesian shield, near Bulawayo, yield an age of 2,640 million years (Holmes, 1954), yet the surrounding rocks — sediments and lavas — are still older; and, what is more remarkable, remains of primitive plants — algal structures — are found there in graphitic limestone (Macgregor 1940, 1941). This provides "indubitable evidence that life has existed for at least 2,600 million years and probably for considerably longer than 2,700 million years" (Holmes). Similarly, signs of organic remains are either found or strongly suspected in the rocks of Lake Superior and Manitoba, which are 2,000 to 2,500 million years old (Barghoorn and Tyler; Rankama).

Thus, direct measurements set the minimum age of the earth's crust at 2,900 million years, the oldest specimens being found in Africa. This confirms also a long-maintained belief that Africa was the first continent to be formed.

It is but natural to expect that the oldest rocks have not yet found their way into man's laboratories, and that the age of the earth's crust is greater than the presently known oldest sample.

An ingenious method, based on data for rocks of widely different ages from 25 to 1,330 million years as determined by Nier, led Holmes (1949) to the calculation of the true age of the earth, or the time during which radiogenic lead has been produced in its materials. The method is one of extrapolation, consisting in the study of the observed relative isotopic abundances within one age group and their theoretical variation with time. The moment when the isotopic ratios, calculated backward for various age groups, become equal is the "beginning." Holmes found in such a manner 3,350 million years for the age of the earth. The oldest analyzed sample used in his calculation was 2,000 million years younger than this figure — a gap which might have caused considerable error in the extrapolation, as was pointed out by Jeffreys.

Recent data as quoted above push the directly observed age limit much farther back in time, and nearer the beginning. Applying the method of extrapolation to modern data, the probable age of the earth results as 3,500 million years (Collins, Russell, and Farquhar, 1953), in excellent agreement with Holmes' former figure, but more reliable, the range of extrapolation being now only a few hundred million years.

The figure of 3.5 thousand million years can at present be accepted as a close approximation to the age of the earth — the time elapsed since its elements were uniformly mixed, probably in a molten state. The same figure, or one perhaps only slightly greater, can be considered the age of the solar system; the formation of the planets and of the earth's crust must have taken relatively short intervals of time.

The uranium and thorium content of iron meteorites is so small that their lead can be assumed to be of primeval isotopic composition, no radiogenic lead having been added in the course of time. If this is so, the present average isotopic composition of lead, uranium, and thorium in the earth's crust indicates an age of 4,500 million years (Houtermans, 1953; Patterson, 1955), in remarkable agreement with a similarly determined age of stony meteorites (Patterson). This would be the time elapsed since the separation of the iron from the silicate phase, which may have taken place in a diffuse state of matter and may have preceded the formation of the planets.

THE AGE OF THE ELEMENTS

Time intervals can be calculated only for radioactive elements with a known rate of decay. According to the well-known laws of radioactive decay, the amount of these elements decreases exponentially with time; calculating their amounts for distant epochs in the past, one inevitably arrives at time limits beyond which the calculated abundances of radioactive isotopes become unreasonably large — greater than those of the presently observed end products, or even greater than the total amount of matter in the universe. Clearly, the radioactive elements can only be of finite age. Now, the rate of decay of radioactive elements is not influenced by external conditions if the temperature remains below 1,000 million degrees and the density below, say, one million times that of water. Neither in the interior of normal (dwarf or "main-sequence") stars, nor in interstellar clouds from which suns and planetery systems are believed to have sprung, do such extreme conditions exist. We may well say that the state of matter in the observable universe requires radioactive decay to proceed relentlessly. As this could happen only for a finite interval of time, it would mean that the observable agglomerates of matter in the universe could also have existed for only a limited time.

Thus, at a remote epoch a building up of the radioactive isotopes must have taken place, in addition to their spontaneous or forced decay. Now, conditions leading to the formation of the heavy radioactive isotopes will throw the rest of the lighter elements into a melting pot, too — will cause their rapid building up and disintegration; this is a trivial consequence of the theory of nuclear structure. The age of the radioactive isotopes is thus almost synonymous with the age of the elements.

According to a method proposed by Russell (1921), a maximum age for the elements can be derived from the relative terrestrial abundances of a radioactive isotope and its end product. It yields a maximum age, because some of the end product must have been created nonradiogenically in the initial "melting pot," when all the elements came into being under extreme conditions of temperature and density. Of the different isotopes, that leading to the lowest estimate of age is to be taken. The upper limit of age of the terrestrial elements thus found equals 5 to 6 thousand million years, less than the double of the age of the earth. The sharpest margin results from the uranium 235–lead 207 ratio. The closeness of the order of magnitude of the upper limit to the age of the earth is significant and makes it likely that the true age of the elements does not differ much from that of the earth — a figure of about 4,500 million years appearing to be plausible.

In these estimates there is some uncertainty from the unknown composition of the earth's interior, which, however, is hardly significant in view of the exponential law of variation of abundance ratios with time. Even a large error in the present ratio will not affect the order of magnitude of the resulting age. The mere presence of radioactive substances is a proof of the temporal origin of the terrestrial elements.

Except for meteorites, there are no data available as to the abundance of radioactive isotopes outside the earth; the above-mentioned time limit refers therefore strictly only to the sample of matter represented by our globe.

Although the relative abundances of the elements (excluding the lightest, which have escaped from small bodies like our planet) in the earth's crust and in the atmospheres of the sun and most stars are very similar, this does not necessarily mean a simultaneous origin for their elements. Only a similar mode of origin is implied.

Several attempts have been made to explain, with more or less success, the origin and relative abundances of the elements by equilibrium conditions inside superdense stars (Klein, Beskow, and Treffenberg; Hoyle; van Albada). Supernova explosions inject the mixture into space, whence it condenses again into new-born stars. Observations of the Crab Nebula, a former supernova, suggest that the product of explosion — the amorphous core of the nebula — is poor in hydrogen, whereas its hydrogen fringe appears to be interstellar gas pushed ahead of the expanding core. We may thus have a double origin for the elements: hydrogen already present in space with an unknown original content of other elements; and the heavier elements enriching the mixture through supernova explosions.

Old stars — those of "Population II" — seem to show, indeed, a smaller metal content than those believed to be more recently formed, suggesting a gradual change in the composition of the medium of which stars are built. If this is so, we need not go to the beginnings of the universe to account for the radioactive isotopes on earth: they may be the products of supernova explosions that preceded the formation of the solar system.

Nevertheless, serious doubts with respect to the latter conclusion are justified. The theory of stellar structure would admit the building up of the lighter metal nuclei in superdense stellar cores (Öpik, 1951; Salpeter, 1952), as well as during the hydrogen explosion of a star that has become hydrodynamically unstable (Öpik, 1953). From this, however, it is a long way to the extreme conditions at which uranium and similar elements of high atomic number can begin to be produced. Although light metals can, indeed, be currently supplied by the above-described mechanism, it is doubtful whether the heavy radioactive isotopes could originate in stellar interiors. More likely, these isotopes have come into being in a more powerful "explosion" which involved the whole universe, namely, that which happened at an early stage of its expansion. In that case the age of at least the heavier terrestrial elements would still be synonymous with the age of the world.

This leads us to another group of theories which explain the observed abundances of all elements, including the heaviest, by their building up from a nonequilibrium, extremely hot mixture (chiefly neutron gas) at an early stage of an exploding universe (Alpher, Bethe, Gamow).

It is possible that the lighter elements (say, those lighter than iron) have originated from two different processes — during the primordial explosion, and currently in stellar interiors — whereas the heavy isotopes were all created at the "beginning of the world"; in such a case, as shown above, the "radioactive" age of the universe, or the time elapsed since the big explosion, is about 4.5 thousand million years. However, unless the possibility of formation of the heavy elements in superdense stellar interiors can be definitely disproved, a certain ambiguity will remain attached to the meaning of this figure.

METEORITES

The pioneer work of Paneth 20 years ago raised hopes that radioactive age determinations of meteorites, based on their helium content, might yield a clue to the age of the solar system at least, or even to that of the whole universe. Unfortunately, the meteorites did not come up to original expectations. Paneth's struggle with this problem, which is not concluded yet, led over disappointments and disclaimers of former results; e.g., he announced that all his determinations prior to 1940 were technically unreliable. Paneth's researches are a remarkable example of a gallant fight for the truth, without bias toward his former work, some of which he rejected as soon as it was found that it did not comply with his own high standards.

The leakage of helium from meteorites to space was one of the many difficulties, and for this reason stony meteorites proved unreliable, so that only data referring to iron meteorites could be fully trusted. From refined analysis of the helium content of the latter Paneth found the ages of meteorites to lie between 100,000 and 9 thousand million years. The higher values represented a puzzle as, for example, they considerably exceeded the upper limit of age for the earth and the solar system as set by the abundances of radioactive isotopes (cf. preceding section).

Now came the latest act of the drama. Bauer (1947) and Huntley (1948) pointed out that part of the helium in meteorites must have been produced by nuclear transmutations, caused by cosmic rays during millions of centuries. This suggestion has now become an established fact, as otherwise the presence in meteorites of the isotope He^3 in considerable amounts (18 to 32 percent of He^4) cannot be explained: radioactive disintegration leads to He^4 only, not to He^3. On the other hand, cosmic rays produce both isotopes in the approximate proportion of 10 He^4 to 3 He^3 atoms (Singer, 1952). This ratio being given, an analysis by the mass spectrograph leads to the determination of the amount of purely radiogenic He^4, which is very much less than the total amount of helium. As a result, the estimated helium ages of meteorites are greatly reduced and, from the provisional data available, hardly attain 1,000 million years. This is much less than the well-established age of the earth and the solar system; therefore, the method is of no avail in estimating the age of the universe. It has been suggested that the meteorites lost their original helium when passing near the sun and melting in its heat; their orbits are sometimes likely to become highly eccentric from perturbations at close approaches to the planets, in which case near passages to the sun become possible. However, unpublished calculations by the writer show that such happenings are very rare, and that the explanation is invalid.

Urey pointed out that iron meteorites are unlikely to contain enough radioactive elements to account for measurable amounts of radiogenic helium. The correlation between the total amount of helium and its isotopic ratio in iron meteorites is highly remarkable. In the opinion of the author of this review the simplest explanation of Paneth's results could be that all the helium is produced by cosmic rays, the absolute amount and isotopic ratio depending upon the original thickness of the protective layer, subsequently lost through ablation in our atmosphere. The time of separation of the stone and iron of meteorites, as determined from the isotopic composition of lead, is consistently found to be 4,500 million years (Patterson, 1951, 1956). This may refer to a preplanetary stage. Potassium-argon-40 ages of stony meteorites are found to be 1,900 to 3,800 million years and 4,700 to 4,800 million years. Evidently there has been little or no escape of argon from stony meteorites. The argon ages would date from the moment of last solidification, thus probably from a planetary or post-planetary stage. Also, these high argon ages of stone seem to indicate again that the helium ages of iron inclusions, often connected with stone, are unreliable.

Meteorites point to an age of the solar system, or its parent nebula, close to 4,500 million years.

THE AGES OF THE STARS

At present there is little doubt that main-sequence ("dwarf") stars depend upon the conversion of hydrogen into helium for their energy source. The correlation of radius and mass, indicating central temperatures of precisely the range required by the corresponding slow nuclear reactions, can hardly be interpreted in a different manner. This knowledge is so well founded that it furnishes a reliable basis for the calculation of time rates of stellar evolution.

To cover radiation losses to space, the sun has to spend an amount of hydrogen very nearly equal to 1 percent of its mass in 1,000 million years. Sirius, a typical star of spectrum AO quite common in the galaxy, emits 13 times more energy per unit mass than the sun, consuming thus 13 percent hydrogen by weight in 1,000 million years. With 60 percent hydrogen originally, the store of energy would last 4,600 million years. There is probably not much mixing in stars outside their central regions (Öpik, 1938); therefore, only about 25 percent of the fuel is available (from the central regions where the temperature is high enough for nuclear reactions to proceed at a not-negligible rate), and the lifetime of Sirius becomes 1,150 million years. It may then become a giant (Öpik, 1938), and ultimately collapse — possibly by throwing off its outer shell in a supernova explosion, leaving behind a remnant which ultimately becomes a white dwarf. The success in calculating "composite" models of red giants (Schwarzschild, 1952), as well as Trumpler's classification of star clusters, lends support to this concept of stellar evolution. The more massive B stars will have a lifetime of a few hundred million years only. This being much shorter than the lifetime of the galaxy, which cannot be younger than the earth, it is concluded that the early-type stars are currently replaced by new stars condensing out of diffuse matter (Öpik, 1938). Where diffuse matter is no longer available, early-type stars are absent and only giants of the corresponding luminosity remain, as is actually observed in globular clusters. Using Baade's terminology (1944), Population II of the globular clusters, the galactic center, and the general galactic background, consists of aging members born at a remote epoch; whereas Population I, connected with the diffuse matter and spiral structure of the galaxy, contains young early-type stars steadily coming into being and dying, in addition to the background of less massive young and old stars, some of the latter existing from the very beginning of the galaxy.

The absence of normal B and A stars from the globular clusters sets their age, as well as that of the galaxy, at more than 1,500 million years.

The energy source of the giants remains a puzzle. If we take their persistent appearance in globular clusters as an indication of their longevity, a more powerful source of energy must be assumed for their maintenance — either gravitation of their superdense cores, or annihilation of matter. On the other hand, these giants may represent short-lived objects in "statistical equilibrium" with the rest of the stellar population — those which blow up or collapse being replaced by others becoming giants. This latter concept would agree with the calculated red-giant models (Schwarzschild) which are supposed not to draw on unknown sources of energy and are short-lived, their luminosities being abnormally high as compared with their masses. The giants of the globular clusters, as well as the short-period variables which should represent a phase preceding the giant stage, would then correspond to stars of more or less similar mass for which the exhaustion of hydrogen has reached a critical limit. Taking the observed luminosities with Schwarzschild's models, the limiting mass would be from 3.0 to 2.0 solar mass, indicating for the clusters an age between 800 and 2,500 million years.

The fork-shaped H-R (Hertzsprung-Russell) diagram of the globular clusters represents apparently the result of aging, in contrast to the continually rejuvenated Population I of our galactic surroundings (the difference in metal content having only a secondary effect). The globular clusters, which are all well outside the galactic plane and are not sharing in galactic rotation, will necessarily oscillate on both sides of the galactic plane, the period of oscillation being less than 100 million years (Oort). Thus, they must have repeatedly gone through the galactic plane. While passing for the first time through the plane, they must have been stripped of all their diffuse matter — which could have been but loosely bound by a gravitational potential of only 1/1000th that of the galaxy — through collision with the diffuse matter near the galactic plane; the mechanism is similar to that visualized by Spitzer and Baade for collisions of galaxies. This would have prevented the subsequent formation of new stars in them. The stellar population of the globular clusters must therefore consist of members of almost the same age, which came into being when the galaxy was formed, and represents thus one of the oldest time indicators. The lower branch of their H-R fork appears to join the H-R diagram of Population I at absolute bolometric magnitude +2; this should be the luminosity of old stars which have now arrived at the end of their career as dwarfs.

The evolution of dwarf stars, without much mixing of their substance, amounts to chemical changes around their central cores, where hydrogen is converted into helium; the composition of the outer regions remains unchanged. Öpik (1951) has followed the evolution of such stellar models by numerical integrations. From these calculations it can be estimated that stars which have nearly exhausted their central store of hydrogen yet remain dwarfs should be about 0.5 mag (or by 60 percent) brighter than "normal" dwarfs of equal mass. If we take this into account, it is estimated that the above-mentioned "ultimate" dwarfs in globular clusters, about 10 times brighter than our sun, should have a mass of $1.7 \odot$. The total duration of the dwarf stage at this mass would be around 4,000 million years.

The numerical value of this estimate may be considerably in error; yet, qualitatively there is little doubt about the soundness of the interpretation which ascribes to the stellar population of the globular clusters the same age as that of the galaxy itself. By essentially the same method, but on the basis of more recent observational data, Sandage (1953) finds an age of about 5,000 million years for the globular clusters. We may take the average of the two estimates, 4.5 thousand million years, as the probable age of the globular clusters, as well as of our galaxy.

Among the many data concordantly pointing to an age of the stellar universe of a few thousand million years, there is one which seemingly strikes a note of discord — some uneasiness may be felt about the high frequency of white dwarfs. If they are remnants of supernovae, which appear only once in a few hundred years, they would have required perhaps 100,000 million years to accumulate. However, at the beginnings of the galaxy, at the time when Population II was formed, star formation must have proceeded at a faster rate than now. The frequency of supernovae, directly related to the frequency of formation of massive stars, may then have been much higher (Schwarzschild and Spitzer). Further, the possibility of white dwarfs being formed in another way cannot be ruled out. Doubts as to the time scale cannot be maintained on such slender evidence.

Besides, a direct estimate of the age of individual white dwarfs can also be made, and this turns out to be in agreement with the other estimates. The energy source of white dwarfs can consist only in the thermal agitation of atomic nuclei (Mestel, 1953) or upon explicit heat — like a kettle of hot water gradually cooling. The time of cooling, until the present state is reached, or the age of a white dwarf can be easily calculated when A, the mean atomic weight of this material, is known. Considering that all hydrogen must previously have been converted into helium, and that, before the "degenerate" stage of a white dwarf is reached, triple collisions at temperatures of a few hundred million degrees will convert all the helium into carbon, and then into lighter metals such as magnesium, we find that $A=24$ can be assumed, and Mestel's highest values for the ages of white dwarfs become equal to 4,000 million years. This may be near the age of Population II and the galaxy, in thrilling agreement with other estimates.

STABILITY OF STAR CLUSTERS AND DOUBLE STARS

The dynamical stability of clusters has been investigated repeatedly, with the result that most galactic clusters will dissolve, either under the tidal action of the galactic center or through encounters with field stars or other members of the cluster, in time intervals of the order of 1,000 million years (Bok, 1934; Chandrasekhar, 1943). Although this statement refers to the future and, theoretically, is compatible with an unlimited past, the probability of simultaneous occurrence of a great number of old clusters which just now have come to the verge of disruption is very small. We may expect an average cluster to be observed in the middle of its lifetime, and assume, therefore, that the age of most clusters is some 1,000 million years or less. Yet, most of them contain early-type stars which cannot be very old. Consideration of the dynamical stability of clusters confirms thus the youth of their members, and adds another argument in favor of the theory that stars are being born continually. Apart from that, no new criterion of age for the galaxy is forthcoming — clusters which are older than their stellar content cannot be observed.

The situation is similar with wide double stars. The distribution of the distances between their components (Öpik, 1924) indicates that equipartition of energy cannot have taken place (Ambarzumian, 1936), and that the binaries could not have been subjected to encounters with field stars for longer than, say, 5,000 million years. On the other hand, the statistical material from which this conclusion is drawn is based chiefly on the relatively luminous A-type binaries which, according to the preceding, cannot have lived to so great an age, anyway.

Thus, conclusions as to age based on the dynamical stability of clusters and double stars are overruled by the shorter lifetime of their components, and can be used only to reaffirm the short time scale of stellar evolution.

THE RED SHIFT OF EXTRAGALACTIC NEBULAE

The observations by V. M. Slipher, Hubble, and Humason, if interpreted in a straightforward manner, indicate a recession of the extragalactic nebulae proportional to distance, or an expansion at a uniform rate of the visible portion of the universe.

Recent developments have shown, in a manner that leaves practically no doubt, that Hubble's scale of distances should be at least doubled. The distances of the nearest nebulae were determined by Hubble from the period-luminosity relation of the long-period cepheids. The zero point of this relation depended upon space absorption in low galactic latitudes, and was known to be inaccurate, but, for lack of better data, it was accepted and used during the past quarter of a century as a basis for work on the structure of the universe. Some cosmological theories actually depended upon the particular value of the zero point and the resulting scale of distances. The unexpectedly large correction in the scale is a shock to all theories involving the so-called cosmological constant. We need not express regret that these theories were created — they were fully justified by the esthetic value alone — but, from the standpoint of economy of thought, the cosmological constant (equivalent to a repulsion) must be suspended from active duty for the time being and put in cold storage until new observational facts sound the trumpet for its revival. It is rather doubtful whether this ever will happen.

The zero point of cepheid luminosities affects only the distances of extragalactic nebulae. Within the galaxy, including the globular clusters, a more reliable criterion of distance is offered by the known luminosities of the short-period cepheids, the so-called cluster-type or RR Lyrae variables. The average luminosity of these Population II high-velocity objects does not depend so much upon space absorption, and is well determined. They were too faint to be observed in the nebulae by Hubble. In the Magellanic Clouds, whose estimated distances depended also upon long-period cepheids, persistent Harvard Observatory searches failed to reveal cluster-type variables, a circumstance sometimes interpreted even as indicating the actual absence of these objects.

Now, at last, numerous cluster-type variables have been found in the Magellanic Clouds (Thackeray and Wesselink, 1953), but about 1.3 mag (or 3.3 times) fainter than expected from the magnitudes of the long-period cepheids. Thus the long-period cepheids are 1.3 mag brighter and all distances based on them 1.8 times greater than was formerly assumed. The apparent diameters and integrated luminosities of globular clusters in external galaxies call for a similar correction (Shapley, 1952), and independent support for these conclusions is forthcoming from other sources (Baade).

This, however, is not the whole story. The recession constant of the nebulae depends entirely on the more distant objects, for obvious reasons; yet in these no variable stars could be observed. Their distances were linked to the cepheid scale of the nearer galaxies through intermediate criteria — the magnitudes of the brightest stars and of the nebulae themselves. Both criteria are of a statistical nature and not only involve various photometric errors, but also depend upon the true dispersion (variety) of the magnitudes of the objects used as standards; the dispersions, and therefore the distances, seem to have been underestimated by Hubble. A comprehensive survey of the problem has been first given by Behr (1951). He concludes that those of Hubble's intrinsic luminosities of the nebulae which are not based on variable stars should be increased by 1.7 mag. Behr was not aware of the need for adjustment of the cepheid scale of the nearest nebulae, and this correction, evidently, must be added to that found by him. The total correction amounts thus to $1.7 + 1.3 = 3.0$ mag, or an increase in the distances of nebulae (except the nearest, which are based on cepheids) in a ratio of 4 to 1. The constant of recession, or the rate of increase of velocity with distance as based on observed red shifts, now becomes 145 km./sec. per megaparsec (3.25 million light-years), only one-quarter of the formerly assumed value. The expansionistic time scales are increased four-fold, and even the shortest will yield more than the lower limit — the age of the earth.

The retention of the cosmological constant by Eddington and Lemaître was justified by the need to extend the time scale; the slow phase of expansion, when gravitational attraction and cosmic repulsion nearly balanced each other, allowed this to be done almost indefinitely. Now, with the increased distances, cosmic repulsion becomes a superstructure of a purely esthetic nature, serving no practical purpose. Besides, Einstein, the originator of the concept, has disavowed the cosmological constant ever since, in spite of the then favorable numerical aspect of the problem.

Without the cosmological constant, the Friedmann-Einstein cosmological models furnish a working hypothesis best suited to deal with the expanding universe. These models are very similar to an ordinary gravitating sphere in uniform expansion. Gravitation, working against expansion, is slowing it down. When the velocity of expansion is below a certain limit, the expansion will be ultimately stopped by gravitation, and contraction will start; when the velocity of expansion equals or exceeds the limit (velocity of escape), gravitation will be unable to stop it and the sphere will disperse into space, expansion never ceasing. According to the general theory of relativity, and without cosmological repulsion, a similar state of affairs in the expanding universe prevails. The first case, when expansion is ultimately stopped by gravitation, would correspond to positive curvature of space, or to closed space and a relapse of the universe, after maximum expansion, into the original state of high density (atom or nebula). The second case would correspond to zero or negative curvature, to open and infinite space, and to a one-way development of the universe by perpetual expansion.

For an expansion constant of 145 km./sec. per megaparsec the line between the two cases is set by a certain limiting value of the *average* density of matter in space (i.e., if all the matter of the universe were spread uniformly over its entire volume, instead of being concentrated into galaxies, stars, and atoms), equal to 3.9×10^{-29} gm./cm.^{3} The volume of the earth filled with matter of so low a density would contain only a mass of 42 milligrams.

The probable value of the average density of matter in space can be estimated in the following way. There are in the universe, on the average, 12 nebulae per cubic megaparsec (Fletcher, 1946). The average mass per nebula, including intergalactic matter, can be estimated from the internal motions in clusters of galaxies according to the "virial theorem" (mean kinetic energy per unit mass proportional to the potential of gravitation); this, of course, depends upon the assumption that the clusters are held together by gravitation. The assumption can nowadays hardly be subjected to doubt, considering that otherwise, with the velocities observed, the clusters would have dispersed long ago; on the contrary, they are gathered so closely together that numerous interpenetrations or "collisions" of the member galaxies of a cluster must have happened during the lifetime of the universe (Spitzer and Baade, 1951). Repeated collisions must have led to "statistical equilibrium" in the distribution of velocities of the member galaxies; the similarity between the radial density distribution of nebulae in these clusters and that of an isothermal gas sphere (de Vaucouleurs) supports this assumption and the validity of the virial theorem. For the Virgo cluster a mass of 500,000 million suns per nebula results with Hubble's scale of distances (Bok), and four times as much with the corrected scale. These data lead to a world density of 2.5×10^{-29} gm./cm.^{3} or 64 percent of the critical density. If the result is taken literally, this would mean negative curvature, an open and infinite space into which the universe is irreversibly expanding.

However, the calculations are not exact enough to warrant unreserved acceptance of such a conclusion. The estimate has come astonishingly close to the critical density, and therefore, within the limits of uncertainty in the data, the alternative case of closed space and limited expansion followed by collapse is also possible. Indeed, Zwicky finds considerable amounts of matter in the space between the galaxies, and favors a world density about 25 times that of our estimate, which would bring it far above the critical value. However, Zwicky's value is a very rough estimate, not based on the virial theorem. Our estimate of 2 million million suns per nebula would ascribe 90 percent of the mass to intergalactic matter (that between the galaxies) and only 10 percent to the galaxies themselves; this figure seems to be more realistic than Zwicky's, which would set the percentages at 99.5 and 0.5, respectively.

It is, perhaps, permissible to speculate on the closeness of the world density to its critical value, and to suggest an intrinsic reason for this near equality of the kinetic energy of expansion and the absolute value of the gravitational potential. The reason should be sought in the past history of the world. For example, an oscillating universe whose maximum world radius greatly exceeds the present value would lead to the above-mentioned near equality except when close to the phase of greatest expansion (which should be far ahead of present time). In that case the time of expansion from the state of greatest density until today is insensitive to the precise value of world density, and depends only upon the rate of expansion; it is practically equal to that of uncurved (Euclidean) space and, with the revised value of the expansion constant, becomes.

$$t = 4,500 \text{ million years.}$$

The figure is surprisingly close to the other estimates, although a considerable uncertainty is involved, the extreme admissible values being, perhaps, from 3 to 6 thousand million years.

This would represent the age of the universe in a restricted sense, or the time elapsed since it was in a highly condensed state. This state cannot yet be described. Lemaître's primeval atom is one of the possibilities. The theory of the origin of the elements, as shown above, does not provide a clue. The same is true of the cosmic rays, which appear to be of stellar origin and whose connection with the prestellar stage of the universe seems to be improbable.

SPACE REDDENING OF THE GALAXIES

This phenomenon, announced by Stebbins and Whitford (1948), and consisting in an increase of the color index of distant galaxies, not accounted for by the red shift, led to far-reaching speculations on observable effects of stellar evolution. The effect seems to be restricted to elliptical nebulae (purely Population II), whereas spirals (mixed populations) do not show reddening. The distant nebulae are observed at an earlier stage of evolution (on account of light time), and it has been suggested that the effect could be accounted for by the red giants of Population II disappearing with time (blowing up or collapsing), which would tend to make the population bluer. However, a multicolor study of the spectral-energy distribution of a distant elliptical nebula has shown that "the result is definitely not that expected from the death of red giants" (Whitford, 1953).

Vaucouleurs (1948) suggested that the effect is due to the depression in the ultraviolet produced by absorption lines and bands. With the red shift the ultraviolet depression is displaced into the blue, making the blue-red color index redder. At least part of the effect can be accounted for in such a manner (Öpik, 1955).

As to the spirals, they are known to contain a considerable amount of nebulosity in emission; this, especially that due to hydrogen, will fill the ultraviolet depression, counterbalancing the absorption. The absence of the reddening for spirals is thus explained without invoking stellar evolution. Over the time intervals involved, evolution may well affect individual stars, but considerable effects upon the entire Population II are unlikely.

ALTERNATIVE HYPOTHESES

It has been repeatedly stressed that the nebular red shift may not indicate recession, and alternative suggestions have been made recently (Freundlich, Shelton). It is difficult to imagine a collisional process of reddening without simultaneous blurring of the nebular images (Atkinson). Further, the nonexpanding universe will be unstable and will end in collapse; or in expansion, if the cosmological repulsion is introduced. Thus, the present state would be exceptional, the normal state being one of Doppler shifts corresponding to real approach or recession. It does not seem advisable to sacrifice the solid concept of recession to a piling up of *ad hoc* new laws and improbable states.

Continuous creation of matter under various aspects (Kapp, Jordan, Bondi, Gold, Hoyle) is another alternative which would dispense with a finite age for the universe. It requires the retention of the cosmological constant (repulsion), or a pulsating variety of it (Kapp). For reasons similar to those given above these theories can at present be assessed only from the standpoint of their esthetic value. It is not easy to imagine observational criteria for them which cannot be explained away.

Perhaps the distribution of masses of the galaxies can provide the least objectionable proof. In Hoyle's expanding universe galaxies will continually grow by accretion, especially large ones with gaseous envelopes firmly bound by gravitation; the envelopes will act as nets catching atoms from intergalactic space, or incorporating whole gaseous envelopes of smaller galaxies which happen to be in their way. They will grow almost indefinitely with time. Their frequency per unit volume in Hoyle's universe will vary inversely as the cube of age, thus more or less as the cube of mass, too; when selected by apparent magnitude, there will be no upper limit of mass and almost no correlation of distance with magnitude. The available evidence implies a frequency of nebulae in space decreasing with the 4/3 power of mass (Holmberg, Zwicky), a definite upper limit of mass (Page), and a correlation of distance with apparent magnitude. What evidence there is, is definitely negative.

CONCLUSION

The rate of irreversible processes in different physical complexes — the radioactive elements, the earth and the solar system, the stars, stellar systems, the galaxy, the observable portion of the extragalactic universe — is such as to suggest an age not exceeding 6,000 million years for the universe in its present form and content. The extragalactic nebulae, with our galaxy and its backbone of Population II, may have been formed some 4,500 million years ago, the sun as a star of Population I coming into being perhaps later.

Cosmological repulsion is a theoretical superstructure which is not necessarily required by the existing observational evidence. The same is true of the continuous creation of matter and the alternative interpretations of the nebular red shift; these are mere possibilities, serving the purely esthetic purpose of denying the universe a temporal origin.

The observed velocities of recession exceed one-fifth of the velocity of light, the energy corresponding to a packing fraction (fraction of mass converted into kinetic energy) of 0.02 per nucleon (proton or neutron). Nothing short of an explosion from the densest-known state of matter — nuclear fluid — could be advocated as the cause. Our knowledge of the present density of matter in the universe is insufficient to decide between the two possibilities: that of open space, in which case the whole universe is an irreversible process of temporal origin, and that of closed space, in which the universe may return to its initial state, implying oscillations — the collapsing universe rebounding from the elastic forces of the nuclear fluid at a state of maximum compression, to begin a new phase of expansion.

It may appear at first sight that, at an advanced stage of collapse, when all individual bodies have melted into a uniform gaseous mass, the gaseous universe may be prevented from further collapsing by the elastic forces of the gas itself, like an oscillating gaseous star of which the cepheids are examples. However, it is likely that, with the enormous kinetic energy of contraction, the universe will first pass quickly through the stage of building up of heavy elements from hydrogen and helium, most of the hydrogen remaining unconverted before the next stage, that of nuclear dissociation and formation of neutron gas, begins — electrons being squeezed into and absorbed by the positively charged atomic nuclei. This is the reverse of the process by which Gamow and others visualized the origin of the elements after the explosion of the primeval atom. Formation of neutron gas absorbs enormous amounts of energy, and this, so to speak, blows the bottom off the resistance of the gas to compression. In such a case, the so-called ratio of specific heats of the gas (mixed with strong radiation) is less than 4/3 and, according to a well-known theorem on the structure of gaseous spheres, the universe becomes intrinsically unstable and cannot cease collapsing while in a gaseous state. Only when the perfect-gas laws no longer are valid, i.e., when the stage of nuclear fluid is reached, will there develop enough resistance to stop the collapse and invert the trend of events.

In the case where open space appears to be required by the physical characteristics of our neighborhood, we never will be sure of its validity for the universe as a whole. The possibility should not be overlooked that what we observe now is merely the metagalaxy — only a step in the hierarchy of physical systems. The observed expansion may refer only to this limited, although large, material system; in other parts of the world conditions may be different. The finite intensity of the sky background has often been advocated to prove the finiteness of the world. However, as shown by C. V. L. Charlier on purely classical lines, an infinite world is compatible with a finite intensity of the sky background if the universe is built on a hierarchical principle, systems of each order (atomic nuclei, atoms, planets, stars, clusters, galaxies, metagalaxies, etc.) being separated by distances considerably greater than their diameters. Such a "hierarchically diluted" infinite universe has a finite and small surface brightness even in the absence of absorption or Doppler shifts.

In the case of closed space the universe (the whole, or the observable metagalaxy), with all its energy content, including radiation, is bound to return to the initial state of nuclear fluid. This course of events is likely to repeat itself, the universe oscillating without external loss, implying an unlimited age in the past and in the future (time here meaning simply a succession of events, irrespective of its numerical value). All the structural phases will return time and again without, however, an "eternal recurrence of all things" in Nietzsche's sense — the individual celestial bodies in successive oscillations would not be identical, nor would their inhabitants. On the contrary, an unlimited variety of combinations and of prospects of evolution would be possible during each phase of the oscillation.

Some have expressed disgust at the idea of an oscillating universe, periodically repeating its general features. The present writer cannot see why this great repetition should claim a lesser esthetic value than, e.g., the annual succession of seasons so praised by poet and layman. Besides, not only is the repetition never literally exact, but, alas, we have no say in the matter — the Plan was laid down without our being consulted beforehand.

SUPPLEMENTARY NOTE ON RECENT DEVELOPMENTS, DECEMBER 1959

During the four years elapsed since the publication of this article no basic changes have occurred in the outlook. New observational data are accumulating slowly, generally confirming the former viewpoints.

Datings of oldest rocks have not yet exceeded the figure of 2,900 million years, although several new determinations have been published. A few determinations may be cited: 2,700 million years for Rhodesian Shield from rubidium-strontium method (Schreiner et al., 1955); 2,900 million years for Rosetta Mine, 2,200-2,500 million years for six other South African localities from lead-isotope method (Bate and Kulp, 1955); 2,500 million years for Wind River Canyon in Wyoming, rubidium and other methods (Aldrich, 1956); 2,800 million years for four Western Australian pegmatites, potassium and rubidium methods (Jeffrey, 1956).

The method of extrapolation backward in time, developed by Holmes and applied to recent data by Holmes (1956), gave 4,500 ±100 million years for the age of formation of the earth's crust, instead of the former value of 3,350 million years; the indicated small probable error may not be quite realistic and may be due partly to subjective elimination of discrepant values. Another determination, made "with mathematical impartiality" (qualification by Holmes) by Russell and Allan (1955), arrived at a figure of 4,300 ± 400 million years. The time of formation of the crust, and probably of the terrestrial globe itself, can thus be set at from 4,000 to 4,500 million years ago, with an uncertainty of a few hundred million years.

The time of separation of meteoritic iron from stone can be determined much more precisely from the isotopic composition of lead; Patterson (1956) finds this as 4,550 ± 70 million years ago and shows that the same age apparently applies to terrestrial lead. This must be the age of formation of the small planets which, in breaking up, later created the meteorites; it is also the probable age of the solar system.

From the isotopic composition of lead it can also be concluded that the age of the elements in the solar system cannot exceed 5,500 million years. If the heavy isotopes are not produced in stellar interiors, this figure would represent also an upper limit to the age of the universe itself (Öpik, 1957), i.e. the time elapsed since its last superdense state.

As to the formation of the elements in stellar interiors and their injection into the interstellar medium in supernova explosions, much of the evidence has been based on the difference in composition between the old stars of Population II, whose atmospheres are poor in metals, and the younger Population I stars which, like our sun, contain a "normal" proportion of metals. The difference has been ascribed to age; it has been assumed that the metal content of the interstellar medium is gradually increasing, and that stars recently formed by condensation from the medium should contain more metals than those formed from the primordial hydrogen gas. Here, however, the dependence of the composition on age is not at all convincing. All the objects of Population II in which the metal abundance has been found to be low, namely the globular clusters as well as single stars of the galactic halo, have high velocities and belong to the halo, and are placed usually at a great distance from the galactic plane; whereas the "normal" Population I stars are of low velocities and belong to the galactic disk, keeping close to the galactic plane. The difference in composition may thus be due to the place of origin, and not to age. The elements heavier than helium in interstellar space are condensed into solid dust grains, concentrated into dark clouds near the galactic plane; the mechanics of this concentration is easily understood, in terms of dust particles losing momentum in a resisting gaseous medium. On the other hand, the galactic halo is almost pure hydrogen or hydrogen-helium gas. The high-velocity stars, originating from, or sweeping through, the halo, will contain little of the metals, whereas the Population I stars of the disk will absorb much more of them from the dust clouds. For stars unmixed in their interiors, the difference in composition may be only superficial, limited to the atmospheres of the stars and due to recent influx of materials from the space in which they move. However, with vast external convective regions, the influx of interstellar matter will hardly influence the composition even of the external layers of a star after its formation.

There is one object which seems to offer a crucial test in the question of the origin of the elements. The galactic star cluster Messier 67 has an old population whose age is about 5,000 million years (Johnson and Sandage 1955), yet whose stars are of "normal" composition as regards their metal content. It points to location, and not to age, as the chief factor determining the composition of stellar atmospheres. Stars recently formed in the spiral branches of our galaxy have the same metal abundance as those in Messier 67. There is no evidence of an enrichment in heavy elements over a period of five billion years. The evidence points definitely to a primeval origin of the elements. In this case the age of the elements of the solar system must be identical with that of the elements in the universe at large. The upper limit of 5,500 million years acquires thus particular significance.

A new time effect has been pointed out by R. H. Wilson (1956), consisting in electromagnetic damping of stellar rotation by the galactic magnetic field. The effect is amply sufficient to explain the slow rotation of the sun and all late-type old stars. Over a time interval of 4.5 billion years the period of rotation of the sun could have been changed from a few hours to the present-day slow value of 25 – 27 days. The one-time "insuperable" difficulty of angular momentum in the nebular theory of the origin of the solar system is thus finally removed, and the age of the sun cannot be much extended without running into the opposite difficulty of explaining why the sun is rotating at all (Öpik, 1958).

In the basic problem of the extragalactic distance scale, Humason, Mayall, and Sandage (1956) find Hubble's constant of recession equal to 180 km./sec. per megaparsec; this corresponds to an age of expansion of 3,600 million years (Euclidean space). Hnatek (1959), from a rediscussion of the magnitudes of nebulae, finds for the same material limiting values which would correspond to an age of from 3,600 to 4,800 million years. A revision of the available evidence by Sandage (1958) leads to an even lower value of Hubble's constant of 75 km./sec. per megaparsec and a corresponding "Euclidean" age of expansion of 8,700 million years, although with a possible uncertainty factor of 2. The result, uncertain as it is, does not yet necessitate revision of our conclusion as to the upper limit of 5,500 – 6,000 million years.

With the suspected space reddening of the galaxies, hopes of finding an indication of quick evolution from observations of distant galaxies have faded, for the present at least, as anticipated in the original report. New observations by Whitford (1956) indicate that the apparent reddening is due, indeed, to the depression in the ultraviolet spectrum of elliptical nebulae being displaced by the red shift into the blue.

New information on the distant regions of the universe is coming in from the observation of radio sources. These sources, mostly galaxies in collision whose gaseous envelopes emit radio waves, are observable to distances far beyond the reach of optical telescopes. Statistics of their distances may ultimately resolve the question of a steady-state versus an expanding or oscillating universe. Some preliminary results have been announced from Cambridge which seem to testify against the steady-state concept (Ryle and Scheuer, 1955); faint radio sources were found to be over-abundant, indicating that at an earlier stage (observed from a distance because of the time lag of radiation) the density of the universe was greater than now, and that the world is thus expanding. Unfortunately, there are ambiguities in the statistical interpretation of the observations, and at present definite conclusions cannot be made (Pawsey, 1958). From the available evidence, however, it appears "that the discrepancy between observation and the predictions of the steady-state model are considerably greater than could be established hitherto" (Ryle, 1959). Thus, observational evidence is against the steady-state, continuous creation model of the universe, although "the results are not yet conclusive" (Ryle).

The observed excess in the number of faint radio sources over that expected from the steady-state principle is by a factor of from 4 to 6 (Ryle). If this is not yet considered sufficient evidence, in the near future we may expect better statistics and a definite answer from the young science of radio astronomy to the fateful question: Is the world at large an exception to the example set by its ever-changing parts, or is it not, as has been suggested in the present article?

E. J. ÖPIK

THORNTON PAGE

The Origin of the Earth

[FROM THE SMITHSONIAN REPORT FOR 1949°]

A LOGICAL SEQUEL *to a discussion of the structure and time scale of the universe is a related problem, and one nearer at hand, the origin of the earth. Thornton Page, astrophysicist, former Rhodes scholar and University of Chicago professor of astrophysics, and consultant of the Johns Hopkins University's Operations Research Office, is now professor of astronomy at Wesleyan University. He frankly admits at the start that no current theory fits all the facts exactly. Early theories have been accepted, then lost favor, only to be later rejuvenated and reinstated. The author passes in review the clues derived from studying the earth's surface, from temperature and chemical investigations, from meteorite analysis, and from observations of the sizes, distances, and orbits of our sun's other planets.*

The recent theories of Weizsäcker, Kuiper, and Urey agree better with the known facts than previous hypotheses, but their consequences have not yet been fully evaluated. One of these consequences is of prime interest in indicating that the formation of planets around suns is a normal process, with the implication that there may be billions of habitable earths like ours.

° Revised as of December 1959 by insertion of addendum at end of article.

W ITH ALL the spectacular success of recent scientific research, it is perhaps refreshing to examine a field so characterized by failure as this one. Although many speculations have been described as "theories," there exists today no real theory of the origin of the earth in the sense of a complete logical structure linking together the vast quantity of pertinent observations collected during the last century.

The most obvious approach to the problem is to study the visible surface of the earth for clues to its origin. This has been done in detail by geologists, geodesists, geophysicists, and geochemists, but it is perhaps not surprising that what they find has more to do with the earth than with its origin. It has been the astronomer, studying the relation of the earth to its surroundings, and the physicist, studying the behavior of matter, who have made the greatest progress in the study of the earth's origin.

Early speculation on the subject was simple and direct because there were fewer observations to explain. The assumption of a divine creation of things as they are was generally accepted until the end of the sixteenth century. Then the revolution in scientific thinking, started by Galileo, turned men from assumptions of a catastrophic origin to a belief in natural development, understandable in terms of what can be seen and measured today. As the astronomical picture became clearer, it appeared that the earth is a relatively small, nearly spherical body moving around the sun together with the other planets, all under the influence of the sun's gravitational attraction. It was soon recognized as scarcely due to chance that all the known planets and their satellites are moving and rotating in the same direction, their orbits nearly circular, and in nearly the same plane. Therefore, in 1755, the great German philosopher-scientist, Immanuel Kant, speculated that the planets and the sun were formed from a single large rotating gaseous cloud, or nebula, which had condensed into smaller rotating parts, these further condensing into rotating planets with their satellites, all moving in the same direction round the nucleus of the nebula which became the sun. Kant's hypothesis explained nearly all of the available observational data within the framework of physics as it was developed at the time.

Later on, about 1800, the French mathematician, Laplace, independently proposed a modified form of the Kant hypothesis which, even though it was not given much weight by its author, soon became widely accepted as the concept upon which much of geology was founded. Laplace went further than Kant in explaining how the primordial nebula condensed into planets. He assumed that in the beginning the nebula was hot and spinning slowly, that the gas contracted as it cooled and therefore increased its spin in accordance with the law of conservation of angular momentum. As the spin increased, he reasoned, rings of gas would be thrown off by centrifugal action and each ring would condense into a planet. It is now recognized that no such condensation of hot gas at the rim of a spinning nebula would take place, but Laplace's speculation was important in that he introduced two new factors: the idea that the earth condensed from hot gases, and the consideration of angular momentum in the solar system.

Not until 1895 was the Laplace hypothesis seriously challenged. By that date geology had come into its own as a science, and T. C. Chamberlin, an American geologist, considered the geological evidence incompatible with the concept of a hot gaseous sphere cooling to become the present earth. Instead, he proposed the planetesimal hypothesis, in which the earth and other planets were built by accretion of cold particles (the planetesimals) which were moving around the sun under its gravitational attraction. Together with an astronomer, F. R. Moulton, he suggested that such planetesimals might have resulted from a near-collision between another star and our sun. The planetesimal hypothesis introduced two new concepts: that the earth was built by accretion of cold solid material, and that another star was involved in forming the solar system. The near-collision presumably being a rare event, this represented a return, in part, to the old concept of a catastrophic origin.

During the last 50 years, most of the thinking on this problem has been divided between the two widely divergent hypotheses of Laplace and Chamberlin. Did the earth start hotter or colder than

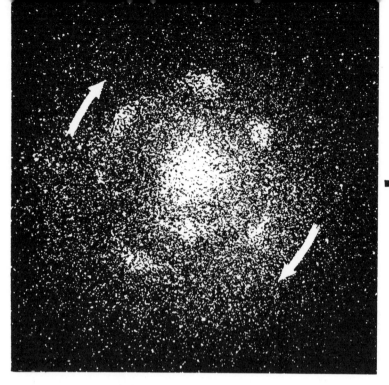

ILLUS. 3—KANT—1755
　　　1. Clotting mass of gas and dust in rotation.

ILLUS. 4—LAPLACE—1796
　　　1. Rotating nebula of hot gas.

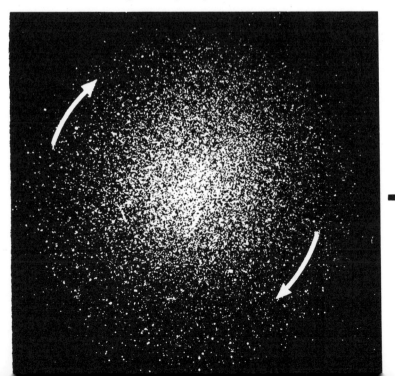

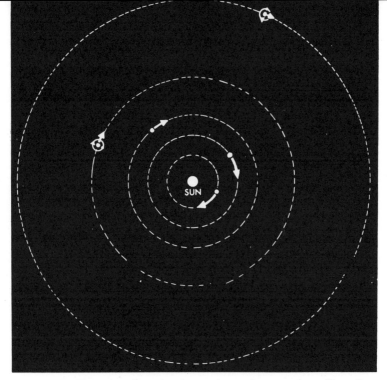

2. *Clots grow by accretion to form planets and satellites. Re-mainder of nebula contracts to form sun.*

2. *Cooling nebula shrinks, spins faster, and is expected to leave rings of gas to condense into planets. The remainder forms sun.*

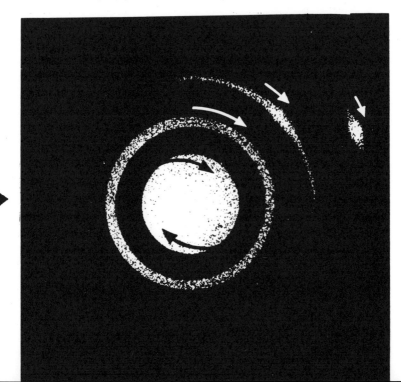

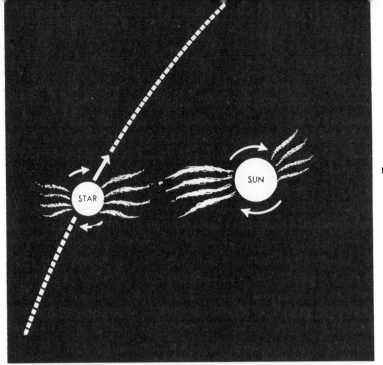

ILLUS. 5—CHAMBERLIN-MOULTON—1900

> 1. *A passing star narrowly misses the sun. Huge eruptions were expected to occur on both as they pass.*

at present? Has it condensed and contracted, or grown by accretion? Was its origin a commonplace occurrence in a nebula (many of which can be seen in the sky), or due to a highly unusual near-collision between stars? Whatever drawbacks these incomplete speculations may have had, they have provided definite concepts on the basis of which further research has been and yet remains to be done.

ILLUS. 6—WEIZSÄCKER—1945 *(opposite)*

> *Vortices formed in the equatorial plane of a nebula of gas and dust rotating about the sun, according to Weizsäcker. Accretion is expected to take place along the heavy concentric circles to form planets and satellite systems with direct rotation and revolution.*

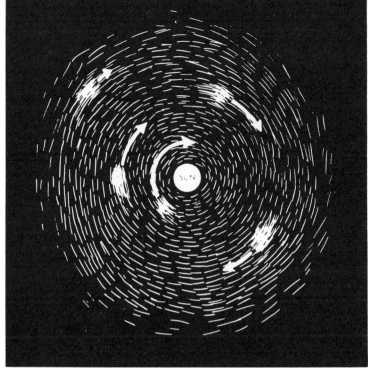

2. *The sun is left with a vast number of planetesimals which con-*
densed from the erupted gases and slowly coagulate to form
planets. The intruding star should also have planets forming.

THE RECORD IN THE ROCKS

In geology it is assumed that we can explain past developments on the basis of processes taking place today, and this assumption has been remarkably successful in tracing geological history to form a consistent pattern. The surface features of the earth can be explained as the expected result of erosion, of glacier action, of volcanism, and of movements of the crust itself, all of which are observed in action now. This reasoning might be expected to lead, step by step, to the origin of the earth.

The sequence of events in earth history is best summarized by the geologic column, a schematic pile of all the rock strata which have been classified, in the order of their formation. After fitting together rocks from all over the world, there are left only four major gaps in the record, when erosion in practically all parts of the earth now above sea level must have eliminated the rock deposits of millions of years. With these four exceptions, the geologic column, fitted together from the results of a century of world-wide geologic prospecting, gives almost as complete and consistent a picture of earth history as if the entries had been made in a diary. It lacks only the number of years intervening between the various geologic eras.

The dates were supplied when the absolute ages of rocks were estimated from their radioactivity, first in 1905 by Boltwood, an American physicist. He measured the relative amounts of lead and helium in uranium deposits. The uranium ore crystallized when the molten magma solidified, and the radioactive uranium has since been disintegrating at a constant but very slow rate to form lead and helium which, in favorable cases, have both remained sealed in the igneous rock with the uranium. The process of radioactive decay has been thoroughly studied in the laboratory by many physicists, including the Curies and Rutherford (who suggested Boltwood's research), and the rate of disintegration accurately measured.

Dating various igneous rocks in the geologic column showed first how very long was the record; the oldest igneous rocks yet dated crystallized about 3 billion years ago. Moreover, there are even older sedimentary rocks through which the molten magma had pushed to form these oldest known igneous rocks; hence the earth must have had surface conditions about 3 billion years ago not radically different from those today. There must have been water and an atmosphere operating to erode rocks and form sand and mud beds. Fossils in somewhat younger rocks indicate that early forms of life existed at least 1 billion years ago when conditions must have been very like those today.

But the geologic column fails to yield the one feature which might provide conclusive evidence on the earth's origin. No rocks yet examined have the appearance of an original crust; they are all either old sediments or solidified magma which pushed up through sediments.

TEMPERATURE AS A CLUE

Trying another tack, we might expect that the earth's thermal history could be traced back to determine its temperature at birth. In deep mines and wells the temperature increases 1° C. for each 125 feet below the surface. Knowing how rocks conduct heat, we find that 10 million million calories of heat are flowing out from the earth's interior each second. If the earth were solid granite, all 7,000 billion billion tons of it, this escaping heat would cool it

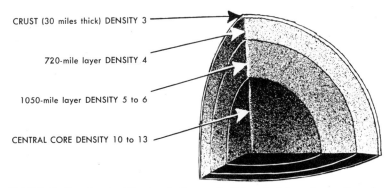

CRUST (30 miles thick) DENSITY 3

720-mile layer DENSITY 4

1050-mile layer DENSITY 5 to 6

CENTRAL CORE DENSITY 10 to 13

ILLUS. 7—Density stratification in the earth. Seismologists, using earthquake waves as a sounding device, have discovered these layers within the earth. They may indicate that the earth was once molten; or they may result from chemical compaction and plastic flow within the earth.

about 1° C. in 3 million years. From this measured rate of cooling is it possible to determine whether the earth was originally molten?

One must be careful in such estimates; not all of this heat comes from cooling the earth, since the radioactive disintegration so useful in determining the age of rocks is also releasing energy. In fact if the measured radioactivity is constant with depth, the outer crust of the earth only 12 miles thick would provide all the 10 million million calories leaving the earth's interior. If the radioactive material goes deeper than 12 miles, the earth must, willy-nilly, be heating up! So the heat now leaving the earth does not give a clue to its original temperature, although it does point to another approach. Since it is improbable that the earth is heating up rapidly, the radioactive material probably is not distributed uniformly throughout the earth but is concentrated in surface layers.

Such a stratification within the earth might have a bearing on the original conditions. For instance, if the earth were once molten, we might expect heavier materials to sink to the center and lighter ones to come to the surface. A variety of measurements do prove that the earth is much more dense at the core than at the surface, and this central condensation was long used to support the concept of an originally molten globe. In fact, the central core itself was generally believed still to be molten. But a few years ago, observations of faint earthquake waves which could only have passed through the core if it were solid, disputed the point.

It is now generally accepted that the earth's interior is stratified in three distinct layers on a central core which is four times as dense as the surface rocks, and although probably as solid throughout as surface rocks, it yields to plastic flow over long intervals of time. (The molten lava of volcanoes is only in local pools liquefied by a temporary release of pressure.) Recent work by geochemists shows that at least some of the stratification is due to chemical compaction, the tremendous pressures favoring the formation of heavier chemical compounds in the interior. There is no satisfactory explanation of the dense core, which must be a material radically different from surface rock. But its existence can no longer be used with certainty to argue that the earth was' once molten.

CHEMICAL CLUES

Geochemical studies give a somewhat better clue to the earth's temperature at birth. Harrison Brown at Chicago has recently shown that all the elements which exist mainly in gaseous form — hydrogen, helium, neon, argon, krypton, xenon — occur in the earth, its seas and atmosphere, to a very much smaller extent than expected from studies of the abundances of elements, both from theory and from observations of the sun and stars.

The low abundance of hydrogen and helium is easy to understand: at temperatures of 500 to 600 degrees Centigrade they would escape from the gravitational attraction of the earth in a few hundred million years because of the high velocities and small masses of their molecules. But the heavier atoms, krypton and xenon, could have escaped in quantity only if the material of the earth were at one time in much smaller pieces, with correspondingly smaller gravitational attraction, or if the earth had for some time a temperature of 10,000 to 30,000° C. Now this is hotter than most stars, and quite impossible for the earth to maintain, so we deduce that early in its history the material of the earth was in separate, small pieces. Since oxygen, nitrogen, and water-vapor molecules are all lighter than krypton (and would therefore escape if krypton did), it appears that the earth's atmosphere and oceans must have been formed from the decomposition of heavier compounds after the earth achieved its present size.

To summarize the best geological evidence: the earth is at least 3 billion years old and its surface conditions of temperature and atmosphere have not changed materially in 1 billion years and not radically in 3 billion years. Its stratified layers from density about 3 at the surface to density about 13 at the center could result from plastic flow and chemical compaction whether or not the earth were originally molten. Finally, the earth lost most of its gases early in life, probably because it was at one time in pieces of too small mass to hold on to light gas molecules.

SHOOTING STARS

An important bridge between geology and astronomy is provided by the meteors. Millions of these small chunks of rock and iron collide with the earth each day, most of them burning up high in the atmosphere. Some of the larger, slower-moving ones reach the ground; there the few collected are the only material from outside the earth available for detailed study. Are they a few remaining planetesimals — or are they visitors from outside the solar system?

Measures of meteor speeds by Whipple at Harvard have established that they are at least members of the solar system. If they came from outside they would be moving much faster than observed. Radioactivity measurements (as in dating rocks, but corrected for the effects of cosmic rays which form extra helium) show that the meteors are between 2 and 3 billion years old, in startling agreement with the earth's age. Their high iron and nickel content has supported the assumption that the earth's core is nickel-iron (so that earth and meteors would have the same over-all composition).

Furthermore, Harrison Brown's recent studies of the chemical compounds present in meteorites show that they were probably at one time under the high pressures and temperatures of a planet's interior. It would seem that, far from being planetesimals, the meteors are the remains of a fair-sized planet which was formed at the same time as the earth, and which broke up in some large-scale interplanetary collision at a later date.

THE GAMUT OF SPECULATION

The astronomer, in his approach to the problem of the earth's origin, started by recognizing a certain order and regularity among the planets, their satellites, and the smaller asteroids, all moving about the sun. The emphasis is shifted from the origin of the earth, as one of the planets, to the origin of the solar system as a whole. The latest trend goes even further in linking the origin of the solar system with the early history or origin of our galaxy of stars and even of the whole universe.

The solar system regularities noted by Kant clearly indicate that the planets had a common origin; ever since Kant's time it has been the fond hope of cosmogonists to establish the exact nature of that origin from further studies of the over-all pattern of the solar system. The first clue of this sort to be noted was the spacing of the planets; they are not at irregular distances from the sun, but spaced approximately in geometric progression — that is, the distances can be calculated roughly from a formula called Bode's law after its discoverer. Since the planets continue to move in the same orbits year after year, this spacing must have been established during their formation.

A second possible clue to the origin lies in the progression of planet sizes — from the smallest, Mercury, which is nearest the sun, increasing through Venus, Earth, and Mars to Jupiter, the largest, then decreasing through Saturn, Uranus, and Neptune to Pluto, a small planet, and most distant from the sun.

Further clues will be noted as we follow, now, the twentieth-century history of speculation on the birth of the solar system, from Chamberlin to Weizsäcker and Whipple. Each of these theoreticians has started either from the Kant nebular hypothesis, or from the Chamberlin two-star hypothesis, and tried to show by more or less exact reasoning that the presently observed solar system would have resulted naturally. Chamberlin and Moulton in 1900 guessed that the close approach of another star to our sun would raise great eruptions on the sun, that hot solar material would condense into small planetesimals moving around the sun and that these planetesimals would later stick together to form the planets by accretion.

In 1917 the English astronomers Jeans and Jeffreys made more exact calculations and concluded that the eruptions would not have taken place; rather, the intruding star would have to side-swipe the sun, peeling off a long filament of solar material which would then condense into the planets. They pointed out that this filament would be thicker in the middle than at the ends, thereby accounting for the progression of planetary sizes.

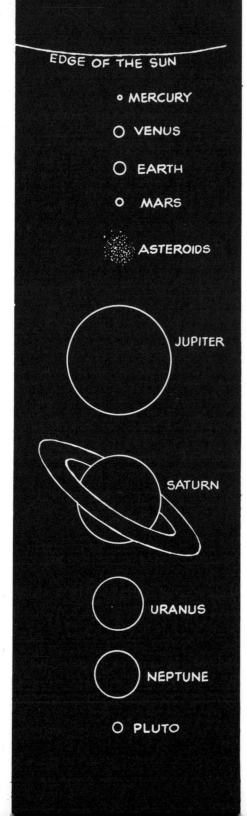

ILLUS. 8—Scale of planet sizes.

The Jeans-Jeffreys hypothesis seemed satisfactory until 1930, when Nölke in Germany and Russell at Princeton pointed out another clue: the angular momentum of the planets. Just as a spinning top would keep on spinning forever if there were no friction, so the planets must have maintained constant angular momentum in their orbits around the sun, since nothing analogous to friction is known in the solar system. If the planets were formed from material pulled out of the sun, this law of conservation of angular momentum requires that the original planetary material must have started moving around the sun with the same angular momentum the planets have today. Russell showed mathematically that a grazing collision with another star could not start the filament of planetary material off with anywhere near enough angular momentum.

In an effort to patch things up, one of Russell's students, Lyttleton, analyzed mathematically the case of a collision between three stars, and found that it was just possible to produce a filament of material moving with sufficient angular momentum about one of them. An English astronomer, Hoyle, showed it was also possible if one of two close stars blew up, as a somewhat asymmetrical nova, propelling itself away and leaving some planetary material moving around the other star.

But these mathematical exercises and the whole sequence of speculations based on the two-star hypothesis were brought sharply to a close in 1939 when Spitzer, another of Russell's students, calculated that the material pulled out of the sun, or any other star, could not condense into planets or planetesimals anyway — it would expand with explosive violence to form a tenuous gaseous nebula!

BACK TO THE NEBULAR HYPOTHESIS

Long before Spitzer had shown that the two-star hypothesis would lead to a nebula, other scientists had been working away on the nebular hypothesis, trying to find some means by which material near the sun would form a group of planets all moving in the same direction in nearly circular orbits and in nearly the same plane. In 1914 a Norwegian physicist, Birkeland, calculated that electrically charged particles shot out of the sun would spiral out in the sun's magnetic field to definite circular orbits at distances depending on the ratio between the electric charge and the mass of the particles. This promising lead was followed further in 1930 by a Dutch meteorologist, Berlage, who assumed the particles were charged atoms. More recently, in 1942, the Swedish physicist, Alfvén, was able to predict by similar reasoning that rings of gas with sufficient angular momentum would be formed around the sun as the sun moved through a nebula, but both he and Berlage have avoided the embarrassing problem of how this gas could condense to form planets.

Lastly in the sequence of nebular speculations, a German physicist, Weizsäcker, has recently investigated in detail the motion of a large cloud of dust and gas in rotation about a massive central body like the sun. From this return to the ungarnished Kant hypothesis he was able to show that, while most of the gas would escape into outer space, the planets could be formed by the accretion of the dust particles over a period of a hundred million years — a short time compared to the age of the earth. The spacing of the planetary orbits Weizsäcker explains in this manner: The inner parts of the rotating nebula would be pulled around more rapidly by the sun's gravitational attraction than the outer parts. Like stirring a bowl of soup near the center, this would set up eddies, and at the boundaries of the eddies the dust would coagulate most rapidly. These boundaries, Weizsäcker calculated, would be spaced approximately in a geometric progression from the sun just as the planets are observed to be.

The Weizsäcker hypothesis accounts for more of the observational data than any of the previous speculations, but because it is so recent a number of its consequences have not been explored and some of the estimates may need revision.

One of the interesting consequences is that the formation of planets should be an extremely common occurrence. Possibly in the process of formation of *every* star the conditions would be correct to form planets. Thus we might expect billions, if not hundreds of billions of planets in our galaxy, the strong likelihood that life has developed on a million or more of these, the high probability that there are other civilizations of mankind, and even the possibility that men on other planets are writing articles on the origins of their solar systems!

THE ORIGIN OF STARS

But where did the original gas and dust come from? How was it started in rotation? One reason the Weizsäcker hypothesis has received so much attention is that a separate line of research on the origin of the stars has provided answers to these questions. The argument hinges on the energy necessary to keep the stars shining.

The closest star — our sun — is radiating energy at such a stupendous rate that no ordinary energy generator could keep it going for the 3 billion years we know it has been shining on the earth. However, it is now known that atomic energy provides the sun's light and heat by a process in which four atoms of hydrogen are converted into one atom of helium and the excess mass changed into radiant energy. The details of this process, which can only proceed at the high temperature and pressure of a star's interior, were established by Hans Bethe at Cornell in 1938. But there are many hot stars thousands of times brighter than the sun (if viewed from the same distance), and a simple calculation shows that they would use up all their atomic energy in a mere 10 million years. Where did these hot bright stars come from if they can last only one three-hundredth as long as the earth has been in existence?

A possible answer was provided in 1947 by Lyman Spitzer at Yale, and Bart Bok at Harvard. Spitzer showed theoretically that diffuse gas and dust which is observed between the stars could, under some circumstances, be compressed by the pressure of radiation from all the other stars, to condense into a new star. Bok observed in the Milky Way certain small dark knots of such interstellar material, which may well be stars in the process of formation. Here is the process of growth by accretion on a much larger scale. This theory is well enough established that Whipple at Harvard has recently proposed that the planets coagulated in the manner postulated by Kant and by Weizsäcker during the formation of the sun itself.

GALAXIES

As we are pushed farther and farther in explaining the origin of our planet, new sources of evidence come into the problem. The next evidence comes from a study of the large groups of stars called galaxies.

Passing from the solar system to the stars is no larger a jump — and no smaller — than from the earth to the solar system. Our galaxy includes all the visible stars and is a correspondingly large system, outside of which the telescope shows many other galaxies. These are believed to be very like our own galaxy — a disk-shaped conglomeration with a mass, determined from its rotation, of about 200 billion star masses. There are about 100 billion stars in a galaxy, the rest of the material being spread between the stars in the form of gas and dust.

The outside galaxies, often called "spiral nebulae," are being studied by Hubble at the Mount Wilson Observatory in California, and by other astronomers with large telescopes. As Hubble looks farther and farther out into space (by taking longer photographic exposures with larger and larger telescopes), he finds more and more spiral nebulae, apparently without limit. In 1925 Hubble and Humason found from the redness of their light that the more distant spirals are receding from us more rapidly than the closer ones, and that the speed of their retreat is in direct proportion to their distance from us. At first sight this appears to leave our galaxy (with our sun and earth) in a central and somewhat unpopular position, with the rest of the universe running away. But a little thought shows that our view of the universe is the same as the view from any one of the other galaxies; each would see the rest receding from him with velocities proportional to their distances from him.

Tracing the motions back in time (there is no evidence that the spirals are accelerating or decelerating) shows that all the spiral nebulae would have been near our galaxy between 2 and 3 billion years ago. The coincidence of this with the age of the earth and the age of the meteorites is too marked to need further comment

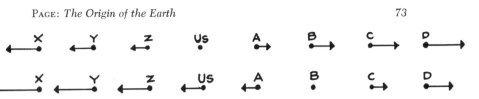

ILLUS. 9—Upper, our view of some spiral nebulae. The arrows indicate veloc-ities. Note that spiral B, which is twice as far from us as spiral A, is receding twice as fast. C, three times as far, is receding three times as fast, and so on. Lower, the view of an observer on spiral B, considering himself to be at rest. It is the principle of relativity that he has just as much right as we do to consider himself at rest. He gets the same view as we do; all the spirals are receding from B with velocity proportional to distance.

— the whole universe seems to have started with a bang about 3 billion years ago!

THE BEGINNING OF TIME

This curious evidence that the spiral nebulae were all close to — if not entangled with — our galaxy 3 billion years ago, means that the formation of the solar system at that time probably took place under conditions somewhat different from those of today. To be sure of the reasoning, we must examine the conditions of 3 billion years ago more carefully; it was this reexamination which led, in 1945, to the most bizarre suggestion of all in this field already rich in speculation. It was put forward by the English biologist, J. B. S. Haldane, and is based on a new theory — or philosophy — of relativity proposed in 1932 by the English mathematician, E. A. Milne. First we shall speak of Milne and his brand of relativity.

To make the reasoning clear we must start with Einstein's ear-lier relativity theory which links space and time in such a way that if one observer is moving at constant velocity past another his measurements of distances and time intervals will differ from those of the first observer, although the relation of time and distance is such that they both observe the same laws of physics. Einstein formulated his relativity on the philosophy that it is simply impos-sible to tell which observer is "at rest." Complicated as it sounds,

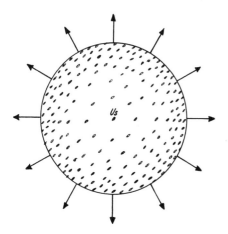

ILLUS. 10—*Milne's picture of the universe. If all measurements are made in atomic time, on Milne's theory, the universe started expanding from a point 3 billion atomic years ago. As we see it now the spiral nebulae shown in the left diagram are all moving away from us and (if we could see far enough) would be much more numerous near the "edge." At this edge the velocity of recession is equal to the velocity of light, so we can never hope to see the edge itself. On the other hand, if clock time is used for all our measurements, the universe is static and the spiral nebulae, as shown on the right above, are uniformly distributed on to infinity. The more distant nebulae are redder because we see them as they were many years ago with "slow" atoms. The "edge" of this picture comes when this reddening gets so extreme that galaxies are no longer visible.*

this scheme has been developed to form a logically complete theory in terms of mathematical transformations. Milne extended the established principles of relativity in his "cosmological principle," which is, in effect, an assumption that the view of the whole universe from one spiral nebula must be the same as the view from any other. Moreover, he has redefined distance measurements in terms of the travel time of light signals, as in radar ranging, thus reducing both time and distance measurements to readings of clocks, in principle.

Milne then raises the disturbing question: How are we sure that our clocks are reading constant intervals of time? In fact, the slowing down of the earth's rotation (which is normally our "master clock") has been measured as one-thousandth of a second per century by comparison with the planets, and we have no philosophically sound assurance that the planets keep "perfect time."

The cosmological principle leads mathematically to two kinds of time, one of which is speeding up relative to the other. Milne has shown that pendulum clocks, the earth, and the planets keep "dynamic" or clock time, while vibrating atoms and radioactive decay have constant period only in "kinematic" or atomic time. There is no philosophical reason for choosing one kind as the "correct" time; if we used a pendulum clock to time atoms we would find, after a very long interval, that the atoms are gradually speeding up in their vibration, if we used an atomic clock we would similarly find that the planets are slowing down in their orbits.

If this is correct — and no one has yet proved it otherwise — the age of the earth is 3 billion *atomic years* as determined from radioactive decay, but it is many more clock years, since in the past the clock year was shorter than the atomic year. (They are equal at present — by definition.)

The coincidence between the age of the earth and the time of recession of the spiral nebulae Milne explains as a result of the difference in these two kinds of time. Since the light we observe from a spiral 100 million light-years away left there 100 million years ago, we are seeing the atoms there ticking off the units of atomic time in use 100 million years ago. Compared to our present atoms, these early atoms ran slow; as a result, the light they emitted is redder than the light emitted now by similar atoms on the earth.

From this effect and his cosmological principle, Milne calculates that in the past infinite number of clock years there were 3 billion atomic years. The origin of the earth, and the time when all the spirals were close to our galaxy, both of them 3 billion atomic years ago, therefore occurred at the beginning of time (since one could hardly expect *more* than infinite time on the clock scale).

Now for Haldane's suggestion, which he calls "A Quantum Theory of the Origin of the Solar System." It is based, as its name implies, on the well-established quantum theory of radiation, and on a mathematical result of Milne's theory: that the universe, as measured in atomic time, has expanded with the velocity of light, starting from a point of zero radius 3 billion atomic years ago.

Since the universe started from zero radius, Haldane was able to pick an early enough instant, just a fraction of a second after the start of atomic time, when the whole universe was but a fraction of an inch in diameter — much smaller than the wavelength of visible light — smaller, by far, than the wavelength of X-rays or gamma rays. (These fractions are too small to write out easily; the first requires 72 zeros after the decimal point, the second, 62!) The wavelengths of radiation in existence in this small universe could scarcely have been bigger than the universe itself, Haldane reasoned, therefore the only radiation in existence was of these incredibly short wavelengths. But the basic principle of the quantum theory is that radiant energy comes only in packets, or "quanta," inversely proportional to the wavelength in size. So, at this early instant all radiation was in giant quanta of very small waves. And the energy of one of these giant quanta can easily be calculated as sufficient to knock one or more planets out of the sun. The even smaller waves at a somewhat earlier instant would have been in quanta with sufficient energy to tear apart stars, and even earlier, to tear apart the galaxies from some primordial globe of matter.

The details of this remarkable suggestion have been carried no farther, but Haldane's investigation points up one important general fact: whether or not Milne's new relativity is accepted, conditions at the time of the origin of the solar system were probably considerably different from those today. If Milne's cosmology is accepted, the relationship between radiation and matter was most radically different. It may seem that this last and most fantastic speculation — which can neither be completely explained nor fully evaluated here — contradicts our former conclusion that the solar system was formed from a rotating nebula of gas and dust. However, the condensation of the planets and the distribution of angular momentum (which have been so difficult to explain in all previous theories) may follow from further mathematical investigation of the first second of atomic time. In fact, if the details can be worked out rigorously, Haldane's suggestion may lead to confirmation of Milne's cosmology, which is as yet lacking.

In an echo of the introductory remarks it scarcely needs to be emphasized that we have no complete theory of the origin of the earth. The reader may be impressed with the diverse investigations involved and with the promise of the latest speculations; or he may notice the infinite regression implicit in any question of origins: if the planets were formed from dust or planetesimals, whence came the dust or planetesimals? if the dust and planetesimals came from a primordial nebula, whence came the primordial nebula? if the primordial nebula was formed by the absorption of a giant quantum by a fragment of matter, whence came the original matter and radiation in the universe? and so on, *ad infinitum* (clock time).

ADDENDUM, DECEMBER 1959

During the years since this article was first published, much has been done to contradict the opening paragraph. We now have, primarily in the work of Gerard Kuiper of the Yerkes Observatory, an acceptable concept of the early days of the sun and solar system, a modification of the Weizsäcker model described on page 70. Working back from the present sizes and masses of the planets, Kuiper computes the sizes and densities of the first condensations in the primordial nebula around the sun, which was at that time of much lower temperature than today. These "protoplanets" must have been from 10 times (Jupiter) to 1,000 times (earth) more massive than the present planets, in order that the escape of gases over the billion years or so of their evolution (while the sun was heating up) would leave the planets as we see them today.

Tracing this development backward even further, by spreading the protoplanet masses out in a symmetrical nebula, Kuiper finds the mass distribution in the primordial solar nebula, and was able to show in 1949 that it would have to break up, of its own instability, into chunks at distances corresponding to Bode's Law (page 67). This result is at once a confirmation of Kuiper's model and an explanation of Bode's Law.

The larger protoplanets, furthermore, would continue the process, forming extensive satellite systems as observed around Jupiter and Saturn, much as the planets were formed around the sun. The details of this process explain why the satellites are rotating slowly and why they did not form further systems of even smaller satellites. Much of the reasoning is based on the theory of tides in the protoplanets and protosatellites, and the evaporation of lighter elements caused by the steadily brightening sun. The evaporated gas was pushed out of the system much as comet tails are pushed out by the light and particles streaming out from the sun today.

Finally, Kuiper shows that some satellites would temporarily escape from their parent planet and some of these would be recaptured as the "irregular" satellites we see today (in orbits of high inclination, or in retrograde sense). He interprets Pluto as such an escaped satellite of Neptune. The asteroids can be understood in terms of a low density of material in the primordial nebula that prevented the formation of a single, larger protoplanet between Mars and Jupiter; the meteors resulted from a collision of two escaped satellites; and the comets are the remnants of the solar nebula far from the sun (beyond Neptune and Pluto).

Of course many other contributions have been made by astronomers, physicists, chemists and geologists over the past dozen years. A good deal more is now known about the compaction of material to form the dense cores of planets. More basically, the measured ages of the earth (from the radioactivity in rocks), the meteorites (also based on radioactivity, as indicated on page 66), the stars, and the whole universe (based on the independent evidence of expansion, as on page 72) have all been increased from 3 billion to about 10 billion years.

A number of other developments, just as fascinating, are closely associated with these current views on the origin of the earth: the origin and evolution of stars, of galaxies, and of the elements themselves. As implied in the conclusion written 12 years ago, we will probably never be sure of actual origins, but we can understand many more of the puzzling regularities of the universe on the basis of these theories — and even see new regularities in what previously appeared as chaos.

THORNTON PAGE

JOHN W. EVANS

Solar Influence on the Earth

[FROM THE SMITHSONIAN REPORT FOR 1954°]

FOR THE MOST PART, *we think of the sun simply as a brilliant globe in the sky that rises in the morning, provides us with light and warmth (in season), and sets at night. This it has been doing to all appearances unfailingly for some billions of years, so that we have come to consider the sun as completely reliable. But to those concerned with radio and wire communication, it is apparent that the sun at intervals acts in strange ways, at times disrupting such communication. These vagaries are of vital importance, particularly to airplane pilots, and it is appropriate that this discussion is presented by John W. Evans, who is Director of the Sacramento Peak Observatory of the Air Force Cambridge Research Center, at Sunspot, New Mexico.*

The worst offenders among the sun's caprices are the "flares" — great outbursts of brilliance on the sun ranging in size up to 100,000 miles in diameter. These are followed by a lowering of the terrestrial ionosphere, which in turn causes radio fadeouts. It is of vital importance to learn how to predict such occurrences, and Government and industrial agencies are uniting in attacking the problem.

° Revised as of November 1959 by insertion of addendum at end of article.

ALTHOUGH THE SUN is the great provider of the neces-
sities for life, most of us know rather little about it simply because
it is so thoroughly reliable. We do not have to worry about whether
we shall receive our daily quota of solar energy tomorrow. A very
long history of unfailing performance justifies the belief that we
shall. In fact, an astronomer friend recently offered to bet me a
dollar at odds of 10 to 1 that the sun would still be shining 1
billion years from now. He made the proviso that he should hold
the stakes. After computing the interest on $1 for 1 billion years,
I decided that this was a mere swindle. The winning of the bet
pales into insignificance compared to the compound interest on a
dollar for a billion years — a figure so large that even our Government has not found a name for it.

Since the sun is so reliable we devote our worries to more
worthy problems, such as whether it will rain in Texas, or whether
the Senators can beat the Yankees, since these matters are highly
uncertain. There are, however, a few peculiar sun worshipers re-
siding on mountain peaks and at other odd places, surrounded by
telescopes and spectroscopes and radio gadgets, who take the sun
very seriously. They are finding that in some things the sun is very
capricious and quite unreliable. Until recently this had so little
effect on our daily lives that we were not even aware of it. But
with the rising complexity of our technology and our dependence
on delicate devices that are vulnerable to small disturbances, we
are becoming increasingly aware of the effects of these minor solar
variations, although most of us do not recognize the sun as the
root of our troubles. It is these minor solar variations and their
terrestrial effects that concern us here.

I am sure you are familiar with the effect of fading on your
radios. Usually stations come in strong and clear from tremendous
distances, but once in a while the signal fades out and all you can
get are local stations within 100 miles or so. While parents of
teenage youngsters may regard this as a blessing, the pilot of a
transatlantic airplane is apt to disagree. Whether we like it or not,

this fading-out of distant radio stations is traceable to the sun. What happens is something like this:

Radio waves are like light. If not disturbed they go in straight lines, and if nothing interfered, we could not receive them any farther away than we can see. In fact, the short high-frequency waves of television have this property, which is the reason a given television station can serve only a small area within 25 or 30 miles. The longer waves of the broadcast band however, can be transmitted to the other side of the world. To get there, they have to travel around the curve of the earth in anything but a straight line-of-sight path. This is possible because the ionosphere serves as a highly reflecting mirror to long radio waves, which bounce back and forth between it and the ground and are thus conducted around the curve of the earth.

That word "ionosphere" is very important in any explanation of solar terrestrial effects. In broadest terms, the ionosphere is that portion of our upper atmosphere which is capable of conducting electricity. Its normal lower limit is some 60 miles above the ground, where the density of the air is less than a millionth of that at ground level, and it extends upward to above 130 miles.

The atmosphere at all heights is composed of myriads of tiny particles known as molecules. There are so many of them that when you take a good deep breath you can be quite sure of inhaling a couple of hundred that were breathed out by Patrick Henry in uttering the words "Give me Liberty or give me death," and have since been thoroughly mixed with the whole atmosphere of the earth. The thought would perhaps be a little unappetizing if Patrick Henry had not used that breath so effectively. Its significance is simply that there are about 200 times as many molecules in a single breath as there are lungfuls of air in the whole of the earth's atmosphere. What I am trying to say is that the molecules of the atmosphere are tiny and numerous. Furthermore they are complicated. They are made up usually of two atoms of oxygen or nitrogen, held together by electric bonds. When one of these molecules is given a sufficient jolt it comes apart. Sometimes the two atoms are separated. When this happens one of the atoms may steal an electron from the other, and both then have an electric charge. Sometimes the jolt merely removes an electron without otherwise disturbing the molecule. Either of these processes is called ionization. The particles resulting from ionization are known as ions and free electrons. Their important property is that they carry a small electric charge and therefore can be pushed around by electric forces, unlike normal molecules.

The ionosphere gets its name and its electrical conductivity from the fact that it contains an appreciable fraction of ions and free electrons. As many as one molecule in every 10,000 may be ionized. It is actually the free electrons that reflect long radio waves. The process of reflection is too complicated to explain here, but I will ask you to endure a crude analogy. Think of the electrons in the ionosphere as an ionospheric screen, like a window screen. The fineness of the mesh of our screen is proportional to the number of electrons per cubic inch in the ionosphere. When radio waves hit the screen, they are caught and thrown back if they are larger than the mesh, but if they are smaller they pass through between the electrons, so to speak, to outer space. Thus the long waves of the broadcast band are reflected, and can be received over long distances around the curve of the earth, while the short TV waves are not reflected, but penetrate through the ionospheric screen, for the benefit of inhabitants of artificial earth satellites and the moon. The ionospheric screen has one other property that is directly responsible for radio fading. Under normal conditions there is good reflection from it when it is in the high atmosphere where the electrons have room to shake themselves without too much interference from neighboring molecules. But if for some reason the screen is pushed down to low levels where there may be a hundred times as many molecules per cubic inch, the screen gets clogged and the radio waves are neither reflected nor transmitted. They are absorbed, and distant stations fade out. The energy of the radio waves stops right there and goes into warming the air. I am sure this fact is not generally known in the halls of Congress. If it were, and our legislators realized that under special conditions they could warm the air of the upper atmosphere while warming that in their immediate vicinity, the condition of the ionosphere would be fixed by law, since any presidential veto would surely be overridden.

While the fading of radio signals is the most familiar solar effect, whether we recognize it as such or not, there are others which I shall discuss presently. The noteworthy fact is that all of them can be traced to disturbances in the ionosphere, and we may justly conclude that the primary solar terrestrial effect from which all observable effects stem, is the influence of the sun on the ionosphere. Now, just what is this influence?

The thing that counts in the ionosphere is the concentration of ions — the number of ions per cubic inch — at various heights above the ground. Normal concentrations vary from about 1 to 3 million ions per cubic inch at different heights.

I have already mentioned that ions are formed when air molecules are subjected to sufficiently large jolts. In ordinary terms, the required jolt is very small. In climbing an inch up the wall a fly expends enough energy to ionize a hundred billion molecules. But it is not altogether easy to ionize a molecule in spite of this. The trick is to concentrate the little bit of energy required on a single molecule. You cannot do it by swinging a baseball bat. The energy is there all right, but it gets spread around among billions of billions of molecules, and no single one of them gets enough to break it in two. The only two things that possess the required energy in sufficiently compact packages to be concentrated on single molecules are the bullets of ultraviolet light known as quanta, and fast-traveling atomic particles of several types, which are known collectively as corpuscles. The very existence of the ionosphere is sure evidence that the earth is being showered continuously with ultraviolet quanta or corpuscles or both. Until recently neither of these agents could be observed directly. They are completely absorbed in the process of forming the ionosphere and never reach the ground. To them the upper atmosphere is like a brick wall, and both ultraviolet quanta and corpuscles expend their energy on it in the process of forming ions. However, even though they were unseen, there were several good reasons for supposing that both corpuscles and quanta were involved in the formation of the ionosphere and that they all came from the sun. It did not take a Sherlock Holmes to pin it on the sun. There simply is no other likely source handy. Furthermore, it was observed that certain events on the sun were often followed by sudden large changes in the ionosphere with such perfect timing that there could be no doubt of a connection. The timing also put the finger on the disturbing agents. When a flare flashed up on the solar surface, the ionosphere on the daylit side of the earth responded instantly. In other words, the disturbing agent had made the trip from the sun to the earth along a straight-line path and with the same speed as the light by which we saw the flare, and must therefore be ultraviolet quanta. Then about a day later a second and more prolonged ionospheric disturbance would set in all over the world long after the flare had died out and disappeared. The one-day time lag was interpreted as the time required for a shower of material corpuscles to travel the 93,000,000 miles from the sun. They were electrically charged and guided in to all parts of the earth by the earth's magnetic field. Hence, both quanta and corpuscles were involved. All this is a nice example of the power of careful step-by-step reasoning to explain phenomena that cannot be directly observed. First it was observed that radio waves were transmitted around the world, and Kennelly and Heaviside explained this by assuming the existence of the ionosphere. Then radio experiments were devised specifically to test this assumption — and it proved correct. It was realized that the ionosphere can be maintained only by incoming ultraviolet quanta or corpuscles; and again it was assumed that the sun must be the source of these. Finally this was confirmed by observation of disturbances on the sun and corresponding disturbances in the ionosphere. Having got this far we have the main outlines of the activity without ever having seen it. As I have described it, it appears much less complicated than it actually was. The scientific method rarely runs smoothly. A theory is advanced. Investigators think it over and give it up, and think some more and give it up some more, until some key discovery convinces them that it is a good idea, or quite impossible. Then they are ready for the next step.

In the case of the ionosphere, theory has received brilliant observational confirmation in the last few years. Scientists of the Naval Research Laboratory and of the University of Colorado have sent rockets into the ionosphere from the White Sands Proving Grounds. They unequivocally recorded the ultraviolet radiation from the sun for the first time. A year or so earlier the incoming corpuscles were also observed directly at the Yerkes Observatory and at Cornell by spectroscopic means, and their velocities were found to vary from a few hundred to more than 2,000 miles/sec.

I think that by now you have anticipated me in seeing how the ionosphere is disturbed by the sun. Its existence is due to a steady stream of ultraviolet quanta and corpuscles from the sun. The intensity of this stream frequently varies violently. These variations cause changes in the density of ions at different heights in the ionosphere. To get back to our analogy, the height and mesh of the ionospheric screen is drastically altered, and detectable effects immediately follow. When the ionosphere is pushed downward into the denser regions of the atmosphere it becomes clogged and absorbs all radio signals, and we have fading.

Radio fading, however, is by no means the only result of abnormal ionospheric conditions. I have discussed it in detail because it probably affects more people than any of the others. The others are equally interesting, and usually result from some other kind of change than a depression of the ionospheric net into the gummy denser air of the lower levels.

The magnetic field of the earth is often affected, quite independently of radio fading. The compass needle points a trifle off its normal direction, and the strength of the field increases or decreases slightly. This is referred to as a magnetic storm. Without delicate magnetometers we would be quite unaware of the most violent magnetic storms because they stimulate none of our five senses. One manifestation of a magnetic storm, however, is often beautifully visible. This is the aurora. Ordinarily the aurora is confined to a narrow zone around the earth in the polar regions. It is a glow high in the ionosphere produced by corpuscular bombardment from the sun, like the bombardment of neon in a neon sign by electrically propelled ions. The solar particles consist mostly of free protons and electrons, and are therefore electrically charged. As they approach the earth they enter its magnetic field which guides them in and concentrates them in the auroral zones around the north and south magnetic poles. Their collisions with air molecules excite the molecules to luminescence, which we see as the aurora. This is the normal state of affairs. When some disturbance on the sun sends out corpuscles at higher speed, they are less easily controlled by the terrestrial magnetic field, and strike the ionosphere in lower latitudes. Thus occasionally the aurora borealis will be seen from the latitude of Washington. When that happens you can be quite sure that a vigorous magnetic storm is in progress.

The exact ionospheric mechanism responsible for magnetic storms is still a matter of debate. However, we can say this much. Just as the earth's field exerts forces on the incoming solar corpuscles, equal and opposite forces are exerted on the field. This is an example of a very fundamental physical law which is so strikingly used in rocket propulsion. Next time you swing a cat by the tail, note that the cat pulls on you as hard as you pull on him. It is the same thing. The earth's magnetic field is quite elastic, and when the solar corpuscles give it a shove it gets pushed out of shape. If you will picture the earth's field as a vast framework of invisible elastic wires held together by the mysterious bonds that we call a field, it will not be too difficult to see that a distortion of this framework at one point will mean accommodating distortions throughout the whole, and at any one place the direction and tension of the wires will be changed. You would get a similar effect if you dropped a stone on a drumhead of balloon rubber. The distortion is greatest near the stone, but the shape of the drumhead is changed at every point. This distortion in the earth's field is what we detect as a magnetic storm and, like the rubber of the drumhead, it is different at different locations on the earth although all locations are affected simultaneously. Since the magnetic storms and abnormal aurorae are apparently caused by the same solar particles, the two usually occur together. This description is a gross simplification of a very complex phenomenon, but the general concept is valid.

One other solar effect is worth our attention. Occasionally when we have an especially intense disturbance in the ionosphere, it produces such powerful electric fields at ground level that wire communications fail. Transcontinental teletypes go completely crazy, and the messages received are nothing but a meaningless jumble of letters, which sometimes come through when no message is being sent at all. Fortunately such spectacular disturbances are fairly rare and quite short-lived.

Because of the practical importance of ionospheric disturbances, particularly to radio communication, many agencies of the Government and industry are intensely interested in doing something about them. A few years ago I could have remarked that you cannot control the ionosphere any more than you can control the weather, but that would be an anachronism in this day of cloud-seeding experiments. The next best thing to making the ionoscope behave itself is to be able to predict its fits of misbehavior. This takes us directly to the cause of all ionospheric disturbances, the sun.

It is for this reason that the Geophysics Research Directorate of the Air Force Cambridge Research Center has built a modern solar observatory at Sunspot, New Mexico, on Sacramento Peak, at 9,000 feet altitude. We know a lot about the sun, but the more we learn, the more we find that we ought to know and do not. In particular, we have learned of a few isolated kinds of solar activities that are associated with ionospheric storms, but so far no one has advanced an acceptable theory of how these activities produce the ultraviolet radiation and blasts of corpuscles that affect the earth. We are like the puppy who observes that the baby's explorations in the clothes closet are often followed by corporal punishment for Fido, an innocent bystander, with no apparent causal connection.

In order to save myself numerous small digressions later, I shall indulge in a long one now to describe the general characteristics of the sun. It is the central body of the solar system, at a distance of 93 million miles from the earth. It contains 99.8 percent of the material of the whole solar system, and to the outside observer the planets and comets revolving around it would appear as interesting but inconsequential trifles in comparison. The sun's diameter is over a hundred times that of the earth and its weight is 332,000 times as great. It is composed entirely of gas, because the temperature of even its coolest parts is so high that the most refractory materials are vaporized. Although it contains oxygen, no combustion takes place because of the same high temperature.

Combustion is the chemical combination of atoms of oxygen with other atoms. The hot atoms of the solar gas move so fast and collide so violently that any two that happen to stick together are instantly knocked apart. Hence the heat and light of the sun are not due to any burning process. Instead, the source of energy is a thermonuclear reaction in the deep interior, which converts 4 million tons of solar mass into energy every second. If this seems like an alarming rate of expenditure of solar material, I can only advise a relaxed attitude. The sun has enough expendable material to keep going at the same rate for a number of billions of years.

Although the ultimate source of energy is deep inside the sun, it is the leakage of this energy through the surface that interests us in considering solar terrestrial effects. The surface has a temperature of about 10,000° F. It radiates a remarkably steady flow of light, the measurement of which has been a major part of the distinguished career of Dr. Abbot of the Smithsonian. He found that, within 1 or 2 percent, the solar energy that can be observed from the ground is constant. This is in marked contrast to the invisible ultraviolet radiations which maintain and are absorbed in the ionosphere.

If we look at the sun through a telescope at almost any time we find its surface pocked with sunspots, great dark circular patches that may be anything up to 100,000 miles in diameter. We know that they are cooler than the surrounding regions and they are the seats of stupendous magnetic fields, but their cause is a mystery. The most remarkable thing about the sunspots is the cyclic variation in their numbers. The sunspot cycle averages about 11½ years. At maximum, many spots are always visible on the solar disk, but at sunspot minimum no spots will be seen for days at a time.

When we equip our telescope with various spectroscopic devices, we can detect other solar features otherwise invisible. I have already mentioned the flares. They are especially important to students of solar terrestrial effects, because, of all solar activities, they are most clearly connected with the most violent and troublesome of ionospheric disturbances. A flare is a very impressive sight. Somewhere near a sunspot it suddenly appears as a small bright point of light on the solar surface. In a matter of minutes it flashes up to its maximum size and brightness, and then slowly fades away to invisibility in half an hour or so. Its full size is about like that of the sunspots, and may be anything from the smallest detectable up to 100,000 miles across. In visible light a flare is a puny thing, which cannot be seen at all without special optical aids that reject most of the light except that of the flare. This appearance, however, grossly belies the true potency of a flare, as the visible tip of an iceberg projecting above the sea belies the great bulk below the surface. It is clear that the great bulk of flare energy consists of ultraviolet quanta and corpuscles. This is evident from the reaction of our ionosphere. When a flare appears a new ionospheric screen very suddenly develops at a height of only about 40 miles, where the interference of air molecules becomes so great that no reflection of radio waves is possible. We have a radio fadeout. An estimate of the energy required shows that the ultraviolet output of a large flare, which might have an area of one-thousandth of the visible hemisphere of the sun, is comparable with the output of the whole normal sun. We conclude that each square inch of the flare would be 1,000 times as bright as a square inch of the normal solar surface, if we could see it in ultraviolet light.

We can draw a further conclusion. The low-level ionization produced by flare radiation appears without any serious changes in the normal ionosphere above 60 miles. In other words, the normal ionosphere, which is completely opaque to the ultraviolet of the normal sun, fails to absorb the quanta from the flare. They penetrate it quite freely and are absorbed in the process of producing ions at the 40-mile level. Hence there must be something different about flare quanta. The difference can only be a difference in wavelength of the radiation. If we were talking about visible light we would simply call it a difference in color, and I am going to refer to this wavelength difference as a difference in ultraviolet color.

The atmosphere of the earth contains many different kinds of molecules, and the percentage abundance of the different kinds varies with height above the ground. Each kind is an efficient absorber of some particular ultraviolet color. It absorbs this color and becomes ionized in doing so. The ultraviolet radiation from the normal sun encounters molecules of a kind that absorb its

particular color at levels above 60 miles. They are not the kind of
molecules that absorb radiation of the different ultraviolet color
emitted by flares, however. Therefore this radiation penetrates to
a lower level where it finds molecules of another kind, which
forthwith absorb it and produce ions. Just which kinds of molecules and which colors are involved is still rather uncertain.

In addition to terrific bursts of ultraviolet quanta, flares emit
equally impressive showers of corpuscles, consisting largely of free
protons and electrons. They travel along at a rate of 1,000 miles/
sec., and arrive at the earth about a day after the flare outburst.
As they impinge on the earth's magnetic field they twist it slightly
out of shape, and some of them are guided down into the ionosphere. We then have a lively magnetic storm, and aurorae appear
in lower-than-normal latitudes.

Although the most spectacular of solar disturbances, flares are
not the only ones to affect the ionosphere. The sunspots themselves appear to emit corpuscles that induce magnetic storms. At
least we blame the sunspots because the magnetic storms tend to
occur a couple of days after a large spot has rotated past the center of the solar disk. However, we have to be careful here, since
we cannot actually see the corpuscles leaving the spots. A sunspot
is only the most visible feature of a much broader disturbance
which we simply call an active solar region. It is the fever thermometer which indicates a deep-seated disorder. Refined observations show the presence of flares, active prominences (which I
shall describe presently), regions of intense brightness in the immediately overlying corona, and brighter-than-normal patches on
the solar surface known as faculae and plages. All these features
share in the 11-year sunspot cycle. Whether it is the sunspot itself
that showers us with corpuscles, or some other member of the
retinue, remains to be determined, and for the present we should
perhaps just attribute the resulting magnetic storms to the active
regions.

More mysterious are the periodic magnetic storms that are clearly solar in origin, but seem to have nothing to do with any dis-
tinguishable solar feature. They come in series, starting with a
small magnetic disturbance. Twenty-seven days later comes a larger
disturbance, and others at 27-day intervals. Successive storms build

up in intensity and then gradually die out. The whole series will include perhaps a dozen recurrences at 27-day intervals. Yet the most refined observational techniques have revealed nothing on the sun that appears to accompany these storms. The evidence for their solar origin is difficult to avoid, however. The 27-day period is exactly the rotation period of the sun. It appears, therefore, that every time a certain patch on the solar surface rotates into a position facing the earth, we are treated to a shower of corpuscles. Just to have a name, we call such a patch an M-region. If the equality of the solar-rotation period and the recurrence of M-region storms were the only evidence we might put it down to a remarkable coincidence. But this is not all. The frequency of M-region storm sequences unmistakably shares in the sunspot cycle. The odd thing about it is that we have most of these magnetic storms around sunspot minima. It appears that the M-regions on the sun do not get along well with sunspots or active regions. We have specific confirmation of this. If we arbitrarily assume that the M-region is the patch of solar surface that was squarely at the center of the solar disk when the corpuscular shower started on its trip from sun to earth, we find that the M-regions avoid the neighborhoods of sunspots like the plague. Furthermore if a sunspot develops in the M-region, the corresponding series of magnetic storms abruptly ends. So we have learned that an M-region is a portion of the solar surface that appears perfectly normal in every other respect to our definitely limited perceptions. One of our efforts at Sacramento Peak is to sharpen our perception enough to identify the M-regions.

I have mentioned prominences in active regions. Of all the objects of astronomy the solar prominences are to me the most beautiful. In variety and form they resemble the clouds of our own atmosphere, but they are, of course, a very different animal indeed. We see them best at the edge of the sun, where they stand up like scarlet flames above the solar surface in beautiful contrast against the dark sky. Aside from their esthetic appeal, they are fascinating objects from the scientific point of view, largely because they are so hard to understand.

A prominence is a great cloud of hydrogen and helium with small impurities of iron, sodium, magnesium, etc. It is usually between 20,000 and 100,000 miles high, with exceptional specimens that rise to a million miles. The variety and complexity of their structure and motions defy description, although there are a few characteristic patterns that serve to classify them. They are too faint to be seen in an ordinary telescope because the glare of scattered light in our atmosphere next to the edge of the sun is so intense that it drowns out the prominences. Fortunately the prominences resemble radio stations in emitting only light of a specific wavelength, while the scattered light is composed of all wavelengths. Just as we can pick out one radio station by tuning to its wavelength and rejecting all others, we can see the prominences through an appropriate filter tuned to their wavelength. In rejecting the other wavelengths, we reject 99.9 percent of the scattered light, and the prominences become visible. The particular red wavelength we usually use is that emitted by hydrogen atoms, so, strictly speaking, we see only the hydrogen in the prominences.

The most puzzling thing about the prominences is their motion, or sometimes their lack of motion. At first sight you may not be surprised to see a motionless prominence apparently floating above the solar surface. You are used to seeing clouds floating around overhead without feeling impelled to report them to the newspapers. The startling thing about the prominences is that there is no air for them to float in. They appear to stay there with nothing whatever to hold them up against the sun's gravity, which is 27 times stronger than terrestrial gravity. The prominences have every appearance of complete ignorance of gravity, whether they are stationary clouds or rapidly moving streamers. We can measure prominence motions quite accurately, and we can calculate how the material ought to move in the sun's gravitational field. Almost invariably the observed motion has no resemblance whatever to the calculated motion.

For explanation we have two choices. We either sacrifice the universal validity of Newton's law of gravitation, or we assume that there are other forces on the sun that oppose gravitation, and sometimes exactly balance it. The first alternative is extremely repugnant. It would mean that in prominences we have found the only example of matter in the known universe that is not subject to Newton's law that every particle attracts every other particle in the universe. The second alternative seems difficult, but we think we are making progress.

The matter composing prominences is highly ionized. Not just 1 atom out of every 10,000, as in our ionosphere, but more like 99 out of every 100. From where we sit on the earth we may regard this as a peculiar condition, but if we look at the universe as a whole we realize that it is not peculiar at all. Fully half of the material universe is just as highly ionized. We just do not realize what an odd place we live in, or that it is this oddity that makes life possible. The ionization in prominences greatly changes the character of the forces that can act on them, other than the action of gravity, which is a function only of mass or weight, regardless of ionization. Ionized materials are conductors of electricity, which means that they are subjected to forces in changing electric and magnetic fields. It is this property of conductors that accounts for the power of an electric motor.

Now we know that the sun is a place of very strong magnetic fields. They have perfectly measurable effects on the spectrum by means of which we can determine their strength. The fields are especially strong and active near the sunspots, and it is precisely here that we find the most active prominences. We can say quite definitely that the solar magnetic fields must have a profound effect on the motion of ionized prominence material. The problem now is to determine whether the fields could account for the observed motions. It turns out to be a very complicated problem about which there is still a great deal of lively controversy among astronomers. The general conclusion at present is that solar magnetism almost certainly controls the motion and support of prominences, but the details of how it is done will not be unraveled very soon.

ADDENDUM, NOVEMBER 1959

The advent of scientific earth satellites has given us a tantalizing peek into the mysteries of the behavior of charged particles in the earth's magnetic field at heights of tens of thousands of miles. We have learned many facts that were unsuspected, but as usual, the increase in knowledge has posed new questions. The geophysicist is in the situation of the child who looks inside the radio to see where the music comes from. There is lots to see where the music comes from. There is lots to see, but what does it all mean? I am hardly a qualified guide to the new exhibits, nor is there space here for even a bare description of them. My purpose is simply to remark that we can expect to see in the near future partial solutions to many of the problems I have mentioned above. The indications are, however, that they are relatively trivial appendages to much broader problems, which will doubtless challenge the best scientific ingenuity for a good many years to come. There is no end to the labors of the scientist, praise God.

JOHN W. EVANS

GERALD S. HAWKINS

The Development of Radio Astronomy

[FROM THE SMITHSONIAN REPORT FOR 1957*]

GERALD S. HAWKINS *is the Director of the Boston University Observatory, and a Research Associate at Harvard College Observatory. His subject, radio astronomy, is so new a science that most of its development has taken place in the last 10 years. Yet in that brief time it has cast new light on the structure of our own galaxy, located nearly 2,000 radio stars, many of them invisible optically, and recorded signals from other galaxies as well as from the sun, Venus, and Jupiter.*

A radio telescope consists essentially of a large parabolic reflector — that at Harvard is 60 feet in diameter — which focuses the radio waves from outer space and feeds them into a special receiver. The cosmic radio noise can then be recorded either over a loudspeaker or on a roll of graph paper. Dr. Hawkins reports the surprising results that have already appeared through the use of this new branch of astronomy and predicts some of the radio ventures out into space that may be expected in the future.

* Revised as of December 1959.

IT IS NOT OFTEN that we can witness the birth and development of a new science such as radio astronomy. Most sciences have had obscure beginnings, and the world has been slow to realize their importance. Astronomy, for example, began with an interest in the stars and the motion of planets long before the beginning of recorded history, but this interest could not develop into a science until after the invention of arabic numerals, which paved the way for the theories of planetary motion several hundred years later. The telescope gave a great impetus to research when in 1609 Galileo discovered the moons of Jupiter and Saturn's rings, but knowledge spread slowly in those days and it took more than 200 years to establish the basic facts of astronomy. We know that the sun is one star among 100 billion in the local galaxy, and in the universe there are probably more than 100 billion other galaxies. With the additional techniques of photography and spectroscopy rapid advances are being made in all fields, so that we can study the atmosphere of the planets, the composition of the stars, and can investigate almost any problem we choose.

On the other hand, the science of radio astronomy has developed at a time when the world seems to be almost at the peak of its technical evolution. The radio sky was first glimpsed by Jansky in 1932. Within 15 years the significance of the new science was realized and then discovery followed discovery with bewildering speed. Radio stars were found, some of which are quite invisible to the astronomer, and others which are coincident with exploding stars and with galaxies in collision. Spiral arms have been mapped out in our local galaxy and radio signals have been detected from the neighboring galaxies in the universe. Nearer home, the sun, Jupiter, and even Venus have been found to be radio emitters. The cause of these signals and the nature of the invisible stars are unknown, and much research effort is being expended at the present time to solve these mysteries.

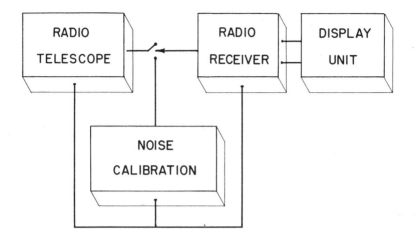

ILLUS. 11—The equipment used by radio astronomers.

THE EQUIPMENT USED BY RADIO ASTRONOMERS

Almost every observation so far has been made with the equipment shown schematically in Illustration 11. Signals are picked up from space by the radio telescope to be magnified in the receiver and fed to a suitable display unit.

Radio telescopes fall into two categories, those with a single directional beam and those with multiple beams. A single beam is formed by the parabolic reflector, as shown in Illustration 14, which acts like an auto headlight in reverse. Waves from a radio star are focused by the paraboloid to form a spotlike image which has a diameter inversely proportional to the aperture of the telescope. Large apertures are expensive and one of the best images that has so far been obtained is ½ degree, given by the new 60-foot disk at Harvard. This emphasizes the main disadvantage of radio telescopes; the definition is extremely poor, not even as good as that of the human eye, but as we shall see later there are ways of overcoming this defect. At the focus of the paraboloid the image is allowed to fall on a dipole element which is formed from two metal rods similar to one side of an H-shaped TV antenna. Electric voltages and currents are induced in the dipole and are fed down a cable into the receiver.

A single beam may be produced in an endless number of ways which can become almost as complicated as the character of the designer. If dipoles are connected together to cover a flat area they are equivalent to a paraboloid telescope of the same area. The array of dipoles, however, will operate only over a narrow band of wavelengths and it is difficult to point the sensitive beam to various parts of the sky. A dipole may have five or more focusing rods placed in front of it to form a Yagi-type antenna which is frequently seen in use with short-wavelength TV receivers. Electrical energy may also be picked up on a long metal helix. Both the Yagi and helix are equivalent to paraboloids with apertures of from 1 to 2 wavelengths.

It is possible to increase the quality of the image by means of the interferometer. Two separate antennas are spaced at either end of a long baseline and the signals are mixed together in the receiver. A radio star perpendicular to the baseline produces signals that are in phase at each antenna. As the earth rotates and the radio star makes an angle with the baseline the signals will differ in phase and tend to cancel out. In this way a radio star produces periodic variations as it rises, passes due south, and sets. Now the effective aperture of the telescope is equal to the length of the baseline, so that a narrow beam can be produced with reasonable economy. Unfortunately, not one but many narrow beams are produced, so that the results become difficult to interpret. Despite this limitation, however, the interferometer has done much valuable work in determining the angular diameter and exact positions of radio stars.

The receiver is similar in many respects to those used in TV, except that the voltage gain is high (~ 10 million) so that the radio noise due to thermal motion of electrons at the input of the receiver is readily detected. In radio astronomy great care has to be taken to maintain a constant gain in the receiver because a fluctuation, say in the temperature of the filaments in the tubes, would produce a variation of noise at the output which would mask the faint signals being detected from space. A standard source of energy is put in place of the telescope to calibrate the receiver as shown in Illustration 11. This is usually a diode vacuum tube since the noise power is accurately known in terms of the current flowing through the tube. To minimize the effect of variations in the thermal noise of the receiver the calibration is sometimes carried out automatically at a rate of 25 times per second. In this way a 25-cycle note is produced at the output and the amplitude of the note is independent of receiver noise, being proportional to the difference between the cosmic signal and the standard source. There will always be slight ripples in the output, however, even with an ideal system, because we are comparing two noise signals which are varying in a random manner about a certain mean level. These ripples can be greatly reduced by integrating the signals over long periods of time.

Recently new designs of receivers have come forward, each using a revolutionary principle. The "Maser" uses a crystal in which electrons are poised ready to transfer from a high energy level to a lower one. A weak radio signal is able to supply enough stimulus to cause the electrons to jump, releasing energy that reveals the presence of the radio signal. The "Parametric amplifier" rapidly alters the components in the tuned circuit of the receiver while the radio signal is being received. The changes produce what can be described as a "pumping action" and the sensitivity of the receiver is considerably increased.

One of the most impressive ways of displaying the noise from the cosmos is to use a loudspeaker system. The sun and local galaxy can be heard as a gentle hiss; the galactic noise remains steady but the storms on the sun swell and fade many times during the course of an hour. Jupiter is the performer that really dominates the air. When heard over a high-fidelity system, its roars and rumbles almost convince one that the Romans were right in their ideas about the gods. For quantitative work, however, it is essential to obtain a permanent record in a form amenable to analysis. If the signal is fed to a milliammeter with a pen attached to the arm, a mark will be made which is proportional to the intensity of the signal. If the mark is made on a roll of paper driven at a constant speed then a precise intensity-time graph is produced. Radio stars

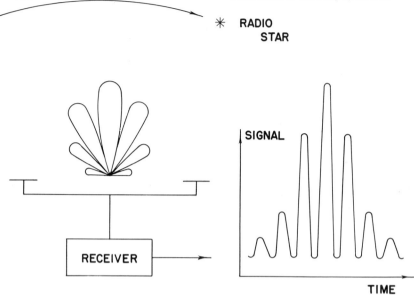

*ILLUS. 12—A radio interferometer and the signal it produces when a radio
star passes through the antenna pattern.*

can be observed by sweeping the telescope slowly across the sky,
for when the star is in the center of the beam the pen gives a maximum deflection. One of the most convenient scanning arrangements is to clamp the telescope and utilize the rotation of the
earth. This has been the preferred method with an interferometer
because the baseline is long and the instrument is mechanically
unwieldy. The sensitive beams are therefore allowed to drift across
a star as the earth rotates and the pen record varies rhythmically
as shown in Illustration 12. A star of small diameter produces well-
defined maxima and minima, but a large source forms an indistinct
pattern. The depth of the minima gives a measure of the diameter
of the radio object. In specialized work, following the rapid movements of gas jets across the sun for example, the interferometer
beam has been made to scan at a fast rate but the method presents practical difficulties and is not often used. The scanning is
performed electrically by introducing a variable phase lag in the
cable from one of the antennas.

SIGNALS FROM THE SUN

There are remarkable differences in the appearance of the sun at different radio wavelengths. Optically we see down through the solar atmosphere to the incandescent layer of gas called the photosphere. This layer is at an average temperature of 6200°C., but occasionally large areas become cooled to about 5000°C. and a dark sunspot appears. Sunspot regions are greatly disturbed and have been likened to storms. Ciné films show that part of the interior of the sun is disgorged to rain down incessantly as streams of white-hot gas. The whole area is pierced by an intense magnetic field which probably has its origin in whirlpool motions below the photosphere. At times a bright flare of light appears near a spot, as shown in Illustration 13, and this is thought to mark the ejection of a stream of charged particles which impinge on the atmosphere of the earth a day or so later, causing beautiful displays of the aurora borealis. Above the photosphere we find the chromosphere, which is a red-colored layer about 10,000 km. thick, visible during a total eclipse of the sun. During an eclipse a white halo is also seen extending outward for about a solar radius. This is the solar corona, an envelope of ionized gas shining with scattered sunlight. It has recently been shown that the outer edge of the corona is at a temperature of a million degrees; this is a helpful clue in explaining some of the peculiar radio effects that have been observed at long wavelengths.

At centimetric wavelengths the sun looks very much the same as it does in the optical band, except that the steady light is now able to pass freely through heavy cloud, rain, or fog. At wavelengths of 20 cm. the sun ceases to be uniformly bright but develops a ringlike halo. Viewed with radio eyes it would appear as a brilliant circle with a dusky center. This is caused by the temperature inversion in the corona where the temperature increases as we move out from the sun. Looking at the center we see the cooler layers below, and looking at the limb we see the hotter layers edge-on. In addition to the limb brightening, starlike points appear on the disk of the sun and contribute to the general radia-

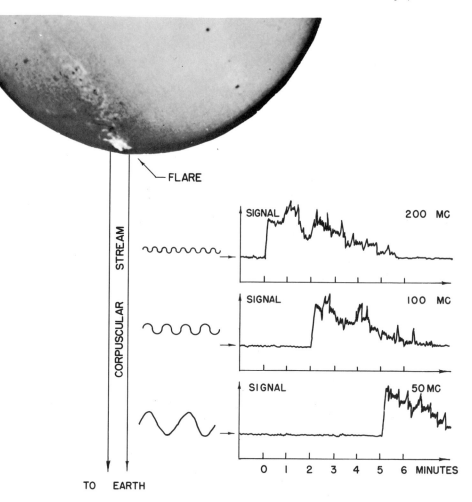

ILLUS. 13—*Radio signals produced by a corpuscular stream as it travels through the atmosphere of the sun. (Photograph taken at the Astrophysical Observatory, Kodaikanal, India.)*

tion. It has been shown that these points occur near the visual sunspots, so at 20 cm. the radio astronomer has a completely reversed image, a dark sun with bright sunspots.

There were further surprises in store for the radio astronomer when he looked at the sun at wavelengths of about 1 meter. A steady signal was observed corresponding to a temperature of a million degrees. To find the exact location of the noise source on the sun an attempt was made to observe an eclipse. Providence has so arranged the distances of the earth, moon, and sun that the circular shape of the moon exactly covers the photosphere. Without this fortunate coincidence our knowledge of the sun would for a long while have been quite sparse. As the moon gradually covered the solar disk it was hoped that the radio signal would disappear at a certain stage of the eclipse and thus reveal the radio source. The observations showed little variation in the signal and even at totality the radio sun was still shining. It was obvious that the radio sun was much larger than the optical, and the radiation was coming from the high corona.

Three types of major radio disturbances are recognized as emanating from the sun. They are noise storms, outbursts, and bursts. A noise storm originates in a cloud in the corona, vertically above a sunspot. The cloud is invisible optically, but on radio wavelengths it shows temperatures of billions of degrees. The enhancement of radio emission may continue for several days, and during the periods of sunspot activity noise storms occur once every five days on the average. If the sun were to behave in the visible spectrum as it does at radio wavelengths the world would have been burnt to a cinder long ago. One of the most spectacular phenomena is the noise outburst which occurs after a solar flare. The flare is usually accompanied by an upward surge of hot gas which leaves the chromosphere with a velocity of about 100 km. per second and then falls back again into the sun. An intense radio source, associated with the surge, moves outward with a velocity of the order of 2,000 km. per second. This movement has been followed in a number of surges with the rapid scanning interferometer and there is evidence that the radio source does not fall back again but leaves the sun completely as a corpuscular stream of electrons and positive ions. As the stream forces its way through the ionized layers in the corona it is able to emit radiation of increasing wave-length. Three receivers would therefore detect the noise one after another as shown in the records of Illustration 13. After a time lapse of about 24 hours the corpuscular stream reaches the earth and excites the atmosphere to make it glow with the beautiful colors and forms of the aurora. A portion of the sun has been presented with majestic pomp to the earth.

RADIO STARS

For many years the astronomer, with modest pride, has felt that he could count with certainty the number of bright stars in the sky. There are many, however, that he would have overlooked be-cause they are invisible optically. Provisionally, these objects are called radio stars but it is certain that most of them are quite dif-ferent from the stars of optical astronomy. The brightest radio star is in the constellation of Cassiopeia. It corresponds in position with one of the faintest nebulae that can be detected with the 200-inch telescope on Mt. Palomar. The nebula was found only after repeated searching near the radio position and it would probably have remained undetected if the radio data had not been avail-able. So far the nature of the object is a mystery. Spectroscopic evidence shows that it is an irregular cloud of gas with violent internal motions and high excitations. The object is known to be within our local galaxy but opinion is divided as to whether the gas is dispersing or condensing, possibly to form a new star.

Cygnus A is the second brightest radio star. It corresponds to an object at a distance of 2×10^{21} km., a distance so great that its light and radio waves take 200 million years to reach us. *Homo sapiens* was certainly not in existence when the radio waves we receive now started on their journey. It is fortunate that the object was not at any greater distance for it would then have been be-yond the limits of the visible universe as seen with the Palomar telescope. By careful photography the telescope shows that a re-markable catastrophe is taking place out there. Two galaxies, two huge systems of stars and gas, are involved in a collision. Illustra-tion 15, figure 1, shows them in contact, but it is hard to imagine that the spots and surrounding halo actually represent a cloud of stars some 3×10^{17} km. across. Collisions of this kind are extremely rare and we would probably have to see well beyond our present range before we found another face-to-face contact like that in Cygnus A. The consequences of galactic collisions have already been studied. Remarkably enough, the stars in the system are hardly affected at all; interstellar distances are so great that the star systems can pass through each other with only minor perturbations. The gas between the stars, however, meets with great violence. Part of the kinetic energy of the collision is emitted as radio waves; indeed, the process is extremely efficient, about 5 percent of the energy being converted in this way. It seems that collision and violent motion in gas clouds are an essential requirement for the formation of a radio source. Cassiopeia A contains gaseous filaments in rapid motion, Cygnus A is formed by gas clouds in collision, and we shall see that other radio stars are associated with this condition. It has probably taken a million years or so for the galaxies to pass through each other. Bearing in mind the fact that light takes 200 million years for the journey, we realize that the actual collision process must have been completed long ago and there will now be left two remarkable galaxies in space cleared of dust and gas, while between them will be a hot gaseous nebula, far larger than any that we encounter in the local galaxy. But these objects will not be visible to astronomers until a million years have passed.

There is one radio star that was observed in A. D. 1054, 12 years before William the Conqueror landed in England. In this year a star in the constellation of Taurus, the Bull, exploded, leaving an object which we now call the Crab nebula. The sudden increase in brightness was seen by Chinese astronomers who faithfully noted the event in their records and stated that the new star was visible by day as well as by night. According to modern terminology this was a supernova. Research shows that about once every 500 years in our galaxy a star reaches an unstable point in its evolution, whereupon the whole star explodes like a giant atomic bomb. The disintegration is complete and all that remains is an expanding ball of gas. Astronomers have checked the rate of expansion spectroscopically and also by taking photographs

ILLUS. 14—The 60-foot George R. Agassiz radio telescope. (Photograph by Robert E. Cox, with permission of Sky and Telescope.)

spaced many years apart. On extrapolating back, they find that the ball was a single point in the year 1054, thus confirming the identification. When the Crab nebula is photographed in the red light of hydrogen, Illustration 15, figure 2, we notice a filamentary structure and it is clear that the nebula is in a violent state of motion. The expansion of gas again acts as an efficient generator of radio waves, although the exact process is still obscure. Inter-

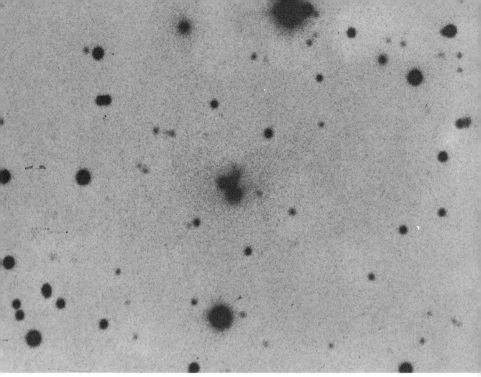

ILLUS. 15–1. *Galaxies in collision. (Photograph by permission of Mount Wilson and Palomar Observatories.)*

2. *The Crab nebula photographed in hydrogen light. (Photograph by permission of Mount Wilson and Palomar Observatories.)*

ferometer measurements show that the whole of the invisible nebula is transmitting, and the radio image fits almost exactly over the photographic image. Another supernova was observed by the famous astronomer Tycho Brahe in 1572, and this too has been identified as a radio star. The last supernova was recorded by Kepler in 1604, so that if the estimated mean rate of one supernova every 500 years or so is correct, there is a high probability that a supernova will occur in our time. This would present a unique opportunity for studying the entire process with all the superb equipment available to the modern scientist.

These three sources in Cassiopeia, Cygnus, and Taurus are among the few radio stars to have been positively identified. Recently a catalog of over 1,900 radio stars was made and the astronomical nature of most of them is still unknown. Much research will obviously be required before this mounting list of mysteries can be solved.

THE MILKY WAY

The original observations of Jansky in 1932 were made on the Milky Way, our local galaxy. Radio interference was found which seemed to be coming from the galactic center. Surveys of the sky have since been made in great detail with wavelengths ranging from a few centimeters up to many meters. The radiation comes from a large elliptical area which is aligned with the general direction of the Milky Way. Optically there are dark obscuring clouds or lanes of dust, but these do not appear on the radio maps because the radio waves pass through them. Dark clouds obscure the center of the galaxy, which is probably the most interesting part, but this region is easily visible to the radio astronomer. So far very little research has been done on the galactic center and this remains an exciting field for the future.

It is not known yet whether the general galactic noise is the combined signal from millions of radio stars or whether it originates in the matter between the stars. In a few years' time, when large radio telescopes are available, it may be possible to see if myriads of faint stars are producing the noise. Meanwhile much speculation goes on as to the exact origin of the signals.

There is one component in the radio spectrum, however, that

is well understood. Radiation has been detected over a small waveband at 21 cm. This emission line is produced by the neutral hydrogen atom. If the spins of the proton and electron are aligned in the same direction there is a tendency for one of the spins to change. The probability of the change is very low so that a hydrogen atom waits several million years before changing. At this time it emits 9.4×10^{-25} joules at a frequency of 1,420 mc. Although this seems an insignificant power output, the number of atoms in the direction of the antenna beam is usually sufficient to give a detectable signal. The signal strength gives a measure of the temperature and space density of the hydrogen, but, what is more important, the exact frequency of the emission gives the velocity in the line of sight. As in the case of sound waves and light waves, the observed frequency of a source is higher when it is approaching and lower when it is receding so that the velocity of the source can be found. By measuring the velocity of the hydrogen with respect to the sun the astronomer is able to go one step farther. The galaxy is rotating about its center and each star follows an orbit which is nearly circular. Stars on the edge of the galaxy travel more slowly than stars near the center. Hence a measure of velocity gives a measure of the distance of a hydrogen cloud from the galactic center and the position of hydrogen in space can be deduced.

Extensive surveys at 1,420 mc. have been made. It is found that the neutral hydrogen is concentrated within the spiral arms of our galaxy. By means of the hydrogen emission these arms may be traced out far beyond the optical limit which is set by interstellar absorption. For the first time we can picture the sun as it is set in one arm of a great spiral system as shown in Illustration 16.

The hydrogen line has been detected in other galaxies besides our own. Recently emission was received from the great cluster of galaxies in Coma Berenices at a frequency of 1,387 mc. Thus the radio signal is at a lower frequency, or reddened, by the velocity of recession of the cluster in the same way that the visible spectrum is shifted. Absorption by hydrogen has also been noted in the noise from the colliding galaxies in Cygnus. Again there is a shift of the radio line which corresponds to the red shift observed optically.

JUPITER

It is scarcely four years since the radio signals from Jupiter were discovered. Many tape recordings have already been made which illustrate the effects that this planet can produce. There are components of the hissing sound which are usually associated with the random motion of thermal electrons. It is unlikely that the noise is really thermal in origin because it is difficult to visualize how high temperatures could be produced on Jupiter. The atmosphere is composed of methane and ammonia and contains clouds at a temperature of $-140°$ C., while the planet itself is presumed to be formed of solid ices, again at a low temperature. Other noises that have been recognized are grinding sounds and rumbles. When analyzed in detail these sounds are apparently composed of a series of two or three pulses following one another in rapid succession.

By an ingenious method it has been found possible to locate the area which is generating the noise. The transmission is spasmodic, some days it is present, other days it is absent, but by observing over long periods of time the noise has been found to vary in synchronism with the rotation of the planet. This defines a north-south line, or line of Jovian longitude on which the source lies. The planet's speed of rotation, as given by observations of clouds in the atmosphere, varies between the Equator and the Poles. The Equator rotates once in 9 hours 50 minutes 26 seconds, and the corresponding figure at the Pole is 9 hours 55 minutes 24 seconds. By timing the variation of the signals the latitude of the source can be obtained. This is, of course, not a very exact determination, and the method is further complicated by the presence of more than one transmitting area. Despite these difficulties the main noise area has already been located. It is close to the famous red spot which has been observed in Jupiter's atmosphere since 1664. Surprisingly little is known about the spot from the optical observations. One hypothesis suggests that it is an island of solid ammonia or methane floating in the dense atmosphere, while at the other extreme it is considered to be the product of an active volcano. Perhaps

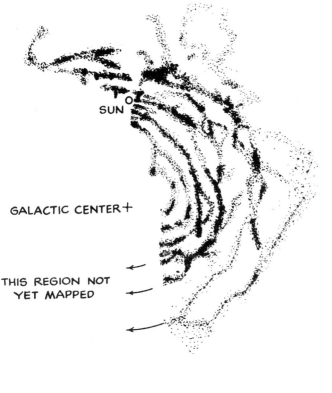

SUN

GALACTIC CENTER +

THIS REGION NOT
YET MAPPED

SCALE

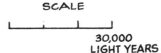

30,000
LIGHT YEARS

*ILLUS. 16—Spiral structure of the local galaxy. (Reproduced by permission of
G. Westerhout and M. Schmidt, Leiden, Holland.)*

the radio observations will help us to determine the true nature of
this disturbance.

Radio observations have given indications that Jupiter may be
surrounded by an ionosphere. The red-spot region does not produce
signals at every position as it rotates. There appears to be an atten-
uation of the noise as the spot approaches the east or west limb and
this has been explained by reflection effects in the ionosphere. The
double and triple pulses forming the rumble are also explained in
terms of the ionosphere. A signal from some disturbance in the at-

mosphere is received by direct transmission to produce the first pulse, while the second pulse is the echo produced by the surface of Jupiter. The third component is reflected from the ionosphere back to the surface before reaching the receiver on the earth.

RADAR ASTRONOMY

We are not limited to passive reception of signals. Great advances were made during the Second World War in the detection of aircraft by means of radio echoes. In the same way a high-power transmitter can be made to send out a series of pulses which will be reflected off celestial objects.

Meteors are the nearest bodies of interest in astronomy, for although they spend many years circulating between the planets, they spend the last second of their lives in the atmosphere of the earth about 60 miles up. The meteor particle collides with the atmosphere at such a high velocity that it completely evaporates, producing heat, light, and ionization. By studying the echoes from the column of ionization it is possible to measure the velocity of the meteor with fair precision. With three or more radar stations one can determine the direction of motion of the meteor. Velocity and direction together define its orbit, or life history, and we can then trace back its path among the planets. Radar observations have shown that meteors are members of the solar system and do not come from the space between the stars. We now believe that meteor fragments are shed by a comet as the icy nucleus of the comet evaporates in the heat from the sun.

Farther out from the earth we come to the moon, and radio echoes have been obtained from the moon by many experimenters. At a distance of 200,000 miles, radar astronomers have to wait for a period of about 2 seconds before the echo returns. The echo is subjected to many effects on its journey to and from the moon and from the way it has changed we can learn many interesting things about the atmosphere of the earth and the surface of the moon. The radio wave forming the echo is formed, of course, from oscillatory electric and magnetic fields which are at right angles to each other. When the electric field is parallel to the receiving dipole a maximum signal is produced. In this way the direction of the field can be determined. It is found that the field is rotated many times as the echo pulse travels to the moon and back. Most of the rotation occurs in the ionosphere of the earth, as it is proportional to the electron density of the transmitting medium and the strength of the magnetic field of the earth. This rotation gives us information about the ionosphere at great heights above the earth's surface.

As the radio pulse is reflected from the surface of the moon the mountain ranges and craters cause interference so that the echo power fluctuates. This effect is not unlike the glitter that is seen when light falls on a rough, shiny object. There are other things that cause the signal to fluctuate more rapidly than the interference from a rough surface, but the origin of these rapid variations is at present unknown.

Radar astronomy will probably never become as spectacular as radio astronomy. With pulse techniques we certainly are making our first venture out into space, and the radio pulse can certainly visit and explore the moon even if mankind at present is limited to the earth. But we will require tremendously powerful transmitters if we are to bounce an echo off our neighboring planets such as Venus and Mars.

Echoes have actually been obtained from Venus at a distance of some 30 million miles, but the returned signals were very weak and did not yield much information. Increased sensitivity, however, may allow us to measure the rotation period of Venus, a measurement which is impossible for astronomers to make because the surface is hidden by dense white clouds.

To reach the nearest star is impossible: even if we did have sufficient transmitter power we would have to wait eight whole years for the echo to return. The output of the natural transmitters of the cosmos is far greater than any we can make on the earth. Cygnus A, for example, on the edge of the visible universe, puts out a power which is more than a billion times greater than our man-made signals. Such considerations help us to realize our insignificant position as earthbound mortals, and impress upon us the grandeur of the natural universe.

H. P. WILKINS

The Mystery of Mars

[FROM THE SMITHSONIAN REPORT FOR 1956*]

THE WORD *"mystery"* in the title of this article might well be changed to the plural form, for many of the telescopically observed features of our neighboring planet raise major questions. Are the so-called *"canals"* natural features, carrying water from the polar ice caps, or are they artificial waterways constructed by intelligent beings in a desperate attempt to survive in a drought-stricken world? Are the large dark patches on Mars' surface vegetation, and if so, is it a primitive form of plant life or a forest of trees? If life does exist on the planet, is it just starting out on the evolutionary road or has it passed its zenith and is now fading away on a dying world? Decisions on such intriguing questions are in the nature of things controversial and speculative, and will only be universally agreed upon when the first spacemen return from a firsthand inspection of the planet's surface.

The author, H. P. Wilkins, is a Fellow of the British Royal Astronomical Society and Past President of the International Lunar Society of London. He has observed the disk of Mars at opposition with many telescopes in Europe and America, and is well qualified to speculate on solutions of the planet's mysteries, as well

* Revised as of November 1959.

as to suggest what future spaceship landings on its surface may expect to encounter.

M̲ARS is preeminently the planet of mystery. Because it is farther from the sun than the earth, it takes longer to complete a revolution, and every two years we overtake it, when it shines in the sky as a bright red star. The red color, suggestive of war and carnage, was the reason why the name of Mars, the Roman god of war, was attached to this planet. The red color of Mars contrasts strangely with the pure white of Venus or the silvery luster of Jupiter and is too pronounced for anybody to mistake it.

Although to the unaided eye Mars seems merely a bright star, a good telescope reveals it as a small full moon, that is to say, we can see the face or disk of this little world. We say "little" because Mars is much smaller than the earth, being in fact only 4,200 miles in diameter. A telescope shows certain markings on the disk, and they move in the course of an hour or two, which proves that Mars turns on its axis and has days and nights just as we do, although they are longer. Instead of turning around every 24 hours as the earth does, Mars requires an extra 37 minutes 22.654 seconds, so that although a smaller world it does not spin round so quickly.

Mars has seasons similar to those of the earth but much longer. They are also more pronounced, because the mean or average distance of Mars from the sun is 48.6 millions of miles greater than that of the earth. From Mars the sun must look smaller, and gives out a proportionally smaller amount of light and heat; we would expect Mars to be a colder world. Mars has an atmosphere, but it is much more rarefied than ours, and it seems safe to say that we would not be able to breathe it because of the deficiency of oxygen, most of which seems to have been absorbed in chemical combination with the surface rocks.

When Mars is comparatively near to us it makes a beautiful picture in a really good telescope. At such times we see a yellowish-red disk, generally with a gleaming white spot at the top and sometimes at the bottom as well, while on the otherwise red background are grayish patches. If the telescope is a very large one, we may also see two specks of light, like small stars, moving rapidly around the planet; these are its two moons or satellites.

But what makes Mars the most interesting of all the planets is not its appearance as seen at any time with a telescope, but the changes which often take place there. The white spots at the top and the bottom mark the north and south poles of Mars. We know that our polar regions are distinguished for their low temperatures and deposits of ice and snow. Seen from space, from the moon, or from Mars, the earth would have gleaming white spots at the top and at the bottom, just as we see on Mars. It is generally believed that these white patches at the poles of Mars are deposits of ice and snow, but they also partly consist of high cirrus clouds. We know this because in photographs of Mars taken in infrared light, which penetrates to the surface, these patches are smaller than as seen in the telescope or on photographs taken in ultraviolet light, which show only the higher-level features.

Confirmation of the belief that Mars has true polar caps is given by the fact that they are largest in the winter time on Mars, begin to dwindle as spring comes on, and are smallest in summer. The cap at the south pole has even been known to disappear altogether, which never happens with the northern one. This is easily understood because when it is summer in the southern hemisphere Mars is nearest to the sun, and therefore receives the maximum amount of heat. It is, however, strange that while the pole is at the center of the northern cap, the south pole is 180 miles away from the center of the southern cap.

The grayish patches on the disk are permanent features, and for a long time were believed to be seas, because water reflects the sunlight less strongly than the land. It is now known that these patches are not seas, although they may once have been so. They are faint in the winter time, but darken as spring gives way to summer, that is to say, as the polar caps melt and the ice and snow are converted into water. This suggests that water has something to do with the darkening, and the consensus is that the dark areas are tracts of vegetation. What this is, whether the vegeta-

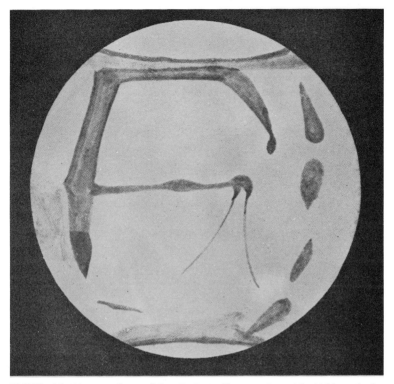

ILLUS. 17—Mars as observed by H. P. Wilkins on June 17, 1954, with the 60-inch Mount Wilson reflector.

tion consists of plants, shrubs, or trees, we cannot say; we only know that it is vegetation of some sort.

These grayish patches are more numerous in the southern than in the northern hemisphere, and encircle the south pole. Many of them run into or join up with each other, but there are isolated patches.

The remaining parts of the disk are uniform yellowish-red and are almost certainly sandy deserts. Indeed Mars appears to be a world on which there is very little water, most of it being locked up in the polar caps. But how does the water released by the melting of the polar caps reach the grayish patches, as it to all appearances does?

It was in 1877 that Mars made one of its close approaches to the earth, and modern study of the planet dates from that year.

One spectacular discovery was that of its two satellites by Asaph Hall with what was then the largest refracting telescope in the world, of 26 inches in aperture. While this discovery came from America, another came from Italy, where Signor Schiaparelli, using a telescope of 8¾ inches in aperture, found a number of straight and narrow lines which he called canali, the Italian word for channels. This was translated into English as canals, and for the first time the world heard of the famous canals on Mars.

For many years nobody else succeeded in seeing the canals, and they were put down to Schiaparelli's imagination, but gradually they were confirmed by other observers with larger telescopes. In 1894 an American amateur, Professor Percival Lowell, built his own observatory at Flagstaff in Arizona, and equipped it with a fine-quality 24-inch refracting telescope for observing the planets, in particular Mars. Professor Lowell's results were of the highest interest, and some of them were very startling, although scientific men have not accepted them in their entirety.

Professor Lowell believed that Mars is a drying-up world, where every drop of water is precious. The inhabitants were in a sore plight; they had to cultivate crops, and the only water available was that in the polar caps. There was only one thing to do. The inhabitants became one community, and constructed a vast network of channels for the water to be conveyed from the polar caps to the regions where it is needed, which are the patches of vegetation. Since open canals would be wasteful and the loss by evaporation enormous, the canals must be covered, and it would be necessary for the water to be helped, for instance, by pumping, in its world-wide journey. Finally certain dark spots, occasionally found at the spots where one canal crosses another, were considered by Professor Lowell as the centers of civilization, the cities of Mars. Lowell implied that the Martians were engineers, and that the canals were artificial waterways dug by them in an attempt to preserve the race in its fight against the encroaching desert.

This fascinating idea captures the imagination, for if true it means that we see on Mars markings made by an alien but intelligent race. In order to distinguish one spot from another, and to compare drawings made by different observers, names have been given to the various spots, the principal ones being shown on the chart, which is on a cylindrical projection. The map, Illustration 18, shows that zero longitude, the Greenwich meridian of Mars, passes through a dark marking shaped like the open beak of a bird. To the left of this is a large, dark and tapering marking, one of the most prominent of the dark patches believed to be vegetation. This is called the SYRTIS MAJOR. From its tip there runs a wide canal, NILUS, which curves round to a dark dot known as COLCE PALUS. Another canal, NEPENTHES, curves from the left side of Syrtis Major, passes a round spot called LACUS MAORIS and ends in another spot, TRITON LACUS. Although the Syrtis Major is always there, its shape varies from time to time. Sometimes it has a long, pointed tip; at other times, as in 1922, the tip is missing, while white patches have been seen hiding a good deal of the Syrtis for a few weeks. These temporary white patches are certainly clouds, and they are often seen over those parts of Mars on which the sun is just rising, as though they form during the night. The canals from Syrtis also vary a good deal in tint, while Lacus Mœris, which on Lowell's theory would be a Martian city, is sometimes small and faint while at others it is large and dark, presumably according to the amount of water available.

The curved edge of Syrtis Major ends at a small round spot, SYRTIS MINOR, about which is a dark streak called MARE TYRRHENUM. On its left is another but larger patch, MARE CIMMERIUM, to which many canals run. The area to the left of Syrtis Major and north of Tyrrhenum and Cimmerium is desert, a sandy waste, in the center of which is another round and dark spot, called TRIVIUM CHARONTIS. This spot is peculiar because occasionally it becomes two separate spots, which after a time reunite. If Trivium is a Martian city, it is situated in a very queer place, right in the middle of the desert. Two canals, one called STYX and the other HADES, connect this desert spot with other canals running up to the north pole, and the water appears to travel along them all the way from the polar cap to Trivium in 12 degrees north latitude.

Still farther to the left, or east, is another dark streak, MARE SIRENUM, on the opposite side of Mars to Syrtis Major, surrounded by desert. East of this is a large light area, in the middle of which is a dark patch from which canals radiate. This spot is sometimes called the "Eye of Mars" because it looks just like an eye; its proper name is LACUS SOLIS, or the "Lake of the Sun." To the south of all these dark areas is a large dusky spot, extending up to the snows around the south pole and called MARE AUSTRALE, or the "Southern Sea." Here and there are a kind of bright islands, such as HELLAS and the THYLES. Between the zero meridian and the Eye of Mars is a pointed dark streak, the MARGARITIFER SINUS or "Pearl Bearing Gulf," and this runs into the tract of vegetation known as the MARE ERYTHRAEUM.

From these dark patches canals run across the northern deserts to dark patches grouped around the north pole. Although there are few of these in the northern hemisphere which, as we have already said, is chiefly desert, one is very prominent and sometimes even more prominent than the Syrtis Major. This dark spot is called the MARE ACIDALIUM, and is connected with the Pearl Bearing Gulf by a wide canal called INDUS. A little to the right, or west, of Acidalium is one of the dark spots in the desert, called LACUS LUNAE or Lake of the Moon. From this spot a wide canal, GAUGES, crosses the desert to the patch of vegetation AURORAE SINUS, near the Eye of Mars. The last desert outpost is the LACUS ASCREUS. Then comes the great desert of AMAZONIA, which extends over 90° of longitude to Trivium Charontis. This desert is crossed by a few canals of which LYCUS, BRONTËS and ORCUS are the largest. Immediately to the west of Trivium is a large white area called ELYSIUM, bordered by canals and with a network of them right up to the pole.

These are the chief permanent markings on Mars, but they are never seen all together. During the winter the polar caps are large, while the canals are then either invisible or can only be traced with difficulty; but as the cap melts, a dark girdle appears around it, probably a temporary polar sea, and then the canals begin to appear. At first only a little bit near the melting snow can be seen, but this gradually gets longer and longer until the whole of the canal is marked out as far as one of the patches of vegetation. Like the canals, these patches are mere shades during the winter, but begin to darken as the canals from the poles fill up, and are very prominent during the summer. With the onset of

ILLUS. 18—Map of Mars (opposite).

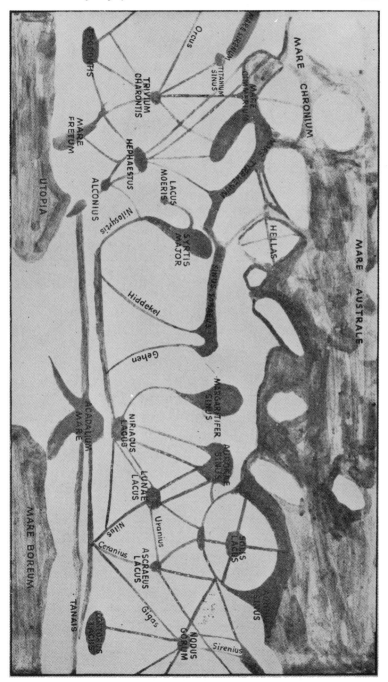

autumn they change from a dark grayish-green to brown, and then become mere shades in winter.

All this fits in beautifully with Lowell's idea of artificial waterways, but there are other opinions. With his 24-inch telescope Lowell saw and drew the canals as narrow and continuous lines, but another eminent observer, Antoniadi, using a larger telescope, the 33-inch at Meudon, near Paris, declared that these narrow lines were illusions. He said that the reason why Lowell saw and drew them as continuous lines was due solely to his telescope being too small to show their true nature. With the great telescope at Meudon, the canals were seen not to be continuous but made up of a series of dots and dashes, arranged one after the other in straight lines. Whether the canals are continuous or not, whether they are natural or artificial, all observers agree that what we see is not the actual ditch, assuming they are ditches, but the vegetation to either side of them. An American observer, John E. Mellish, declares that with the 40-inch refracting telescope at the Yerkes Observatory, the largest instrument of its type in the world, the canals appeared as cracks, wide and eroded down, comparatively shallow and filled with water. Some of the very wide canals were distinctly seen to be darker in the center, and resembled ditches filled with water and with marshes and vegetation along their sides. The dark, round spots, which Lowell believed to be cities, oases in the desert, were seen by Mellish as craters, presumably of volcanic origin, and also filled with water.

We have three opinions about these mysterious canals. The first regards them as ditches dug by the Martians and indicative of an advanced civilization, the work of superhuman intelligences. The second does not attempt to decide whether they are natural or artificial, but denies that they are continuous features, declaring them to be series of isolated and apparently quite separate spots. The third regards them as natural features, in fact cracks in the surface and therefore natural waterways.

The regular appearances of the isolated dark spots, Lowell's cities, were also to some extent broken down into collections of separate dots with the Meudon telescope. On the other hand, Mellish regards them as craters, and therefore regular. That there is life of some sort on Mars is now generally admitted, but the question to be answered is whether this consists merely of vegetation, possibly with some elementary animal life, or whether there exist on Mars today, or have existed in the past, creatures somewhat resembling man, beings capable of reasoning and of constructing civil engineering projects on a scale far exceeding anything which man has achieved on the earth.

This question of whether we have brothers in the sky, or at any rate on Mars, is of the utmost importance. If there are intelligent beings on Mars it is not impossible that they may seek to communicate with us, or even to leave their drying-up planet and migrate to our pleasantly watered and warmer world. Is it possible for highly organized beings to exist on Mars?

We already know that the diameter of Mars is 4,200 miles, to which we can add that this globe is not as closely packed as the earth, the density being 3.94 times that of water, while the figure for the earth is 5.52. The small diameter and the low density mean that the mass of Mars, the amount of matter in it, is only slightly more than one-tenth of that of the earth. The surface of Mars, or its area, is not quite three-tenths and the intensity of gravity at its surface is not quite four-tenths (more precisely 0.38) that of our globe.

The low surface gravity is just about sufficient to allow the planet to retain an atmosphere composed of oxygen and nitrogen, with some water vapor. The red color and the spectroscopic evidence that there is little free oxygen in the atmosphere mean that much of the free oxygen the atmosphere probably once possessed has entered into combination with the surface rocks. The amount of water vapor is limited, but still sufficient for the formation of polar caps and occasional morning mists and clouds. The true water-vapor clouds can be distinguished from what appear to be dust or sand storms by their white color. The yellowish clouds which have attracted the attention of the best observers are thought to be sand storms, in which the sandy surfaces of the deserts are whirled aloft by air currents. There must be winds on Mars; but judging from the manner in which clouds of any kind tend to rise and hang over the same region, without drifting far, it seems that the atmospheric currents are usually ascending or descending, probably associated with temperature variations.

The mean temperature on Mars must be much lower than that on the earth, because the planet is so far from the sun and also on account of its rarefied atmosphere. The best authorities believe that the maximum temperature at noon on the equator is somewhere between 50 and 60 degrees Fahrenheit. From this maximum it must fall rapidly as the poles are approached, and also both in the early morning and the late afternoon for places on the equator. Mars is certainly a cold world, but it is also a dry one; to this it may be added that Mars is a smooth world.

Despite Mars being a small, dry, and cold world, there seems to be some analogy between the conditions on Mars and some of the more arid regions on the earth. A mysterious thing about the red planet is the fact that although it is smaller than the earth but larger than the moon, and thus fits in between them, it is much more smooth than either. The moon clearly tells us that smallness of a planetary globe is no bar to its having a rough and mountainous surface, but on Mars it is doubtful whether there are any mountains higher than the Welsh hills or the highlands of Scotland. Some authorities have set the maximum height much lower, around 2,000 feet, and talk about the featureless horizon on Mars and how, owing to the sharp curvature of its surface, the ground must seem to rise up like a huge convex shield, especially in the desert regions.

The great barrier to increasing our knowledge of Mars is an insurmountable one, namely distance. This, together with the limitations imposed by our atmosphere, renders it certain that the largest telescope man can ever construct will fail to solve the problem of the type of Martian life. It is possible that we will eventually learn more about this alien form of life by radar than by visual or photographic means, unless such means are located somewhere comparatively close to the planet, perhaps on one of its moons.

Every time that Mars comes to opposition, and is therefore most favorably situated, enthusiastic and hopeful people "tune in" with powerful radio sets in the hope that they may pick up signals from the Martians. In 1924 and again in 1926 reports appeared in the press of certain unidentified "pips" which might, but almost certainly did not, originate from Mars. Assuming that intelligent beings exist and attempt to contact us, the difficulty here would be to make anything out of the sounds, as it is in the highest degree improbable that they would make use of our terrestrial Morse code!

More nonsense has been written about Mars than about any other planet. The only thing which science has established is the almost certain existence of plant life on Mars, and the possibility that some form of animal life may also exist. Beyond this we cannot go unless the field is thrown open to speculation, when of course there is no limit. There may be people on Mars and they may be anything you like to imagine, but we know nothing about them, and up to the present time nothing has been picked up which suggests that they are attempting to contact us.

It seems reasonable to conclude that if intelligences do exist, they should most earnestly desire to leave their in many ways inhospitable world, and visit ours. Even if they did succeed in the construction of practical spaceships capable of traveling to the earth, our dense atmosphere would prove a serious and possibly fatal barrier. Just as we would be asphyxiated if we attempted to breathe the thin atmosphere of Mars, so the Martians would be drowned by immersion in our dense atmosphere. Only in the higher regions near the summits of our loftiest mountains, could they hope to survive, at least for several generations and until they became acclimatized to their new environment.

Mystery still surrounds the canals, bound up as they are with the greater mystery of life. As a telescopic object, Mars is often rather disappointing to casual observers. People imagine that we know more than science admits, and expect a large telescope to show the planet like a huge full moon with canals clearly revealed, and possibly even see the canal boats which are imagined as passing to and fro along these waterways. The actual view shows a small and not always round disk of a yellowish-red color, on which the polar caps may be plain enough, as are the darker markings, while the canals generally appear as rather diffused streaks. Should the atmospheric conditions be imperfect, as is usually the case, the view is even more disappointing, as the whole thing is "fuzzy" and unsteady.

The proper place to solve the mystery of Mars is from one or another of its satellites. The nearer to the planet is the larger, and may have a diameter of around 15 miles, while it is so close to the planet (only 3,900 miles from its surface) that it has to scamper around it in 7 hours 39 minutes 26.65 seconds. The outer moon is only 10 or 12 miles in diameter, and takes 1 day 6 hours 21 minutes 15.86 seconds to complete a revolution at its distance of 12,900 miles from the surface.

The inner moon, PHOBOS, actually takes more than three revolutions around Mars while the planet turns around once, so to the Martians it must seem *to rise in the west* and set in the east. On the other hand the outer moon, DEIMOS, revolves around Mars in a period which is less than 6 hours longer than that of Mars itself, and to the Martians must seem to move very slowly across the sky. Deimos rises in the east and sets in the west, in the same manner as the sun and the stars. As seen from Mars it would look like a bright star; its disk would be rather difficult to detect with the naked eye.

Both these moons are totally eclipsed at every "full moon," and also they frequently eclipse the sun. The solar eclipses are never total, for even the nearer and larger moon, Phobos, can only appear about a third of the diameter of the sun. There are no total eclipses of the sun for the Martians; they are either partial or annular. The shadow cones which the moons cast from the side turned away from the sun never reach the surface of Mars. There are also eclipses of Deimos by Phobos, but the latter moon moves so quickly that it only eclipses the sun or occults Deimos for a short time, in both cases measured in seconds. As luminaries they must cut a poor figure, for the total amount of light they afford during the night is far inferior to that afforded by our single moon.

Owing to their small dimensions and their proximity to Mars, the moons are difficult telescopic objects. The period of visibility is a couple of months either side of the date of opposition, amounting to three or four months at intervals of two years. Even the largest telescopes fail to show any detail on their tiny disks; indeed, it requires considerable attention to make out their disks and to distinguish them from stars.

In 1952 Mars was farther from the earth than in 1954, but higher in the northern sky, and thus better placed for observers in

Britain. On May 17 the writer and Patrick Moore, observing together with the writer's 15¼-inch reflector, saw Deimos clearly for more than half an hour, following it until it had drawn so close to Mars as to be lost in the glare. Moore has also caught Phobos with certainty with his 12½-inch reflector, describing it on April 28, 1952, as "unmistakably seen, but excessively faint even with Mars outside the telescopic field; on the very limit of visibility with this instrument, at least to my eyes."

These moons add to the mystery of the red planet. Perhaps they were two of the hundreds of minor planets which revolve around the sun between Mars and Jupiter, captured by Mars during a close approach in the past. They are mere lumps of rock; we are not even sure that they are globes, and it is not impossible that they may have a somewhat irregular shape, as some of the minor planets seem to have. Eros is an example of a small body, about the size of the moons of Mars and perhaps slightly larger, which comes quite near to the earth at certain times and varies greatly in brightness. It has been suggested that this may be caused by Eros being a rough and practically shapeless rocky mass.

Owing to its proximity Phobos cannot be seen from the Martian polar regions, as it is always hidden by the curvature of the surface of Mars. In the equatorial zone it passes overhead, and must look considerably larger when high up in the sky than when near the horizon. A few moments' thought will be sufficient to show that Phobos is considerably nearer when overhead, and therefore looks as big as it possibly can.

If Mars is inhabited by intelligent beings, and if they have telescopes of equal power to ours, it would be easy to find out whether these little moons also are inhabited. The rarefied atmosphere would enable high powers to be used, bringing Phobos within a mile and Deimos to within four miles. However, both moons are certainly barren worlds, being devoid of atmospheres and appreciable surface gravity. They would be admirably suitable for observatories, and may be used as such during the coming era of space travel. What a view of Mars could be obtained from Phobos! Seen from this little world Mars would look over 80 times larger than the moon does to us, and would go through all its phases in less than eight hours.

To ourselves Mars does not always look round, but may appear gibbous, that is to say like the moon three days before or after full. At such times we can see a little bit of the darkened or night side of Mars. Along the line dividing the darkened from the sunlit portion of the planet (the "terminator," to use the correct and technical term), the sun is either rising or setting. This line is generally smooth, but occasionally is irregular owing to the presence of bright projections or spots. When such are seen they can only be viewed for a short time before being carried into the bright or the darkened portion, owing to the rotation of Mars on its axis. Although fiction writers, for example H. G. Wells in his fantasy *The War of the Worlds,* have ascribed these bright spots to flashes from a stupendous gun which was being used by the Martians to project cylinders to the earth, there is no doubt that they are clouds floating in the Martian atmosphere at a considerable distance above the surface and thus catching the sun's rays.

But there are other bright spots, not floating in the atmosphere but on the surface. They appear in the equatorial regions during the summer and autumn on Mars. Usually they lie on or close to the borders of one or more of the patches of vegetation, such as Syrtis Major or Margaritifer Sinus. These white spots develop markedly during the hot season, and, although we are not sure what they are, the plausible suggestion has been made that they may be cultivated areas or, in other words, crops.

Certain canals occasionally show activity of another kind; they become double! What was previously seen as a long, linear marking now has a companion running parallel to it a short distance away. They look exactly like a rail track, and may maintain their parallel nature for hundreds of miles. They are somewhat rare, and the majority of the canals are always seen as single; moreover, they seem to be confined to the desert regions. The appearance is exactly as though the companion canal were a reserve channel which may be brought into use if the circumstances warrant it. They have been the subject of much discussion; some people regard this double aspect as an illusion, without, however, explaining in a convincing manner how the illusion could arise and why only some of the canals are subject to it.

We have already seen that Antoniadi claimed to have resolved the canals into a series of dots and dashes with the great telescope at Meudon. On the moon there are certain dusky streaks on the slopes of some of the craters which are approximately the same apparent width as those of the Martian canals. By this is meant that they look to us about the same size; in reality, the Martian canals are much larger, and it is only distance which dwarfs them to the size of the lunar streaks.

The writer has carefully examined these streaks with the same great telescope which was used by Antoniadi, and actually used the same eyepieces. In small or comparatively small telescopes the streaks on the crater slopes look just like the canals of Mars, that is to say, simple and uniform lines or bands. But with the giant telescope at Meudon the streaks were clearly resolved into dots and dashes, presenting a perfect analogy to what Antoniadi found on Mars.

It seems to be established that not only the ordinary and single canals but also the double ones are in reality made up of discontinuous fragments. It cannot be a mere accidental arrangement of the dots in a straight line, but must be a real feature of the surface. That is to say, the dots and dashes are either the widest portions of continuous cracks, assuming that the canals are cracks, or they have been deliberately placed in these positions, assuming Lowell's ideas to be true. In either case, we can safely assume that all parts of the cracks or ditches are too narrow for us to see except where the enlargements (the dots and dashes) happen to be. It must be remembered that those astronomers who accept the conclusions of Antoniadi draw the discontinuous fragments as arranged in lines. *Unless there is some underlying linear arrangement, no suggestion of continuous streaks would be recorded.*

Now it is contrary to scientific spirit to assume an artificial origin unless a natural cause is proved inadequate. It is also very difficult to distinguish between natural and artificial structures unless we have a more or less complete knowledge of the regions in question. If the earth could be observed with some supertelescope on the moon or Venus, both natural and artificial features would be seen. The latter would be such things as towns, cities, and perhaps some of the larger canals. Unless observations were conducted during their actual construction, it would be very difficult to de-

cide whether the Panama and Suez Canals were natural or artificial. We know that these canals are partly natural, in the existing
lakes, and partly artificial, in the cuttings executed by man; but
without this knowledge, an observer on another world could not
decide. We are in the same position as the imaginary observer;
the canals came into being before telescopes were invented. Although Lowell thought that he detected a few new canals in
previously undisturbed parts of the surface, this has not been confirmed by others, and all the canals have an unknown antiquity.
Even if Lowell's theory should be proved, it might still be found
that the artificial portions are extentions and adaptations of previously existing natural features. The majority if not all of the
markings on Mars are natural features; and although they may
seem strange to us, owing to their unfamiliarity, they are the logical result of the conditions prevailing on the planet, in exactly the
same manner that crater mountains are the natural result of the
forces which molded the lunar surface. On any planet the works
of its inhabitants must be mere superficial scars in comparison
with the operations of Nature — unless the inhabitants deliberately
adopt a policy of self-destruction, to which rational beings are
naturally averse.

Time enters into the discussion, although it is generally overlooked. The present era is one of life-bearing for the earth, but
on Mars might be quite different. For all we can tell, the greatest
life-bearing era on Mars may now be long past; on the other hand,
it may still lie in the future. The present desertlike appearance of
Mars suggests that it is more likely that maximum life existed in
the past than that it should still lie in the future. It looks as though
the life which still exists on Mars is but a feeble reflection of what
once existed. Mars may well prove to be a world in its old age
and approaching extinction, for owing to its small size it would
run through its stages of planetary evolution more rapidly than
the earth.

The favorable opposition of Mars in 1924 was observed by pro-
fessionals and amateurs alike. At the Jungfrau Observatory, in the
Alps, at an altitude of 11,660 feet, Professor Schaerer noted that
the canal Tartarus and part of the Mare Cimmerium were cloud
covered. According to some press reports, light flashes were also

seen, apparently of the same nature as lightning. At the Yerkes Observatory the two moons "shone like chips of star dust." At this opposition the first attempts were made to "listen in to Mars." A 24-valve wireless set was set up in Dulwich Village, and it was stated that strange signals were picked up in the early morning which were very clear and resembled dots in the Morse code, arranged in groups of four and five. It was stated that these sounds were not Morse and could not be identified as coming from any station on this earth. They continued, intermittently, for about three minutes. Nothing, however, came of this, and it seems probable that the dots were a combination of atmospherics and heterodyning or interference between various stations. In 1924 radio was in its early stages, and these signals almost certainly had a terrestrial origin. Reports of the picking up of similar signals were received from abroad; in America, for example, where it was stated that they alternated between a long wavelength of 25,000 meters and a short wave of 75 meters.

At the previous opposition, in 1922, Professor Slipher at Flagstaff had photographed a large white cloud which hung for four days over the edge of the Pearl Bearing Gulf.

A close approach took place in 1909, when Mars was observed by Antoniadi and also by the French observer M. Jarry-Deloges. In this year Syrtis Major had a pointed tip, while among the strange changes noted were those in the canal Phison, which appeared double on September 14 and 16, but single on September 15. It seems possible that it was partly veiled by clouds on the latter date. The Lake of the Sun was elongated in 1909, and a complicated system of canals was seen to radiate from it.

What appeared to be clouds projecting from the surface were seen by Antoniadi on October 10, 11, and 12, 1924, while other clouds were seen over Hellas. In 1924 most of the dark areas were very much darker than usual, which suggests that the proximity of Mars to the sun (it being summer in the southern hemisphere) may have favored the development of vegetation. The polar cap soon showed dark rifts within it, and began to break up into detached pieces which were especially well seen on August 23.

The opposition of 1926 was remarkable in many ways. It was not so close an approach as that of 1924, but the planet was higher up in the sky for northern observers. A special feature of this year was the large number of clouds which were seen to distort the terminator of the planet. Two such clouds were seen to the southwest of Syrtis Major on September 15 by Antoniadi, while on December 15 at least three such clouds were noted to the east of the Lake of the Sun or the Eye of Mars. At times the whole planet seemed to have masses of clouds or mists drifting over it, now hiding this and then that feature on the surface. The canal Nepenthes and Lacus Mœris, to the left or west of Syrtis Major, were very broad and dark in this year, while the Mare Tyrrhenum was clearly resolved into separate patches which in all probability were more intensive areas of vegetation.

A very large cloud apparently floating at a great height above the surface was seen on March 16, 1929, by the same talented observer, Antoniadi. Very few of the canals were seen this year, when the planet was farther from the earth than during the previous two oppositions.

A vast *yellow* cloud was seen from August 23 to 27, 1909, by Antoniadi covering much of the surface around the Trivium Charontis, while in December 1911 another such cloud appeared to the south and southeast of Syrtis Major and could be seen changing its shape and size from November 3 to December 23. This cloud stayed for a long time over this part of Mars, in contrast with the majority of such clouds, which usually disappear fairly quickly. It is certain that the yellow and the white clouds differ in their composition, and this has an effect on the length of their visibility.

If we compare the drawings of the earlier observers, made before the canals were recognized as such in 1877, we can still trace, although faintly, some of the principal canals, which proves that these strange features are not of recent development, but are permanent. We can also find traces of clouds and other indications of variations among the dark patches, showing that the weather conditions on Mars have not altered appreciably during the last 100 years.

But in addition to the temporary changes introduced by clouds, we also find others which affect the dark patches, such as changes in their shapes, a growing-out more than usual at this point and a withdrawal at another. These changes are more interesting than those due to mere clouds, as they must mean some alterations in the patches of vegetation themselves. It may be that they arise from the amount of sunshine at the time, coupled with temperature changes, but it is not impossible that some at least are due to the activities of some other form of life — that is to say, deliberate interference with the growth at the places where the changes are noted. Perhaps the soil is exhausted in these places, with the result that vegetation fails for a time, and it is not impossible that the failing is due to the excessive "reaping" in those areas. It must be remembered that what look to us like small features are in reality objects covering many square miles of the only fertile areas on this otherwise arid planet. It is even possible that the changes are due to the failing of some new kind of vegetation deliberately introduced as an experiment.

An opposition of Mars took place in 1954, but the planet was too low in the sky for successful observations in Britain. At one time it rose only 10 degrees above the southern horizon, and under such conditions no useful observations could be obtained. The writer was then in the United States, where Mars was at a much greater altitude, in the southern States over 27 degrees, and advantage was taken of the great American telescopes. Among other instruments the planet was observed with the 60-inch reflector at Mount Wilson Observatory and also with the 40-inch refractor at the Yerkes Observatory; the latter instrument is the largest refracting telescope in the world.

As seen from Mount Wilson in early June, the ice cap at the south pole was very large and surrounded by a dark band. There is nothing unusual in this, for the melting cap is *always* seen to be surrounded by a dark band, and the cap was beginning to melt. But what *was* very unusual was the intense blueness of the markings, more especially the so-called "seas" in the southern hemisphere. Before the cap has appreciably contracted these are normally of a grayish hue, and are not pronounced. That this blue color was real was proved by observations with filters of various tints; the blue came through clearly. There was also a lot of cloud in the atmosphere of Mars as shown on the drawing, Illustration 17, which was made with the 60-inch Mount Wilson reflector on June 17. That night only two of the canals could be seen, but it was clear that they were continuous streaks and *not* made up of a series of dots and dashes. Later on when Mars was examined with the Yerkes 40-inch refractor, numerous canals were detected, and they all appeared to be uniform streaks strongly suggestive of cracks in the surface, while the oases, several of which were seen, suggested craters, presumably filled up with some dark-colored matter. At Yerkes the blue nature of the markings was again evident, almost vivid when contrasted with the reddish regions. They prompted the remark that perhaps Mars too was experiencing unusual weather. It will be remembered that Britain and Europe had a very wet and unsettled summer in 1954.

With the other and smaller telescopes, such as the 26-inch refractor at the Naval Observatory, Washington, D. C., and the 15½-inch refractor at the Washburn Observatory, Madison, the same general results were obtained. At Yerkes the outer moon of Mars, Deimos, was seen close to the planet itself without requiring any shielding of the planet. Even in the great Yerkes telescope this tiny moon appeared as a point of light and not as a disk. Phobos, the inner moon, was always either behind or in front of the planet on the particular occasions when I was observing with these magnificent instruments. The clouds persisted, and with the Yerkes instrument a large white one was clearly seen projecting beyond the limb of Mars.

Mars was in opposition in 1956 and again in 1958. On both occasions the writer observed the planet at Meudon Observatory, using the 24-inch Cassegrain reflector. The most striking feature of the 1956 opposition was the excessive faintness of the markings owing to the persistence of extensive blue haze in the Martian atmosphere. Of the "canals," only a few vague streaks were detected.

The markings were much easier to detect in 1958. In the telescope the yellowish-red tint of the surface was very pronounced in strong contrast with the bluish-green areas.

The diminution in the extent of the polar cap and the manner in which it broke up into detached portions followed the pattern of previous oppositions. A study of the polarization of the light reflected from the dark areas indicated a degree of humidity sufficient for the existence of some form of life. Yellow and white patches of mist or cloud were also observed but again only a few diffused streaks indicated the positions of the more prominent "canals."

Now that men have sent a rocket which landed on the surface of the moon and another which, passing around the moon, photographed the other side, it is no longer pure fantasy to anticipate a similar attempt in the case of Mars. If and when men actually land on the planet they may find that the dark areas are depressed portions of the surface, probably retaining some moisture. They may be old and now almost dried-up sea beds. They are covered by vegetation of a type peculiar to the planet, but, like all life, made up of cells. Some low form of animal or insect life may also be found, but it is highly unlikely that any kind of intelligent life will be encountered.

There have been other attempted explanations of the dark and permanent markings on Mars. One of the most recent is that of Dr. D. B. McLaughlin, of the University of Michigan, U. S. A. A summary of this new theory was given in the American astronomical journal Sky and Telescope, vol. 13, No. 11. According to this account Dr. McLaughlin believes that the dark areas are not caused by vegetation, as most astronomers think, but are due to drifts of volcanic ash. The volcanic dust originates in active volcanoes, which are supposed to be at the tips of fan-shaped markings. It is suggested that the general wind circulation of the planet causes the dust and ash to be deposited in the places where we see the dark markings. The green color is ascribed to the reaction of carbon dioxide and the scanty moisture with the ferromagnesian minerals to form chlorite and epidote, which are green in color. The canals Dr. McLaughlin believes to be partly ash and partly volcanic rifts; this idea was, however, suggested long ago by the late Alfred Russel Wallace.

The objection to this theory is the presumed existence of volcanoes on Mars. There may be volcanoes on Mars, but that the ash or dust from them would always be blown by winds to the same points on the planet is a weak point unless we assume that there are certain irregularities in the surface which also enter into the shaping of the dark areas. Also, this theory does not take into account the seasonal changes which affect both the dark areas and the visibility of the canal system.

We have considered the evidence which observations have given as to the presence of water on Mars, even although the indications are that the amount is small. Also, the seasonal changes in the dark markings, their altered colors and the way in which the canals begin to make their appearance as the polar caps melt, the certain if occasional presence of clouds or at least mists on Mars, and the general appearance of this most fascinating planet all combine to suggest that Mars is largely a waterless desert and that the dark areas are really tracts of vegetation that owes its life to what water can be conveyed along the natural waterways or canals. Perhaps the future will show that Lowell, with his imaginative but magnificent idea of their having been dug in the past by a race of intelligent beings in a vain effort to ward off the inevitable drying-up of their world, was right after all; but this is not likely to happen until the first spaceship has touched down on the alien and strange landscape of the red and green planet. Then will come the time when men may settle on the planet; then, perhaps, the name will be changed from that of the god of war to that of the god of peace, and men will live freely in their new environment.

FRED L. WHIPPLE

Meteors

[FROM THE SMITHSONIAN REPORT FOR 1957°]

IN THE SUBJECT of this article we come to a union between outer space and the surface of our planet, for in meteorites — those portions of large meteors which survive the passage through the atmosphere — we have the only tangible objects from outer space that can be handled and examined here on earth. The study of the meteors themselves is a fascinating one, both from the point of view of enlarging our knowledge of the universe and from its intimate association with present-day attempts to conquer space.

The author, Fred L. Whipple, is the Director of the Smithsonian Astrophysical Observatory, which now operates the so-called Moonwatch project — the visual tracking of artificial earth satellites. He is also professor of astronomy and ex-chairman of the department of astronomy at Harvard. He has been investigating meteors for many years, and in this article he summarizes his conclusions and those of other workers, on meteoric origin, orbits and velocities, and on new methods of meteoric research. The study involves meteoritic objects than range in size from microscopic dust particles to great celestial bombs that have scarred the earth with craters up to 50 miles in diameter (the latter fortunately mostly in the remote past).

° List of references to literature omitted.

137

The continuous shower of meteoric material constitutes a definite hazard to any proposed type of space vehicle, and meteor investigations are an essential element in the success of man's entry into outer space.

SOLID BODIES from space continuously bombard the earth at a rate of thousands of tons per day. Fortunately for the life forms on the earth, the earth's atmosphere serves as an admirable buffer to protect them from this constant astronomical shellfire.

The slowest meteorites strike at a speed of 7.0 miles per second, the speed with which the earth attracts particles that fall from rest at great distances. The speed of faster ones depends upon their origin and direction of motion. Bodies belonging to the solar system travel in closed orbits around the sun at velocities up to the parabolic limit of 26.3 miles per second at the earth's distance from the sun, while the earth itself moves about the sun at a speed of 18.5 miles per second. The highest velocity of impact occurs, of course, when one of these nearly parabolic particles strikes the earth head-on, so that the total velocity reaches a maximum of 45 miles per second.

Illustration 19 shows how the collisions occur. The fastest meteorites tend to strike on the morning side of the earth and the slow ones catch up on the evening side.

These meteoritic projectiles vary in size from minute particles to very large ones, and are classed as follows: Meteoritic dust, telescopic and radio meteors, photographic and visual meteors, fireballs, detonating bolides, meteorite falls, and, finally, crater-producing meteorites.

Meteoritic dust ranges from barely visible specks down to microscopic objects, limits in size being set by the sun's ability to blow away particles about 1 micron (0.00004 inch) in diameter. Micrometeorites are heated as they strike the earth's upper atmosphere, at an altitude from 130 to 100 km., but because of the small ratio

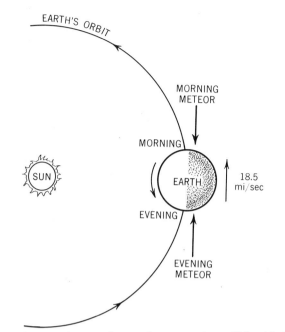

ILLUS. 19—Schematic diagram showing how meteorites collide with the earth.

of their mass to surface area, they can radiate away the heat of impact fast enough to prevent heating above the melting point of ordinary materials such as iron or silicates. Thus many of these particles, as has been shown by Öpik and the writer, can reach the surface of the earth without being greatly damaged. The larger particles in coming through the atmosphere may be melted and fused into small globules by this process without losing much of their mass.

Larger particles, perhaps of the order of a thousandth of a gram or greater, produce enough light by friction with the earth's atmosphere to be visible as telescopic meteors and produce enough electrons to give radar echoes as radio meteors. Both the telescopic and radio techniques can, of course, be used to observe much brighter meteors, and the lower limit of their sensitivity is well below that of the naked eye. Meteors visible to the naked eye fall in the category of visual meteors; today the extremely sensitive Super-Schmidt meteor cameras in New Mexico can photograph nearly to the limit of naked-eye visibility.

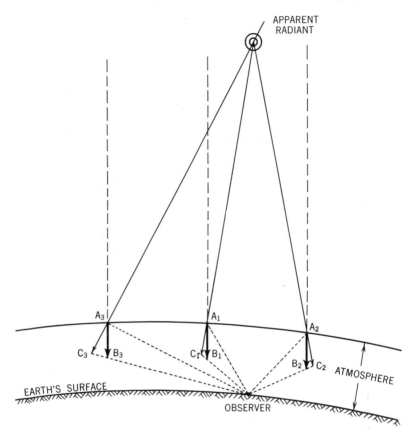

ILLUS. 20—Trails and radiant of a meteor shower. Above the atmosphere the parallel dashed lines show the real paths of the meteors A_1, A_2, and A_3; solid lines show their apparent paths. In the atmosphere the arrows AB show the real meteor paths, and the arrows AC show the paths as they appear to the observer.

On certain days of the year meteors occur in showers, when the earth happens to cross a stream of meteoric particles in space. All the meteors in a shower strike our atmosphere in parallel paths so that all their trails, when extended backward on the sky, tend to meet in a point, or radiant (Illus. 20). The shower is then named for the constellation in which the radiant appears. Some meteor streams are uniformly dense so that when the earth crosses their orbit we can always count on a good display — for example, the Perseid meteors from August 9–14, and many bright Geminid meteors on December 12–13. Occasionally, as on October 9, 1946, meteors seem to fall almost like rain, occurring as frequently as one a second.

As we consider larger and larger bodies we find that with increasing size they penetrate more deeply into the earth's atmosphere and appear as brighter and brighter meteors. If a meteor is bright enough to produce a flash of light that illuminates buildings at night or produces shadows, it is called a fireball. If it is accompanied by a delayed rumbling, caused by its breaking up in the lower atmosphere, it is called a detonating bolide. For these larger bodies the atmosphere is less effective as a shield, so that sizable pieces of these celestial cannonballs survive the atmospheric friction and fall to the ground. These fragments we call meteorites, which we collect and preserve in our museums as our only tangible samples of the great universe that exists beyond the earth's atmosphere. Perhaps we are fortunate that this sampling rate is so low; otherwise more of us would suffer the rare and undesirable experience of Mrs. Hodges in Alabama, who, on November 30, 1955, was injured when a meteorite penetrated her house and struck her on the hip.

The collection of meteorites in the Smithsonian Institution is one of the largest and most valuable in the world. These rare specimens are continuously used by scientists in their attempts not only to discover the origin and history of the meteorites themselves, but also to understand the general laws of supervelocity ballistics involved in the meteor's course through the earth's atmosphere. (See Illus. 21.)

For bodies even larger than the average meteorite, the earth's atmosphere finally ceases to be an effective barrier. Thus irons or stones weighing hundreds of tons or more are affected scarcely at all in falling through the earth's atmosphere. They plow into the ground at supersonic speeds and explode, to produce immense craters. These explosions are literally like those made by huge bombs because of the enormous kinetic energy of the meteorite. The extremely rapid motion endows each pound of the meteorite with much more energy than that contained in a pound of the most powerful chemical explosive. This energy is instantly released when the earth's surface stops the meteorite. A crater-forming meteorite of atomic-bomb energy fell in the general region of Vladivostok in 1947 and produced a great many craters over a large area of ground. In 1908 an even larger fall, of greater than H-bomb energy, occurred near Pultusk in Siberia. It leveled the trees radially from the point of impact for some 50 miles.

No huge craters have been formed by meteorites in historic times, but the great Barringer meteor crater in Arizona, now some 600 feet deep and nearly a mile across, represents the greatest of such celestial visitations in the United States. The largest meteorite crater in the world is probably the one in the New Quebec (Ungava) area in Canada, which is nearly 3 miles in diameter. The crater is now an almost perfectly round bowl, partially filled with water to form a beautiful lake, standing unique in a great area of granite that was once covered by glaciers.

The geological evidence proves that even more powerful celestial bombing has been directed toward the earth in past geological periods than these craters suggest. The Harvard geologist Daly gave convincing evidence that the great Vredefort dome in South Africa was once a meteorite crater some 50 miles in diameter. In the hundreds of millions of years since it was formed the crater has been filled by sediments, tilted over at a considerable angle, and its edge greatly eroded. Many astronomers suspect that such fossil craters on the earth are "blood relatives" to the great craters that we see on the moon. Baldwin has strongly supported this view in his book, *The Face of the Moon,* 1949, and scientific evidence is accumulating to support his theory.

The great meteorite craters and the meteorites themselves present myriad fascinating problems. Since I cannot do even summary justice to both meteorites and meteors I must regretfully abandon the former and discuss meteors alone in the remainder of this article. Before leaving the subject of meteorites, however, I must mention that the majority of meteoriticists favor the theory that many or most of the meteorites originated in two or (many?) more small or minor planets, which have mutually collided and broken up to form both the asteroids and the meteorites. A com-

ILLUS. 21—A stony meteorite from the collection of the Smithsonian Institution, found in Tulia, Swisher County, Texas, showing how the
leading face of a stony meteorite is altered in flight through the
atmosphere.

etary origin, as we shall see, is indicated for most of the smaller
bodies that produce the usual visual and subvisual meteors. Thus
the sources of meteors and meteorites still constitute a major area
of research.

For nearly a century, since Schiaparelli identified the Perseid
meteor shower as being associated with the comet of 1862–III,
astronomers have accepted a cometary origin for recurrent meteor
streams. At the same time, most investigators have agreed that
broken fragments of small planets must contribute to the sporadic
meteors, those that do not appear in showers. There have, however, been great disagreement and much discussion as to whether
some of the meteorites and some of the meteors may not be visitors
from interstellar space rather than from our solar system. To distinguish interstellar from solar-system meteors we need only measure their speeds and trajectories through the atmosphere. After
correcting for the resistance of the atmosphere, the rotation and
attraction of the earth, and the earth's motion about the sun, we
can calculate the meteor's original speed and its orbit about the
sun. If the speed was less than 26.3 miles per second, the orbit
was closed, i.e., elliptical, and the body belonged to the solar system. If the speed exceeded 26.3 miles per second, the orbit was
open or hyperbolic, and the body came from out among the stars.

The visual methods, unfortunately, have not been adequate to
settle this long-standing controversy over the origin of meteors.
Even though extremely sensitive and quick in detecting faint fast-
moving meteors, the eye is not an accurate measuring device for
determining the precise geometry either of altitudes or of angular
velocities across the sky. Within recent years the photographic
method has been developed to a high level of sensitivity with its
natural accompaniment of extreme precision in the measurement
of heights, trajectories, and velocities. Even more recently an entirely new technique, the measurement of radio reflections by
radar methods, has become a vital tool in the study of meteors.

Let us begin with the photographic techniques and follow them
with a résumé of the radio techniques for studying meteors. The
first long and systematic photographic meteor program was conducted by Elkin of Yale Observatory from 1893 to 1909. He used
two telescopes (Illus. 22) and in front of each telescope he placed

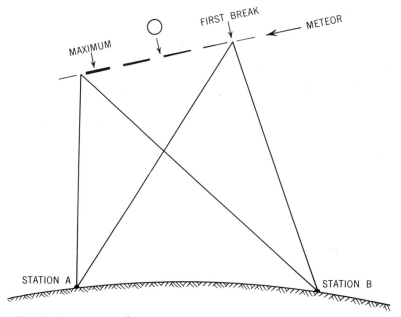

ILLUS. 22—Diagram showing a meteor photographed simultaneously from stations A and B; the circle represents a common point on both photographs of the trail.

a rotating shutter and recorded its speed of rotation by means of a chronograph. Unfortunately, he used such a short base line, about 2 miles, that the geometry of most meteor trails was poorly determined, so that he could not obtain accurate heights, velocities, and trajectories of meteors. In 1936 the writer initiated a similar method, making use of the two stations operated by the Harvard College Observatory in Cambridge, Mass., and at Harvard, Mass., about 24 miles apart. The small Harvard patrol cameras at these two stations simultaneously photographed approximately half a dozen bright meteors per year.

After World War II, meteors and related upper-atmospheric problems and supervelocity ballistics became of such interest that the United States Naval Bureau of Ordnance supported an extensive meteor program at the Harvard College Observatory. This support made possible the design and construction of special cameras. James G. Baker designed the Super-Schmidt meteor camera

ILLUS. 23—The Baker Super-Schmidt meteor camera.

shown above and the Perkin Elmer Corporation has constructed
six of these remarkable instruments, two for the Naval Bureau of
Ordnance, two for the United States Air Force, and two for the
Dominion Observatory of Canada. Four of these cameras have
been operated in New Mexico for the past several years by the
Harvard College Observatory, supported by the Office of Naval
Research and the United States Air Force, while the work of re-
ducing the data has also been supported by the United States
Army, Office of Ordnance Research.

The Baker Super-Schmidt camera has the unique optical design
shown in Illustration 25: the aperture is 12¼ inches and the focal
length only 8 inches, which gives the amazingly fast focal ratio of
F/0.65. The effective focal ratio, including the obstruction by the
photographic film, is still F/0.85. Along with this remarkable speed

the instrument has a field diameter of some 55° without the rotating shutter, reduced to 53° by the shutter, which is supported inside the second glass shell and which revolves only about an eighth of an inch away from the spherical surface of the film. The film itself constituted a considerable problem because the emulsion has to rest on a spherical surface with an accuracy of 0.0005 inch and with a radius of curvature of only 8 inches. A process of molding photographic film, suggested by the Eastman Kodak Co., has been developed at Harvard, so that various types of blue-sensitive and panchromatic emulsions can be satisfactorily heated and molded to this high curvature without serious fogging or appreciable changes in the sensitivity of the emulsion.

Illustration 24 shows an example of a meteor doubly photographed with the Super-Schmidt meteor cameras at two stations. The breaks in the trails were introduced by the shutter, which revolves at the rate of 1,800 r.p.m. and cuts off the light for ¾ of each shutter cycle. During the open part of the cycle, which occurs each $\frac{1}{60}$ of a second, a segment of the meteor trail is photographed.

Without the shutter to reduce the over-all exposure time, on a moonless night in New Mexico we would be limited to only 2 to 3 minutes instead of the 8 to 12 minutes which we can now use effectively. Illustration 26 shows a photograph of the Organ Mountains in the neighborhood of Las Cruces, N. Mex., made with a 2-second exposure at midnight, with full moon. The circle in the center of the photograph is produced by the supporting hole for the rotating shutter and not by the moon.

Since 1952, some 6,000 meteors have been doubly photographed by these cameras in New Mexico. The photographs provide a surprisingly large quantity of information about meteoric phenomena in the atmosphere. We can determine the path of the meteor with an error of only a few feet, its velocity with an error of less than one part in a thousand, and measure its deceleration, caused by the resistance of the atmosphere, to a significant accuracy at several points along the longer trails. Dr. L. G. Jacchia, who has been in charge of the reduction and analysis of the data, finds that the faster meteors enter the atmosphere at an altitude of about 75 miles, and generally die out by an altitude of 50 miles. Some of the slowest meteors are first photographed well below 50

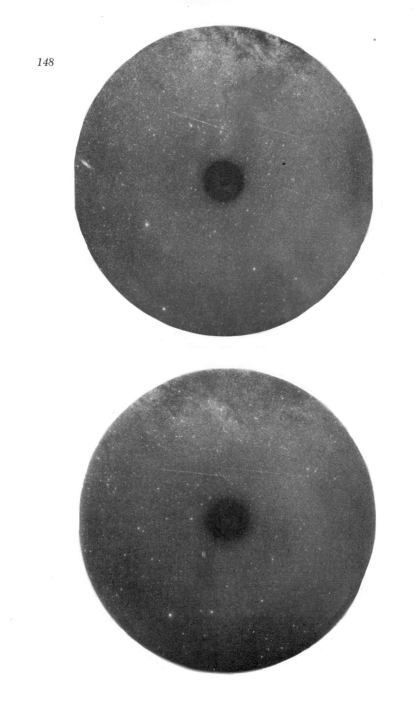

ILLUS. 24—*Two photographs of a Perseid shower made simultaneously from two stations in New Mexico.*

miles altitude and the largest of these has been followed down to an altitude of about 25 miles. The fastest meteors are scarcely slowed down at all by the resistance of the atmosphere, but their surface rapidly disintegrates under the heat or friction of the atmosphere. When the meteor disappears practically nothing remains of its original mass, although the final particle is still moving at only a slightly reduced velocity. Some of the very slowest meteors move at speeds of only 7 to 8 miles per second; in one case only could we trace the meteor's speed down to about 5 miles per second.

In considering the large amount of light and heat generated by these small bodies as they pass through the earth's atmosphere, we must remember that their original kinetic energy corresponds to many times that of an equal mass of a high explosive such as TNT. Hence the energy of friction is adequate to remove and destroy the body before the remaining nucleus can be much slowed down by atmospheric resistance.

Among some 500 photographic meteors that have now been analyzed for velocities and orbits, we find no certain cases of meteors moving in hyperbolic orbits. That is, there are no meteors that certainly originated from interstellar space. If they exist, they

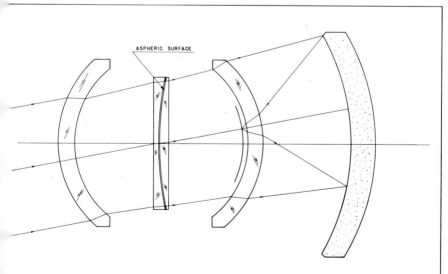

ASPHERIC SURFACE

ILLUS. 25—Design of the optics of the Baker Super-Schmidt meteor camera.

*ILLUS. 26—The Organ Mountains near Las Cruces, N. Mex., photographed
with a 2-second exposure at midnight, in full moonlight, by a
Super-Schmidt camera. The center circle was produced by the
support from the rotating shutter, not by the moon.*

must constitute not more than 1 percent of the total number of
photographic meteors observed. Furthermore, the writer has shown
that at least 90 percent of the photographic meteors pursue orbits
similar to those of comets of both long and short period. If any
average naked-eye meteors come from a broken planet the number does not exceed 10 percent of the total number observed and
probably is under 1 percent. Illustration 27 shows the distribution of
comet and meteor orbits arranged according to an arbitrary cri-

terion, K, introduced by the writer. The quantity K is defined as follows:

$$K = \log_{10}\left(\frac{q'}{1-e} \right) - 1 \qquad (1)$$

where q' is the aphelion distance in astronomical units and e is the orbital eccentricity. The logarithmic quantity is the inverse square of the aphelion velocity.

Out of 1,600 known asteroids only 3 give positive values of the K criterion while some 13 of the shorter period comets give negative values, as seen in Illustration 27. Approximately 10 percent of the sporadic and shower meteors have negative values of

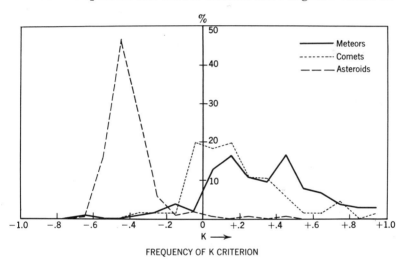

FREQUENCY OF K CRITERION

ILLUS. 27—The frequency of the criterion K among meteors, comets, and asteroids.

K, indicating the possibility, but not the certainty, that they may be of asteroidal origin. Orbital inclination is highly correlated with K in the sense that small values of K are associated with orbits of low inclination. Illustrations 28 and 29 show the orbits of some meteors, both sporadic and in streams, as determined photographically at Harvard.

Although 21 meteor streams could be recognized from the first 144 photographic meteors, only 15 streams in all are yet certainly

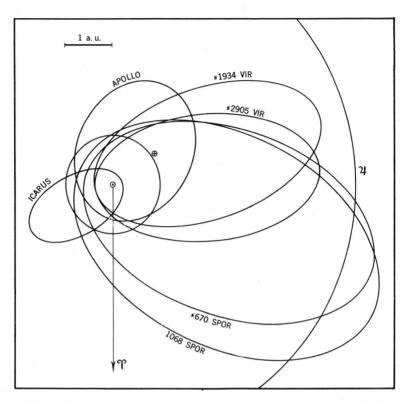

ILLUS. 28—The orbits of two sporadic meteors and two streams of the Virginid shower, with the orbits of the asteroids Icarus and Apollo for comparison.

ILLUS. 29—The orbits of three δ-Aquarid meteors (q=0.07 A. U.)

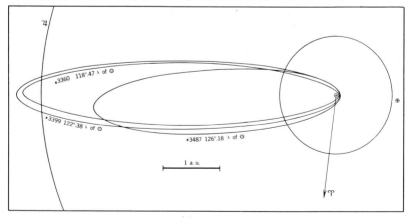

identified with individual comets. Only a few of these identifications have been made photographically. Twelve streams and their definite identifications with comets are indicated in table 1. The extensive discussion of comets, orbits, and meteor streams by Porter in his book *Comets and Meteor Streams*, New York, 1952, is highly recommended to those who are interested in the details of these relationships.

Perhaps the most interesting of these associations is that between the Taurid meteors of October and November and Encke's comet, the comet of shortest period, 3.3 years. The individual meteoric bodies in this stream are so widely distributed about the orbit of Comet Encke that the meteors can be seen to enter the earth's atmosphere from two moving radiants, one below the plane of the earth's orbit and one above it. Gravitational disturbances, or perturbations, by Jupiter have so distributed the orientation of the various orbits that an extraordinarily large volume of space is filled by particles that have been ejected from Comet Encke. Illustration 30 shows the orbital shapes for both Encke's comet and the Taurid meteors. Whipple and Hamid have shown that some of these particles were ejected from the comet approximately 5,000 years ago and another group more recently, about 1,300 years ago. It is not entirely clear whether these ejections represent unusually rapid disintegrations of the comet at those times, possibly by asteroidal collisions, or whether the perturbing action of Jupiter has been such as to make it possible for us now to observe only those meteors that were ejected at those two times. The latter hypothesis appears to be the more likely.

Probably a comet ejects meteoric material continuously, at least every revolution near the time of perihelion passage. It is an interesting commentary on these conclusions that the Taurid meteor stream had been first identified as a hyperbolic meteor stream by earlier investigators.

Our measures of the detailed meteoric photographic processes give us added information concerning the nature of the bodies that produce the ordinary visual or photographic meteors. Jacchia showed that the irregular bursts in the light curves of some meteors were accompanied by a shortening of the lifetimes. He concluded that bursts in these meteors represent a rapid disintegration

TABLE 1.—*Comets and associated meteor streams*

Comet stream	q (A. U.)	P (yrs.)	Orbital elements				
			le	ω	Ω	i	π
1861 I	0. 921	415.	0. 983	213°4	29°9	79°8	243°4
Lyrids	0. 918	>50	0. 969	213. 9	31. 8	79. 9	245. 6
1910 II	0. 587	76. 0	0. 967	111. 7	57. 3	162. 2	169. 0
η Aquarids							
Orionids	0. 542	21. 4	0. 930	86. 8	29. 8	163. 2	116. 5
1951 c	1. 159	6. 1	0. 654	170. 4	94. 3	21. 7	264. 7
June Draconids							
1862 III	0. 963	119. 6	0. 960	152. 8	137. 5	113. 6	290. 2
Perseids	0. 951	95. 1	0. 955	151. 2	138. 1	113. 7	289. 3
1946 V	0. 996	6. 6	0. 72	171. 8	196. 2	30.7	8. 1
October Draconids							
1950 e	0. 338	3. 30	0. 847	185. 2	334. 7	12. 4	159. 9
Taurids (N)	0. 320	3. 13	0. 849	298. 4	221. 8	3. 2	160. 2
Taurids (S)	0. 372	3. 49	0. 835	111. 9	45. 1	5. 4	156. 9
Arietids (S)	0. 296	2. 64	0. 845	122. 2	27. 2	6. 0	149. 5
β Taurids (Day)							
ζ Perseids (Day)							
1866 I	0. 977	33. 2	0. 905	171. 0	231. 4	162. 7	42. 4
Leonids	0. 985	37. 5	0. 918	173. 7	235. 0	162. 5	48. 7
1852 III	0. 861	6. 6	0. 756	223. 3	245. 9	12. 6	109. 1
Andromedids	....	6. 6	....	....	....	....	....
1917 I	0. 190	145. 3	0. 993	121. 3	87. 5	32. 7	208. 8
Monocerotids	0. 186	....	1. 002	128. 2	81. 6	35. 2	209. 9
1939 X	1. 022	13. 6	0. 821	207. 0	269. 8	54. 7	116. 8
Ursids	0. 915	14. 37	0. 845	212. 2	264. 6	52. 5	116. 8

Orbital elements for the comets: Baldet and de Obaldia (1952).
Orbital elements for the meteor streams: Whipple (1954).

or fragmentation of the meteoric body at irregular intervals along their trails.

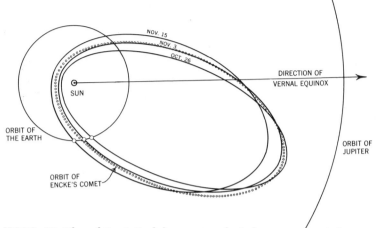

ILLUS. 30—The orbits of Encke's comet, and of three meteors of the associated northern Taurid shower that struck the earth's atmosphere on the dates shown.

Measurements of the slowing down of meteors, or atmospheric resistance, lead to the determination, for each meteor, of the quantity, surface-frontal-area divided by the mass. A knowledge of the atmospheric density, now provided by rocket techniques, enables us to determine the quantity $m^{1/3}\rho_m^{2/3}$ where m is the mass of the meteoric body and ρ_m its density. If we knew the amount of light that should be produced by a given meteoric mass at a given velocity we could immediately calculate, from the light curve and the velocity measurements, the initial mass of the body. Unfortunately, the theoretical determination of this so-called luminous efficiency is not yet possible. Thus, in the meteoric problem, we find relationships that involve the mass, the density, and the luminous efficiency, but we cannot determine any one of these quantities separately. Knowledge of any one, on the other hand, would lead us immediately to accurate determinations of the other two quantities for observed meteors.

Since there is every reason to believe that the energy available for light production cannot exceed the original kinetic energy of

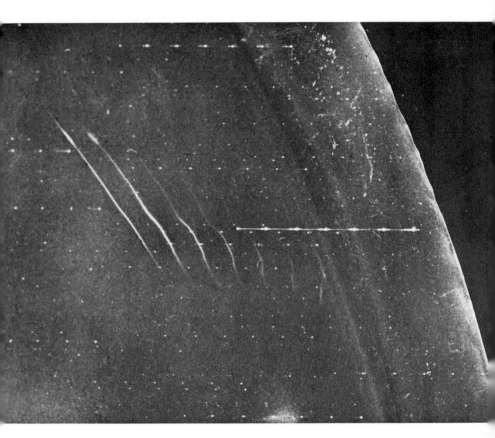

ILLUS. 31—

1. A persistent meteor train. Multiple photographs at the intervals of 2 seconds show the fading and distortion. (J. R. Coultis).

the body, an upper limit to the density of the meteoroid and a lower limit to its mass can be approximated. The writer found from such calculations that the densities of meteoric bodies must be of the order of unity, the density of water, or less.

Recently, Allan F. Cook and the writer have developed a technique for measuring the masses of meteors. We measure the motions in persistent meteor trains, the faint light left along the trails of fast bright meteors after the body has passed. Photographs of such trains, made by opening and moving the Super-Schmidt meteor cameras at 2-second intervals after bright meteors had passed, make it possible to measure winds in the high atmosphere (see Illus. 31, fig. 1). In one case of a multiple-photographed

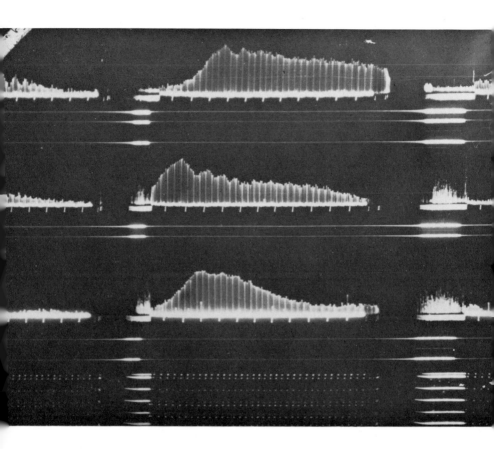

2. *Record of radio pulses from a meteor. (J. G. Davies, Jodrell Bank, England.)*

double-station train, it was possible to measure the forward or coasting momentum of the meteoric gases and trapped air masses. This first result indicates that the density of a meteor is as low as 0.05 gm./cm^3 or $\frac{1}{20}$ the density of water.

If a body is much less dense than water but is still made of ordinary earthy materials, one would expect it to be exceedingly porous and, therefore, exceedingly fragile. McCrosky, who has been studying the fragmentation problem in photographic meteors, finds that among the faint meteors some 20 percent become luminous almost instantly instead of increasing their light gradually as the well-behaved meteor does. He concludes that these bodies must become visible because of sudden fragmentation of the entire meteoric mass. He finds indeed that this fragmentation occurs at a nearly constant pressure introduced by the resistance of the atmosphere, a pressure of only one-third of a pound per square inch. Many of the meteoric masses are so fragile that a block a foot or two in height would crush at the bottom under its own weight, at normal gravity.

Thus we have evidence that meteoric bodies from comets are extremely fragile, of low density, and, therefore, very porous. This conclusion is to be expected from the writer's hypothesis concerning the nature of the comets from which this debris has been ejected. According to this theory, the nucleus of a comet is a conglomerate of interstellar or interplanetary dust formed from gases at a temperature of only a few degrees absolute, perhaps when the sun and planets were formed. Cometary activity is then the result of solar heating that vaporizes ices at the surface of the cometary nucleus. These ices include ordinary ice from water, solid ammonia, possibly even solid methane, and other compounds of carbon, nitrogen, and oxygen with hydrogen.

The remaining meteoritic material, made of the heavier, less volatile compounds in the original dust, must remain very loosely cemented. Most of this material is fragmented into extremely fine particles by the cometary ejection process, but a small amount of it holds together sufficiently well to form the cometary streams of meteors and the sporadic meteors from comets.

One would expect, on the basis of typical cosmic abundances, that the initial cometary nucleus might be about the density of water and that the final density of the meteoritic material might be the order of one-third the density of water. On the other hand, it is very likely that the initial dust in space consists of extremely porous masses, comparable to low-density smoke particles observed from artificial sources. Hence the cometary nucleus itself can be of very low mean density, and the final meteoritic fragments even more porous and rare. It is not certain whether we shall be able to recover such fragile fragments on the surface of the earth, because of their violent interaction with the earth's atmosphere. Tiny ones may come through without being seriously damaged.

While the photographic method of studying meteors was being

perfected, a radically different and powerful technique came into use. Chamanlal and Venkataraman, of India, heard whistles from continuous-wave radio transmitters, audible simultaneously with the occurrence of bright meteors. Pierce at Harvard and Hey at Cambridge, England, working with a pulse transmitter and receiver on the same frequency, observed transient echoes from meteors. A number of investigators rapidly developed methods for detecting the ionization, or electron columns, produced as meteoric bodies plunge through the earth's atmosphere. The methods fundamentally depend upon the fact that the electromagnetically vibrating waves from radio transmitters set the individual electrons into synchronous vibration. The electrons, because of this induced vibration, act as independent transmitters and send out radio waves of the same frequency. Thus a column of electrons effectively reflects a radio wave as the electrons along the column resonate in phase with the initial radiation. The reflection is much like that of light from a shiny cylinder.

Without becoming involved in the complexity of electronic techniques we can understand, qualitatively, one of the most useful methods of tracking meteors by radio, and of determining meteoric velocities. In Illustration 32 we see that as the ionization trail of the meteor progresses through the atmosphere, re-radiation (reflection) from the electrons in the trail occurs along its entire length to the head of the meteor. A relatively wide antenna beam can cover the entire trail. At an early part of the trail, say point *a* in Illustration 32, the distances from the radio transmitter to the successive positions along the trail and back to the receiver will vary rapidly as we move along the trail. Hence the returning waves will be successively in and out of phase because the radio wavelength, only a few meters, is very small compared to the distance, 100 or more kilometers. Little "reflected" radiation, therefore, will reach the receiver when we add up the contributions for an appreciable distance along the trail.

As the meteor approaches the so-called reflection point of the trail, where the line from the radio to the trail meets it at perpendicular incidence, we see that a considerable length of the trail will be at almost the same distance from the radio transmitter. Echoes from this region will return to the receiver in phase and

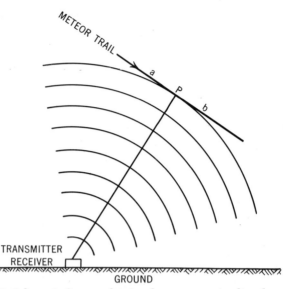

ILLUS. 32—*Schematic diagram showing the geometry of radio echoes reflected
from the ionization trail of a meteor.*

add up to produce a perceptible signal. The problem of the theoretical signal strength of the received echo, as the meteoric body
moves along the trail, was in reality solved more than 100 years
ago by Fresnel, who calculated the effect of such phase phenomena for light scattered by a line. The resulting signal strength as
a function of distance along the trail is shown in Illustration 31,
figure 2. The echo grows in intensity as reflection point is reached,
then increases beyond this value to a maximum in a very short
time; then as it slowly fades out it oscillates in strength with increasing distance from the reflection point. For a specified wavelength of the radio waves, such a curve yields the angular velocity
of the meteor at a point where it passes perpendicular to the line
of radio sight.

Ordinary radar techniques with pulses measure the time required for the radio signal to travel from the transmitter to the
trail and back to the receiver again, and hence the distance to the
reflection point. The angular velocity coupled with the distance
then determines the true spatial velocity of the growing ion column, and therefore of the meteoric body in its trajectory. This

method and similar related methods for measuring meteor velocities were developed chiefly by scientists in England.

From more than 10,000 measurements of meteoric velocities, McKinley concludes that the velocities determined even from very faint radio meteors, somewhat below naked-eye visibility, do not indicate a statistically significant number of hyperbolic velocities, beyond the parabolic limit of 72 km./sec. Similarly, Almond, Davies, and Lovell at Manchester, England, come to the same conclusion from a more detailed analysis of fewer meteors, observed from radiants near the apex of the earth's motion in the early morning hours, and from the antapex direction in the early evening hours. At present, no clear evidence for the existence of any hyperbolic meteors has been found by radio-meteor astronomers. The general uncertainties in the methods of observation, however, permit the possibility that as many as one-half of 1 percent of the total might come from outer space.

The radio technique is capable of detecting meteors whose luminosity is 100 times fainter than that of meteors we can detect visually. The radio and photographic results are in full agreement and indicate that at least 99.5 percent of all the observed meteors are certainly members of the solar system.

A method of determining the radiant points of meteor streams by means of radio echoes was developed by Clegg. Later Aspinall, Clegg, and Hawkins carried out a continuous survey of stream radiants using twin antenna beams. Radio echoes were obtained in turn in each antenna, as the earth rotated, and the time of appearance of long-range echoes gave the time of transit and declination of the radiant.

An extremely important property of the radio technique was first demonstrated when Hey and Stewart discovered extremely dense meteor streams in the daylight hours, particularly in May, June, and July. Thus the radio technique has the enormous advantage over the photographic that it can operate for 24 hours of the day regardless of sunlight, moonlight, or other sky illuminations. It is interesting that one of the daylight streams, according to the results of Clegg, Hughes, and Lovell, turns out to be a recurrence of the Taurid meteor stream contributed by Encke's comet. In a sense, the writer predicted the existence of this stream, although in 1939 he had no premonition that radio techniques might eventually be developed to observe it. It seemed quite likely, however, that bright fireballs from the other intersection of the Taurid stream with the earth's orbit might be seen emanating from the general direction of the sun.

Davies of Manchester has recently developed a most remarkable method for using radio techniques, to measure not only the velocity of a meteor, but also its trajectory and spatial orbit. Davies' method depends upon simultaneous observations from three stations, and provides meteor velocities and orbits for particles several times smaller than those visible to the eye. He finds that these smaller bodies move in orbits that are smaller and more nearly circular than those of the larger photographic meteors. The explanation of this observation will bring us around, full circle, to the problems of the micrometeorites.

Van de Hulst and Allen have demonstrated that micrometeorites are sufficiently numerous near the plane of the earth's orbit to scatter most of the sunlight seen in the zodiacal light, the twilight glow along the zodiac near sunrise or sunset. They find also that along the line of sight near to the sun these small particles diffract the sunlight and scatter it sufficiently to form an appreciable fraction of the solar corona (see Illus. 33). The corona, of course, consists also of sunlight scattered by electrons as well as extremely strong bright lines from the million-degree gases in the sun's huge extended atmosphere. From his calculation of the scattering and diffracting power of the micrometeorites near the plane of the earth's orbit in space, van de Hulst estimates that some 10,000 tons of this fine dust should fall on the earth per day. He also concludes that most of the dust particles are smaller than 0.03 cm. (0.01 inch) in diameter. This estimate of the total fall on the earth is more than 1,000 times greater than Watson's earlier estimate based upon the infall of larger pieces of meteoritic material. Some direct substantiation of van de Hulst's conclusion, however, is given by the fact that noises of meteoric impact on high altitude rockets have been recorded by Bohn and Nadig, of Temple University, and by Berg and Meredith, of the Naval Research Laboratory.

Pettersson and Rotschi find also that deep-sea oozes contain ap-

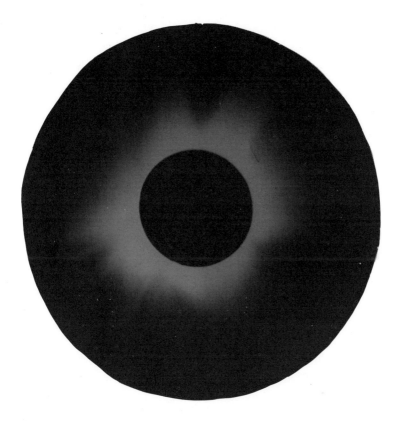

ILLUS. 33—The solor corona photographed by Harvard during the 1937 solar eclipse.

preciable quantities of nickel which may possibly derive from this interplanetary dust.

The writer has recently shown that a few tons of cometary dust injected into the solar system each second would be adequate to maintain the zodiacal light indefinitely. The particles are continuously lost by collisions among themselves, by the gravitational effects of the planets, particularly Jupiter, by the interstellar wind produced by the sun's motion through the interstellar gas, by the action of sunlight according to the Poynting-Robertson effect, and by corpuscular radiation from the sun in the form of outgoing hydrogen protons. Öpik has shown that the extended solar corona also adds drag to these little particles. The three latter effects cause the particles in the zodiacal cloud to spiral slowly in toward the sun, the rate depending upon the size of the particle. Piotrowsky has also shown that the grinding of the asteroids may produce sufficient material to maintain the zodiacal cloud. At the moment it is not possible to distinguish certainly between these two hypotheses but other evidence suggests that the cometary source is much the more important. Observational and theoretical advances should settle the question definitively within the next few years.

Now we can bring together, to complete this discussion, radio meteors, photographic meteors, the zodiacal light, micrometeorites, comets, and corpuscular radiation from the sun. If meteoric densities are typically as low as our single measure suggests, the discrepancy van de Hulst found between the total influx of zodiacal particles and meteoritic masses disappears. He measured the integrated dimensions of the interplanetary matter rather than its mass; hence a low density would reduce his estimate many times. Furthermore, the low density would increase the older estimate of the total meteorite masses, and hence remove the discrepancy entirely.

The continual bombardment of meteoritic debris of course constitutes a real hazard to rockets, artificial satellites, and space vehicles, which may be subjected to erosion or puncture. Elaborate ballistics experiments and careful calculations have shown, however, that optical surfaces exposed to space should not be affected functionally in less than about a year, and that for the presently planned small satellites, the rate of puncture will be, on the average, only about once in five days.

Probably about 2,000 tons of meteoritic debris fall on the earth from inteplanetary space each day. This large mass, however, is still quite negligible compared to that of the earth. In five million years the total accumulation would add up to only an inch over the entire surface.

Although some of our discussion has led beyond the borderline of scientific certainty, I have attempted to distinguish clearly between proven fact and hypothesis. By thus stepping over into unexplored areas, we can see more clearly the exciting possibilities of future research and, at the same time, appreciate some of the great progress already made in this rapidly growing field of astronomy.

ACKNOWLEDGMENTS

I am particularly grateful to Miss Frances W. Wright for the use of table 1 and for her assistance in preparing the figures. Dr. Gerald S. Hawkins has been very helpful in assisting in matters pertaining to radio-meteor astronomy, and Mrs. Lyle Boyd and Dr. Richard E. McCrosky have contributed to the final manuscript.

W. C. ROENTGEN

The X-Rays

[FROM THE SMITHSONIAN REPORT FOR 1897]

THIS ARTICLE *is in the nature of a flashback, enabling us to recall how recent is the origin of all our current marvels of scientific application. Toward the close of the last century came a host of entirely unexpected discoveries that changed the entire concept of the structure of matter. Electromagnetic waves, radioactivity, cathode rays, X-rays, and the electron, all were added to the physicists' tool kit in the closing years of the 1800's. With these revolutionary new tools, the rapidly accelerating scientific advance of the first half of our century was made possible.*

At the time of his discovery of X-rays, Roentgen was professor of physics and director of the physical laboratory at Würzburg, Germany. For his epoch-making work he was awarded the Rumford medal of the Royal Society, London, and, in 1901, the Nobel prize for physics. He reported his original discovery of X-rays and his subsequent researches on them in successive issues of a leading German scientific periodical. Translations of these writings are given here as they appeared in a Smithsonian Report of the time. They will serve to remind us of how much we owe to the brilliant scientists of half a century ago who made basic discoveries of previously unknown natural laws.

166

I. UPON A NEW KIND OF RAYS*

1. If the discharge of a great Ruhmkorff induction coil be passed through a Hittorf vacuum tube, or a Lenard's, Crooke's, or similar apparatus containing a sufficiently high vacuum, then, the tube being covered with a close layer of thin black pasteboard and the room darkened, a paper screen covered on one side with barium-platinum cyanide and brought near the apparatus will be seen to glow brightly and fluoresce at each discharge whichever side of the screen is toward the vacuum tube. The fluorescence is visible even when the screen is removed to a distance of 2 meters from the apparatus.

The observer may easily satisfy himself that the cause of the fluorescense is to be found at the vacuum tube and at no other part of the electrical circuit.

2. It is thus apparent that there is here an agency which is able to pass through the black pasteboard impenetrable to visible or ultraviolet rays from the sun or the electric arc, and having passed through is capable of exciting a lively fluorescence, and it is natural to inquire whether other substances can be thus penetrated.

It is found that all substances transmit this agency, but in very different degree. I will mention some examples. Paper is very transmissible.†

I observed fluorescence very distinctly behind a bound book of about 1,000 pages. The ink presented no appreciable obstacle. Similarly fluorescence was seen behind a double whist pack. A single card held between the fluorescent screen and the apparatus produced no visible effect. A single sheet of tin foil, too, produces

---

* Translation of paper by Professor Roentgen in the *Sitzungsber. Würzburger Physik-Medic. Ges.*, Jahrg. 1895, as reprinted in *Annalen der Physik und Chemie (Neue Folge)*, vol. 64, p. 1, 1898.

† By the transmissibility of a substance I designate the ratio between the brightness of a fluorescent screen held behind the body and that which the screen would have under the same conditions in the absence of the interposed substance.

hardly any obstacle, and it is only when several sheets are superposed that their shadow appears distinctly on the screen. Thick wooden blocks are transmissible. Slabs of pine 2 or 3 centimeters thick absorb only very little. A plate of aluminum about 15 millimeters thick diminished the effect very considerably, but did not cause the fluorescence to disappear entirely. Blocks of hard rubber several centimeters thick still transmited the rays.*

Glass plates of equal thickness behave very differently according to whether they contain lead (flint glass) or not. The first class are much less transmissible than the second.

If the hand is held between the vacuum tube and the screen, the dark shadow of the bones is seen upon the much lighter shadow outline of the hand. Water, carbon bisulphide, and various other liquids investigated proved very transmissible. I could not find that hydrogen was more transmissible than air. The fluorescence was visible behind plates of copper, silver, lead, gold, and platinum, when the thickness of the plate was not too great. Platinum 0.2 millimeter thick is still transmissible, and silver and copper plates may be still thicker. Lead 1.5 millimeters thick is practically impenetrable, and advantage was frequently taken of this characteristic. A wooden stick, of 20 millimeters square cross section, having one side covered with white lead, behaved differently when interposed between the vacuum tube and the screen according as the X-rays traversed the block parallel to the painted side or were compelled to pass through it. In the first case there was no effect appreciable, while in the second a dark shadow was thrown on the screen. Salts of the metals, whether solid or in solution, are to be ranged in almost the same order as the metals themselves for transmissibility.

3. These observations and others lead to the conclusion that the transmissibility of equal thicknesses of different substances depends on their density. At least no other characteristic exerts so marked an influence as this.

The following experiment shows, however, that the density is not the sole factor. I compared the transmissibility of nearly equally thick plates of glass, aluminum, calcspar, and quartz. The

---

* For brevity's sake I employ the word "rays," and in distinction from others make use of the expression "X-rays."

density of these substances is substantially the same, and yet it was quite evident that the calcspar was considerably less transmissible than the others, which are about alike in this respect.

4. All bodies became less transmissible with increasing thickness. For the purpose of finding a relation between transmissibility and thickness I have made photographic exposures, in which the photographic plate was partly covered with a layer of tin foil consisting of a progressively increasing number of sheets. I shall make a photometric measurement when I am in possession of a suitable photometer.

5. Sheets were rolled from platinum, lead, zinc, and aluminum of such thickness that all appeared to be equally transmissible. The following table gives the measured thickness in millimeters, the relative thickness compared with platinum, and the specific gravity:

	Thickness.	Relative thickness.	Specific gravity.
Platinum	0.018	1	21.5
Lead	0.05	3	11.3
Zinc	0.10	6	7.1
Aluminum	3.5	200	2.6

From these values it may be seen that the transmissibility of plates of different metals so chosen that the product of the thickness and density is constant, would not be equal. The transmissibility increases much faster than this product falls off.

6. The fluoresence of barium-platinum-cyanide is not the only action by which X-rays may be recognized. It should be remarked that they cause other substances to fluoresce, as for example the photophorescent calcium compounds, uranium glass, common glass, calcspar, rock salt, etc.

It is of particular importance from many points of view that photographic dry plates are sensitive to X-rays. It thus becomes possible to fix many phenomena so that deceptions are more easily avoided; and I have where practicable checked all important observations made with a fluorescent screen by photographic exposures.

It appears questionable whether the chemical action upon the silver salts of the photographic plate is produced directly by the X-rays. It is possible that this action depends upon the fluorescent light which, as is mentioned above, may be excited in the glass plate, or perhaps in the gelatine film. "Films" may indeed be made use of as well as glass plates.

I have not as yet obtained experimental evidence that the X-rays are capable of giving heat. This characteristic might, however, be assumed as present, since in the excitation of fluorescent phenomena the capacity of the energy of the X-rays for transformation is proved, and since it is certain that of the X-rays falling upon a body, not all are given up.

The retina of the eye is not sensitive to these rays. Nothing is to be noticed by bringing the eye near the vacuum tube, although according to the preceding observations the media of the eye must be sufficiently transmissible to the rays in question.

7. After I had discovered the transmissibility of various bodies of relatively great thickness I hastened to investigate whether or not the X-rays were refracted in passing through a prism. Experiments with water and carbon bisulphide in mica prisms of 30 degrees refracting angle showed no deviation either when observations were made with the fluorescent screen or with the photographic plate. For comparison, the deviation of light rays was observed under the same conditions. The refracted portion lay from 10 to 20 centimeters distant from that not refracted. With prisms of hard rubber and aluminum of about 30 degrees refracting angle I obtained exposures on a photographic plate which perhaps indicated a slight refraction. This is, however, very doubtful and the deviation is, if present, so small that the index of refraction for X-rays in these substances cannot exceed 1.05. I could not observe with the fluorescent screen any deviation in these cases. Experiments with prisms of the denser metals have so far yielded no certain results on account of the slight transmissibility and the consequent decrease of the intensity of the transmitted ray.

In consideration of these results on the one hand, and on the other of the importance of the question whether or not the X-rays in passing from one medium to another undergo refraction, it is very gratifying that this question may be investigated by other means than by the help of prisms. Finely pulverized bodies in suitable layers allow but little light to pass, in consequence of refraction and reflection. If now the X-rays are transmitted equally well through powder as through the coherent substance, equal masses being presupposed, it is proved that neither refraction nor regular reflection is present in any marked degree. This experiment was performed using finely pulverized rock salt finely divided silver, obtained by electrolysis, and the zinc dust so frequently utilized in chemical processes. In no case was any difference in transmissibility between the powder and the coherent substance detected either by the use of the fluorescent screen or the photographic plate.

It follows of course from the results thus obtained that the X-rays cannot be concentrated by the use of lenses; and, indeed, a great hard rubber lens and a glass lens actually proved without effect. The shadow of a round rod is darker in the middle than at the edges, while that of a tube which is filled with some substance more transmissible than the material of which the tube is composed is darker at the edges than at the center.

8. The question as to the reflection of X-rays is so far settled by the experiments already explained that no marked regular reflection was to be found with any of the substances examined. Other experiments, which I will here pass over, lead to the same results.

Nevertheless an observation should be mentioned which indicated at first glance an opposite result. A photographic plate shielded from the action of light rays by a black paper was exposed to X-rays so that the glass side was toward the discharge tube. The sensitive film was partially covered with bright plates of platinum, lead, zinc, and aluminum, arranged in a star-shaped figure. Upon development it was observed that the darkening of the film under the platinum, the lead, and especially the zinc, was distinctly greater than in the other parts. No such effect was produced by the aluminum. Thus it seemed as if the three metals mentioned reflected. However, there were other causes to be conceived which might have produced the increased darkening, and in order to be sure I performed a second experiment, interposing a thin sheet of aluminum foil (very transmissible to X-rays, but not to those of the ultraviolet) between the metals and the sensitive film. Since in this case again practically the same result was obtained, the fact of reflection of X-rays by the metals above mentioned is established.

Taking this result together with the observation that powder is as transmissible as coherent substance, and further, that bodies with rough surfaces behave in the transmission of X-rays and also in the experiments just described exactly like polished bodies, the conclusion is reached that there is, as before remarked, no regular reflection, but that the bodies behave toward X-rays in the same manner as a turbid medium with reference to light.

As I have not been able to discover any refraction in the passage from one medium to another, it appears as if the X-rays travel with equal velocity in all bodies, and hence in a medium which is everywhere present and in which the particles of the bodies are embedded. These latter act as a hindrance to the propagation of the X-rays, which is in general greater the greater the density of the body in question.

9. In accordance with this supposition it might be possible that the arrangement of the molecules of the body would exert an influence on its transmissibility, and that, for example, a piece of calcspar would be unequally transmissible for equal thicknesses when the rays passed along at right angles to the axis. Experiments with calcspar and quartz gave, however, a negative result.

10. It will be recalled that Lenard, in his beautiful experiments on the transmission of the Hittorf cathode rays through thin aluminum foil, obtained the result that these rays are disturbances in the ether, and that they diffuse themselves in all bodies. We may make a similar statement with regard to our rays.

In his last research Lenard has determined the relative absorption of different substances for the cathode rays, and in determining the same for air at atmospheric pressure has given the values 4.10, 3.40, 3.10 as referred to 1 centimeter thickness according to the density of the gas in the discharge tube. Judging from the length of spark observed, I have, in my researches, generally employed tubes of about equal exhaustion and only seldom those of much greater or less density. Using the photometer of L. Weber, the best at my command, I compared the intensity of fluorescence on the screen in two positions distant 100 and 200 millimeters, respectively, from the discharge tube. From the results of these experiments, agreeing well with each other, it appeared that the intensity varies inversely as the square of the distance. Hence the air absorbs a much smaller portion of the X-rays passing through it than of cathode rays. This result is in accord with the observation above mentioned, that it is possible to distinguish fluorescence at 2 meters distance from the discharge tube.

Most other substances are, like the air, more transmissible for X-rays than for cathode rays.

11. Another very noteworthy difference between the behavior of the cathode rays and the X-rays was exhibited in that I was unable to produce any deviation of the latter by the action of the most powerful magnetic fields. The property of being subject to deviation by magnets is, on the other hand, very characteristic of the cathode rays. Hertz and Lenard have observed various kinds of cathode rays which "are to be distinguished by their differences in their capacities for exciting phosphorescence, in their absorptibility, and in their deviation by the magnet," but a considerable magnetic deviation was to be observed with all of them, and I do not believe that this characteristic would be given up except for the most urgent reasons.

12. According to the results of experiments particularly directed to discover the source of the X-rays, it is certain that the part of the wall of the discharge tube which most strongly fluoresces is the principal starting point. The X-rays therefore radiate from the place where, according to various observers, the cathode rays meet the glass wall. If one diverts the cathode rays within the tube by a magnet, the source of the X-ray is also seen to change its position so that these radiations still proceed from the end points of the cathode rays. The X-rays being undeviated by magnets cannot, however, be simply cathode rays passing unchanged through the glass wall. The greater density of the gas outside the discharge tube cannot, according to Lenard, be made answerable for the great difference of the deviation.

I come therefore to the results that the X-rays are not identical with the cathode rays, but that they are excited by the cathode rays in the glass wall of the vacuum tube.

13. This generating action takes place not only in glass, but as I observed it in apparatus with aluminum walls 2 millimeters thick, exists also for this metal. Other substances will be investigated.

14. The warrant for giving the title "rays" to the agent which

proceeds from the wall of the discharge tube arose in part from the quite regular formation of shadows appearing when more or less transmissible substances are interposed between the generating apparatus and a phosphorescent screen or photographic plate. I have many times observed and sometimes photographed such shadow forms, in whose production there lies a particular charm. I have, for example, photographs of the shadow of the profile of a door which separates the two rooms, in one of which was the discharge apparatus, in the other the photographic plate; of the shadow of the hand bones; of the shadow of a wooden spool wound with wire; of a set of weights in a box; of a compass in which the magnetic needle is quite inclosed in metal; of a piece of metal which is shown to lack homogeneity by the use of X-rays, etc.

The propagation of the X-rays in right lines is shown by pinhole photography, which I have been able to do with the discharge apparatus covered with black paper. The picture is weak, but unmistakably correct.

15. I have much sought to obtain interference phenomena with X-rays, but unfortunately — perhaps on account of their slight intensity — without result.

16. Experiments have been begun to see if electrostatic forces can in any way influence X-rays, but these are not yet finished.

17. If the question is asked what the X-rays — which certainly are not cathode rays — really are, one might at first, on account of their lively fluorescent and chemical action, compare them to ultraviolet light. But here one falls upon serious difficulties. Thus, if the X-rays were ultraviolet light then this light must possess the following characteristics:

(*a*) That in passing from air into water, carbon bisulphide, aluminum, rock salt, glass, zinc, etc., it experiences no notable refraction.

(*b*) That it is not regularly reflected by these substances.

(*c*) That it cannot be polarized by the usual materials.

(*d*) That its absorption by substances is influenced by nothing so much as by their density.

In other words, one must assume that these ultraviolet radiations comport themselves quite differently from all previously known infrared, visible, and ultraviolet rays.

I have not been able to admit this, and have sought some other explanations.

A kind of relation seems to subsist between the new radiation and light radiation, or at least the shadow formation, the fluorescence, and the chemical action, which are common phenomena of these two kinds of radiation, point in this direction. It has been long known that longitudinal as well as transverse vibrations are possible in the ether, and according to various physicists must exist. To be sure, their existence has not, up to the present time, been proved, and hence their characteristics have not thus far been experimentally investigated.

Should not the new radiations be ascribed to longitudinal vibrations in the ether? I may say that in the course of the investigation this hypothesis has impressed itself more and more favorably with me, and I venture to propose it, although well aware that it requires much further examination.

WÜRZBURG, PHYSIK. INSTITUT D. UNIV., *December, 1895.*

II. UPON A NEW KIND OF RAYS (ABSTRACT)[*]

As my work must be interrupted for several weeks, I take the opportunity of presenting in the following some new results:

18. At the time of my first publication I was aware that the X-rays have the property of discharging electrified bodies, and I intimated that it was the X-rays and not the cathode rays passing unchanged through the aluminum window of his apparatus which produced the effect described by Lenard on electrified bodies at a distance. I have, however, delayed publication of my experiments until I could present conclusive results.

These can be obtained only when the observations are carried on in a room which is not only completely insulated from the electrostatic forces emanating from the vacuum tube, the conducting

[*] Translation of a portion of the paper by Professor Roentgen in the *Sitzungsber. Würzburger Physik-Medic. Ges.*, Jahrg. 1895, as reprinted in *Annalen der Physik und Chemie*, vol. 64, p. 12, 1898.

wires, the induction apparatus, etc., but is also closed to the air which comes in the neighborhood of the discharge apparatus.

For this purpose I had a box constructed by soldering together zinc sheets, and this box was large enough to contain me and the necessary apparatus, and was airtight with the exception of an opening which could be closed by a zinc door. The side opposite to the door was mostly lined with lead, and immediately adjacent to the discharge tube an opening 4 centimeters wide was cut in the lead and zinc wall, and its place filled up airtight with aluminum foil. Through this window passed the X-rays to be investigated. I have with this apparatus verified the following results:

(*a*) Positively or negatively electrified bodies placed in air are discharged when immersed in X-rays, and the action is the more rapid the more intense the radiations. The intensity of the rays is determined by their action upon a fluorescent screen or a photographic plate.

It is in general immaterial whether the electrified substance is a conductor or nonconductor. Thus far I have discovered no difference in the behavior of different bodies relative to the rapidity of their discharge, or between positive or negative charges. These points are, however, open to further investigation.

(*b*) When an electrified conductor is surrounded by a solid insulator, as for example, paraffin, the radiation produces the same effect as would the flashing of the insulating shell by a flame placed in contact with the ground.

(*c*) If this insulator be in its turn closely surrounded by a grounded conductor and both itself and this outer conductor be transmissible to X-rays, the action of the X-radiations upon the inner conductor is unnoticeable with the apparatus at my command.

(*d*) The observations recorded under (*a*), (*b*), and (*c*) indicate that the air through which X-rays pass possesses the property of discharging any electrified bodies with which it comes in contact.

(*e*) If this be indeed the case, and if the air retains for some considerable time this property imparted to it by the X-rays, it must be possible to discharge electrified bodies not themselves under the influence of X-rays by bringing to them air which has been subject to these radiations.

19. One may satisfy himself in various ways that this is the case.

The following, though perhaps not the simplest method, may be mentioned:

I employed a brass tube 3 centimeters wide and 45 centimeters long. At 1 centimeter's distance from one end a portion of the tube was cut away and replaced by a thin sheet of aluminum. At the other end there was introduced a brass ball, which was supported by a metal support, and this end was closed airtight. Between the brass ball and the closed end of the tube a side tube was soldered in, which was connected with an air-pump. By this means a current of air was made to flow by the brass ball, after having passed the aluminum window. The distance from the ball to the window was 20 centimeters.

I mounted this tube in the zinc box in such a manner that the X-rays entered the tube at right angles to its axis, and the insulated ball lay outside the reach of these rays, in the shadow. The tube and zinc box were placed in contact and the ball was connected with a Hankel electroscope.

It was shown that a charge on the ball, whether positive or negative, was not influenced by X-rays so long as the air remained quiet in the tube, but that a marked diminution of the charge was produced by sucking a strong current of air through. If the ball was kept at constant potential by connecting it with accumulators, and a continuous current of air was kept flowing in the tube, an electrical current was set up just as if the ball was connected with the walls of the tube by a conductor of high resistance.

20. In section 13 of my first article it was stated that the X-rays may be generated not only in glass but in aluminum. In conducting experiments in this direction no solid bodies were found which were not capable of producing X-rays when under the influence of cathode rays. I know no reason to suppose that liquids and gases also do not act similarly.

Different substances, however, possess this property in different degrees. For example, if cathode rays are caused to fall upon a plate of which one-half is composed of platinum foil 0.3 millimeter thick and the other half of aluminum 1 millimeter thick, one may observe in the photographic image taken with the pinhole camera that the platinum foil sends out many more X-rays from the side bombarded by the cathode rays than does the aluminum on the same side. But from the back side of the plate there go out almost no X-rays from the platinum, while the aluminum sends out a relatively large number. These latter rays are generated at the front layers of the aluminum and pass through the plate.

It should be remarked that these observations have a practical significance. For the generation of X-rays of the greatest possible intensity my experience recommends the employment of platinum. I have used for some weeks with advantage a discharge apparatus having a concave mirror of aluminum as cathode, and as anode a platinum plate placed in the center of curvature, and at an angle of 45 degrees with the axis.

21. The X-rays proceed from the anode with this apparatus. As I have concluded from experiments with apparatus with various forms, it is immaterial with regard to the intensity of the X-rays whether they proceed from the anode or not.

WÜRZBURG, PHYSIK. INSTITUT D. UNIV., *March 9, 1896.*

III. FURTHER OBSERVATIONS ON THE PROPERTIES OF X-RAYS (ABSTRACT)*

1. If between a discharge tube sending out intense X-rays† and a fluorescent screen one interposes an untransmissible plate so placed that it shades the whole screen, one can still observe a luminosity of the barium-platinum cyanide. This luminescence is still visible when the screen is close up to the plate, and one is at first inclined to regard the plate as transmissible. When, however, one covers the fluorescent plate with a thick glass slide the fluorescence becomes much weaker, and it completely disappears when instead of using the glass plate one covers the screen with a lead

* Translation of a portion of the paper by Professor Roentgen in the *Sitzungsber, k. preuss. Akad. Wiss.* Berlin, Jahrg. 1897, as reprinted in *Annalen der Physik und Chemie*, vol. 64, p. 18, 1898.

† All the discharge tubes mentioned in the following communication are constructed according to the principle given under section 20 of my second communication. A great part have been obtained from the firm of Greiner & Friedrichs, in Stützerbach i. Th., to whom I wish to express my thanks for the great quantity of material which they have supplied to me without cost.

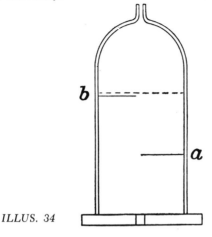

cylinder 1 millimeter thick, which passes entirely over the head of the observer and is closed by the untransmissible plate.

The phenomena described might be due to the diffraction of rays of great wavelength or to the sending out of X-rays by the objects surrounding the discharge tube, such, for example, as the air through which the rays pass.

The latter explanation is the true one, as may be easily shown by the use of the following apparatus. Illustration 34 shows a thick-walled glass bell jar 20 centimeters high and 10 centimeters in diameter, which is closed by a thick zinc plate inserted with cement.

At *a* and *b* are lead shelves of the form of segments of a circle, each of an area somewhat greater than half the cross section of the jar. At the end of the glass jar is a zinc plate with a central opening covered with a collodium film, and the two plates above mentioned prevent X-rays which have passed through this opening from reaching the part of the jar which lies above the lead plate *b*. Upon the upper side of this plate is a fluorescent screen which fills almost the whole cross section of the jar. This screen can receive neither the direct rays nor those a single time diffusely reflected from solid substances, as, for example, the glass walls. Before each experiment the jar is filled with dust-free air. When X-rays are allowed to enter in such a way that they are all received by the lead plate *a* there is no fluorescence to be observed at *b*. When the jar is inclined so that the rays can pass through the space between *a* and *b* the fluorescent screen is illuminated over that portion not covered by the plate *b*. When the jar is connected with an air pump the fluorescence becomes weaker the further the exhaustion proceeds, and when air is admitted the intensity again increases.

I found that no noticeable fluorescence was excited by simple contact with air through which X-rays had shortly before passed, so that it follows that the air while it is receiving X-rays also sends them out in all directions.

If our eyes were as sensitive for X-rays as they are for light rays, an actively operating discharge tube would appear to us like a light burning in a room uniformly filled with tobacco smoke. It might perhaps be that the colors of the rays coming direct would be different from those sent out by the air particles.

The question whether the rays sent out by bodies are the same as those they receive, or, in other words, whether this phenomenon is due to diffused reflection or to an action similar to fluorescence, I have not thus far been able to decide. It may be readily shown that the rays coming from air particles are photographically active, and this characteristic makes itself manifest in a most unwelcome manner. In order to guard against this effect it is necessary in long exposures to protect the plate by appropriate lead screens.

2. In order to compare the intensity of the radiation from the discharge tubes, and for various purposes, I have made use of a contrivance which is constructed similarly to the Bouguer photometer, and which, for the sake of simplicity, I will call a photometer. A rectangular piece of sheet lead 35 centimeters high, 150 centimeters long, and 0.15 millimeter thick is supported vertically on a piece of board in the center of a long table. On each side of this sheet and movable upon the table stands a discharge tube. At one end of the lead strip is a fluorescent screen* so arranged that each

---

* In this and other experiments the Edison fluorescent screen has proved very useful. This consists of a stereoscopic case which can be secured light-tight to the head of the observer, and whose pasteboard bottom is covered with barium-platinum cyanide. Edison employs Scheelite in place of barium-platinum cyanide; but for many reasons I prefer the latter.

half is vertically radiated upon. In the measurements the arrangements were adjusted until the two parts were equally bright.

Some remarks made upon the use of this instrument may not be out of place. First of all it should be noted that the determinations are rendered much more difficult because of the unsteadiness of the sources of radiation. The tubes are sensitive to each irregularity of the interruption of the primary current; and such frequently occur with the Dupret and especially with the Foucault form of interrupter. Many repetitions of each measurement are therefore necessary. Second, I may indicate upon what factors the brightness of a given fluorescent screen depends which is acted upon by a shower of X-rays so rapid that the observer's eye cannot detect the intermittent character of the illumination. This brightness depends (1) upon the intensity of the radiation proceeding from the platinum plate of the discharge tube; (2) very probably upon the nature of the rays falling on the screen, for, as will be shown, different kinds of radiation are not equally active in exciting fluorescence; (3) upon the distance of the screen from the source of the rays; (4) upon the absorption which the rays experience in their journey to the fluorescent screen; (5) upon the number of discharges per second; (6) upon the duration of each separate discharge; (7) upon the duration and the strength of the after light of the barium-platinum cyanide, and (8) upon the radiation to the screen from the surrounding bodies. In order to avoid errors, one must bear in mind that he has to do with a matter which is as if he were conducting experiments to compare by the aid of fluorescence two intermittent light sources of different colors and was obliged to carry on his experiments within an absorbing shell and in a turbid or fluorescing medium.

3. According to section 12 of my first communication, the source of the X-rays is the place where the cathode rays meet the discharge tube and the X-rays radiate outward in all directions. It is now of interest to investigate how the intensity of the rays varies with the direction.

For this investigation the spherical form of discharge apparatus with a well-polished platinum plate inclined at an angle of 45 degrees to the direction of the cathode rays is best adapted. Without other aid, there appears evidence in the uniformly bright fluorescence which is visible in the hemispherical glass wall above the platinum plate that there are no great differences in the intensity of the illumination, so that Lambert's law cannot hold. However, this fluorescence may be largely excited by the cathode rays.

For the purpose of more exact investigation experiments were made with the photometer upon the intensity of the rays emanating from several tubes in various directions, and I have besides exposed photographic films which were bent in a half circle to a radius of 25 centimeters about the platinum plate as a center. In both experiments the varying thickness of the glass at different parts of the tube walls entered as a serious disturbing factor, because the X-rays were thus unequally absorbed in the various directions. It was, however, possible to make the thickness of the glass approximately uniform by the interposition of thin plates.

The result of these experiments is that the radiation upon an imaginary hemisphere constructed upon the platinum plate as a center is nearly uniform almost to the borders of this hemisphere. I could detect a slight diminution of intensity at an emanation angle of 80 degrees, but this diminution is relatively small, so that the principal part of the change in intensity occurs between 89 and 90 degrees. I was not able to detect any difference in kind between rays emitted at different angles.

In consequence of the distribution of intensity of X-rays, just described, it follows that images of the platinum plate formed in the pinhole camera, whether upon the photographic plate or the fluorescent screen, will be more intense the greater the angle which is made by the platinum plate with the screen or photographic film, providing this angle does not exceed 80 degrees. By appropriate arrangements which enabled me to make a comparison between images formed simultaneously by radiations from the same tube on screens at various angles this result was confirmed. A similar case of intensity distribution is found in optics in connection with fluorescence. If a few drops of a solution of fluorescein be allowed to fall into a square trough of water, and the trough be illuminated by white or violet light, it will be noticed that the brightest fluorescent light goes out from the edges of the slowly sinking column of fluorescein, or, in other words, from the places where the angle of emanation of the fluorescent light is the greatest. As Stokes has remarked, referring to a similar experiment, this appearance depends upon the fact that the light exciting the fluorescence is considerably more absorbed by the fluorescein solution than is the fluorescent light. It is worth mentioning that the cathode rays which generate the X-rays are much more strongly absorbed by platinum than the X-rays, and it may therefore be surmised that there exists a similarity between these two processes, the conversion of light into fluorescent light and the conversion of cathode rays into X-rays. There is as yet, however, no firm ground on which to rest such a conclusion.

With reference to practical applications, the observation of the distribution of intensity of the rays proceeding from the platinum plate has some value in connection with the formation of shadow pictures by means of X-rays. In accordance with the observations above recorded it is to be recommended that the discharge tube be so arranged that the rays employed for formation of pictures be those making a large angle, though not much exceeding 80 degrees, with the platinum plate. In this way the sharpest possible delineation will be obtained, and if the platinum plate is flat and the construction of the tube such that the rays proceeding obliquely pass through not much greater thickness of glass than those going out at right angles to the platinum plate, then no material loss in intensity will be experienced in this arrangement.

4. In my first communication I designated as the transmissibility of a body the ratio of a brightness which a fluorescent screen held behind the body at right angles to the rays bears to its brightness in the absence of the interposed body, but under conditions otherwise identical. Referring the transmissibility to unit thickness we obtain what may be called the specific transmissibility. This will be the dth root of the transmissibility where d is the thickness of the transmitting layer measured along the direction of the rays. In order to determine the transmissibility I have since my first communication made use principally of the photometer described above. The two parts of the fluorescent screen having been brought to equal brightness, the plate of the substance to be investigated, as for instance, aluminum, tin, glass, etc., was interposed before one of the tubes, and the distance of one or other of the discharge tubes was altered so that the screen became again

uniformly illuminated. The ratio between the squares of the distances of the platinum plates from the screen before and after the interposition of the body under investigation gives the value of the transmissibility sought. By interposing a second plate its transmissibility may be found for rays which have already passed through one plate of the same kind.

In this procedure it is assumed that the brightness of a fluorescent screen is inversely proportional to the square of its distance from the source of the rays, and this can only be the case on condition, first, that the air absorbs or emits no X-rays, and, second, that the brightness of the fluorescent light is proportional to the intensity of the radiation falling upon it. The first condition is certainly not fulfilled, and it is questionable whether the second is or not. I have therefore first satisfied myself, as already set forth in section 10 of my first communication, that the deviations from strict proportionality are so slight as to be negligible for the purposes of experiment in the case at hand. Again, with reference to the fact that X-rays are secondarily radiated from bodies under their influence, it may be remarked, first, that no difference was to be detected with the photometer between the transmissibility of a single plate of aluminum 0.925 millimeter thick, and of 31 superposed plates each of 0.0299 millimeter thickness, giving a total thickness of 0.927 millimeter; and, second, that the brightness of the fluorescent screen was not appreciably different whether the plate was placed close up to the screen or at a considerable distance from it.

The results of these experiments on transmissibility are for aluminum as follows:

Transmissibility for rays falling vertically.	Tube			
	2	3	4	2
The first, 1 millimeter thick, aluminum plate	0.40	0.45		0.68
The second, 1 millimeter thick, aluminum plate	.55	.68		.73
The first, 2 millimeters thick, aluminum plate		.30	0.39	.50
The second, 2 millimeters thick, aluminum plate		.39	.54	.63

From these and similar experiments with glass and tin we may draw the following result: if a body be imagined to be made up of successive layers with their faces perpendicular to the direction of the X-rays, each of these layers will be more transmissible than the one next preceding. In other words, the specific transmissibility of a body is greater the thicker the body. This result is completely in accord with observations which may be made by photography of a tin scale as described in section 4 of my first communication, and also with the fact that occasionally in photographic shadow pictures, the shadows of thin layers, as for example the paper used in wrapping the plate, came out relatively strong.

5. If two plates of different substances are equally transmissible this equality will not in general be retained for another pair of plates of the same substances with thicknesses altered in the same ratio. This fact may be shown very easily by the use of thin sheets, as, for example, of platinum and aluminum. I used for this purpose platinum foil 0.0026 millimeter thick and aluminum foil 0.0299 millimeter thick. I found in one instance that 1 sheet of platinum was equally transmissible with 6 sheets of aluminum; but the transmissibility of 2 sheets of platinum was less than of 12 sheets of aluminum and about equal to that of 16 sheets of the latter metal. Using another discharge tube, I found 1 platinum equals 8 aluminum but 8 platinum equal 90 aluminum. From these experiments it follows that the ratio of thicknesses of platinum and aluminum of equal transmissibility is less the thicker the sheets under examination.

6. The ratio of the thicknesses of two equally transmissible plates of different material is dependent on the thickness and the material of the body, as, for instance, the glass wall of the discharge tube, through which the rays have to pass before they reach the plates investigated.

7. The experiments described in sections 4, 5, and 6 relate to the alterations which the X-rays proceeding from a discharge tube experience in their transmission through different substances. It will now be shown that one and the same body may for the same thickness be unequally transmissible for rays emitted from different discharge tubes.

In the following table are given the values of the transmissibility of an aluminum plate 2 millimeters thick for the rays given out by different tubes:

	Tube.					
	1	2	3	4	2	5
Transmissibility for vertically incident rays of a 2-millimeter thick aluminum plate	0.0044	0.22	0.30	0.39	0.50	0.59

The discharge tubes were not materially different in their construction or in the thickness of their glass wall, but varied in the density of the gas within them, and hence in the potential required to produce discharge. Tube 1 required the least and tube 5 the greatest potential, or, as we may say for short, the tube 1 is the "softest" and tube 5 the "hardest." The same Ruhmkorff in direct connection with the tubes, the same circuit breaker, and the same current strength in the primary circuit were used in all cases.

Various other substances which I have investigated behaved similarly to aluminum. All are more transmissible to rays from harder tubes. This fact seemed to me particularly worthy of attention.

The relative transmissibility of plates of different substances proved also to be dependent on the hardness of the discharge tube employed. The ratio of the thickness of platinum and aluminum plates of equal transmissibility becomes less the harder the tubes from which the rays proceed, or, referring to the results just given, the less the rays are absorbed.

The different behavior of rays excited in tubes of different hardness is also made apparent in the well-known shadow picturing of hands, etc. With a soft tube a dark shadow is obtained in which the bones are little prominent; when a harder tube is used the bones are very distinct and visible in all their details, whereas the softer portions are less marked, and with very hard tubes even the bones themselves become only weak shadows. From these considerations it appears that the choice of the tube must be governed by the character of the objects which it is desired to portray.

8. It remains to remark that the quality of rays proceeding from one and the same tube depends on various conditions. Of these the most important are the following: (1) The action of the interrupter,* or, in other words, the course of the primary current. In

---

* A good Duprez interrupter works more regularly than a Foucault interrupter; the latter, however, conserves the primary current better.

this connection should be mentioned the phenomena frequently observed that particular ones of the rapidly succeeding discharges excite X-rays which are not only more intense, but which also differ from the others in their absorption. (2) The character of the sparks which appear in the secondary circuit of the apparatus. (3) The employment of a Tesla transformer. (4) The degree of evacuation of the discharge tube (as already stated). (5) The varying, but as not yet satisfactorily known, procedure within the discharge tube. Separate ones among these conditions require further comment.

The hardness of a tube had been considered to be brought about solely by the continuation of the evacuation by means of the pump; but this characteristic is affected in other ways. Thus a sealed tube of medium hardness becomes gradually harder by itself — unfortunately to the shortening of the period of its usefulness when used in a suitable manner for the production of X-rays, that is to say when discharges which do not cause the platinum to glow or at least to glow weakly are passed through. A gradual self-evacuation is thus effected.

With a tube thus become very hard I took a very fine photograph of a double-barreled gun with inserted cartridges, which showed all the details of the cartridges, the inner faults of the Damascus barrels, etc., very sharply and distinctly. The distance from the platinum plate of the discharge tube to the photographic plate was 15 centimeters and the exposure 12 minutes — comparatively long in consequence of the small photographic action of the very slightly absorbable rays (see below). The Duprez interrupter had to be replaced by the Foucault form. It would be of interest to construct tubes which would make it possible to use still higher potentials than before.

Self-evacuation has been above assigned as the cause of the growing hardness of sealed tubes, but this is not the only cause. There are changes in the electrodes which produce this effect. I do not know the nature of these changes.

The observations recorded in these paragraphs and others not given have led me to the view that the composition of the rays proceeding from a platinum anode of a discharge tube depends upon the frequency and form of the discharge current. The degree of tenuity, the hardness, is important only because the form of the discharge is thereby influenced. If it were possible to produce the proper form of discharge for the generation of X-rays in any other way, the X-rays might be obtained with relatively high pressures.

9. The results appearing in the five preceding paragraphs have been those most evidently to be derived from the accompanying experiments. Summing up these separate results, and being guided in part by the analogy which holds between the behavior of the visible radiations and X-rays, one arrives at the following conclusions:

(*a*) The radiations emitted by a discharge tube consist of a mixture of rays of different absorbability and intensity.

(*b*) The composition of this mixture is in a marked degree dependent on the frequency and form of the discharge current.

(*c*) The rays receiving preference in absorption vary with different bodies.

(*d*) Since the X-rays are generated by the cathode rays and have in common with them various characteristics — as the exciting of fluorescence, photographic and electrical actions, an absorbability depending in a marked degree on the density of the medium traversed, etc. — the conjecture is prompted that both phenomena are processes of the same nature. Without committing myself unconditionally to this view, I may remark that the results of the last paragraphs are calculated to raise a difficulty in the way of this hypothesis. This difficulty consists in the great difference between the absorption of the cathode rays investigated by Lenard and the X-rays, and second that the transmissibility of bodies for the cathode rays is related to their density by other laws than those which govern their transmissibility for X-rays.

With regard to the first point, considerations present themselves under two heads: (1) As we have seen in section 7, there are X-rays of different absorbability, and the investigations of Hertz and Lenard show that the cathode rays are similarly to be discriminated. While the "softest" tubes investigated generated rays much less subject to absorption than any cathode rays investigated by Lenard, yet there is no reason to doubt the possibility of X-rays of greater absorbability, and cathode rays of less. It therefore appears probable that in future investigations rays will be found bridging over the gap between X-rays and cathode rays, so far as their absorption is concerned. (2) We found in section 4 that the specific transmissibility of a body becomes less the thinner the plate passed through. Consequently, had we made use in our experiments of plates as thin as those employed by Lenard it would have been found that the X-rays were more nearly like those of Lenard in their absorbability.

10. Besides the fluorescent phenomena, there may be excited by X-rays photographic, electric, and other actions, and it is of interest to know how far these various manifestations vary in similar ratio when the source of the rays is altered. I must restrict myself to a comparison of the first two phenomena.

A hard and a soft tube were so adjusted as to give equally bright fluorescence as compared by means of the photometer described in section 2. Upon substituting a photographic plate in the place of the fluorescent screen it was found, on development, that the portion subject to the rays from the hard tube was blackened to a less degree than the other. The rays, through producing equal fluorescence, were thus for photographic purposes unequally active.

The great sensitiveness of a photographic plate even for rays from tubes of medium hardness is illustrated by an experiment in which 96 films were superposed, placed at a distance of 25 centimeters from the discharge tube, and exposed five minutes with due precautions to protect the films from the radiations of the air. A photographic action was apparent on the last film, although the first was scarcely overexposed.

If the intensity of the radiations is augmented by increasing the strength of the primary current, the photographic action increases in the same measure as the intensity of the fluorescence. In this case, as in the case where the intensity of the radiation was increased by an alteration of the distance of the fluorescent screen, the brightness of the fluorescence is at least approximately proportional to the intensity of the radiation. This rule should not, however, be too generally applied.

11. In conclusion, mention should be made of the following particulars:

With a discharge tube of proper construction, and not too soft, the X-rays are chiefly generated in a spot of not more than 1 or 2 millimeters diameter where the cathode rays meet the platinum plate. This, however, is not the sole source. The whole plate and a part of the tube walls emit X-rays, though in less intensity. Cathode rays proceed in all directions, but their intensity is considerable only near the axis of the concave cathode mirror, and, consequently, the X-rays are strongly emitted only near the point where this axis meets the platinum plate. When the tube is very hard and the platinum thin, many rays proceed also from the rear surface of the platinum plate, but, as may be shown by the pinhole camera, chiefly from the spot lying on the axis of the mirror.

I can confirm the observation of G. Brandes that the X-rays are able to produce a sensation of light upon the retina of the eye. In my record book appears a notice entered in the early part of November 1895 to the effect that when in a darkened chamber near a wooden door I perceived a weak appearance of light when a Hittorf tube upon the other side of the door was put in operation. Since this appearance was only once observed, I regarded it as a subjective, and the reason that it was not then repeatedly observed lay in the fact that other tubes were substituted for the Hittorf tube which were less completely evacuated and not provided with platinum anodes. The Hittorf tube furnishes rays of slight absorbability on account of its high vacuum, and, at the same time, of great intensity on account of the employment of a platinum anode for the reception of the cathode rays.

With the tubes now in use I can easily repeat the Brandes experiment.

Since the beginning of my investigation of X-rays I have repeatedly endeavored to produce diffraction phenomena with them. I obtained at various times, when using narrow slits, appearances similar to diffraction effects, but when modifications were made in the conditions for the purpose of thoroughly proving the accuracy of this explanation of the phenomena it was found in each case that the appearances were produced in other ways than by diffraction. I know of no experiment which gives satisfactory evidence of the existence of diffraction with the X-rays.

WÜRZBURG, PHYSIK. INSTITUT D. UNIV., *March 10, 1897.*

L. HENRY GARLAND

The Scientific Importance
of X-Rays

[FROM THE SMITHSONIAN REPORT FOR 1946*]

To ILLUSTRATE *what widespread results may derive from a single basic scientific discovery, there is presented a recent review of the present-day uses of that invaluable tool of physician and physicist — the X-ray. The author, Dr. L. Henry Garland, is clinical professor of radiology of the Stanford University School of Medicine and was formerly Commander, M.C., U.S.N.R. He has received the gold medal of the American College of Radiology, the distinguished service award of the American Cancer Society, and other honors, and is the author of sections of medical books and of many articles in medical journals. Dr. Garland believes that in spite of the many spectacular recent developments in medical science, the X-ray will after yet another half-century still be regarded as one of the most important scientific discoveries of all time.*

The author describes modern X-ray equipment and reviews the wide range of scientific fields to which the use of X-rays has spread. These include anatomy and physiology, physics and chemistry, biology, and, most important of all, medicine. After outlining

* Revised as of November 1959.

in detail the value of X-rays in diagnosis and treatment, Dr. Garland looks forward to the expected future developments which will make of X-rays an even more potent weapon in the attack upon disease. He concludes by reminding us of our debt to Professor Roentgen.

> *Come, come, and sit you down; you shall not budge;*
> *You go not, till I set you up a glass*
> *Where you may see the inmost part of you.*
>   (Hamlet, Act III, Scene 4, lines 23–25.)

THE DISCERNING English dramatist wrote these amazingly prophetic lines some 300 years before a modest German physicist announced the discovery of a "new type of rays." Yet, had he known, Shakespeare hardly could have penned a more apt description of a fluoroscopic examination — aided, it is granted in this instance, by a mirror, in which the good Queen of Denmark might "see her inmost part." To continue the remarkable coincidence, the Queen, like many an apprehensive patient, replies to Hamlet:

> What wilt thou do? Thou wilt not murder me?

And Polonius cried forth:

> What ho! help, help, help!

Before the days of shockproof X-ray equipment, such a scene might have taken place in a radiologist's office; today it should be a rarity (unless Polonius were confronted with the statement for an unusually prolonged and complicated series of examinations).

In the 65 years which have elapsed since Roentgen's announcement there have been many developments in medical science which, at first glance, might seem to dwarf the tremendous importance of the discovery of X-ray. These developments include the perfection of antitoxic sera, of remarkable antibiotic agents (the sulfa drugs, penicillin, and similar molds), of stored blood or blood derivatives, of open heart surgery and organ transplantation, and finally of planned atomic disintegration. Yet we believe it is safe to hazard the guess that in another 50 years we still shall look upon the X-ray as one of the developments of major scientific import of all time, as well as one of the most valuable weapons for medical care. We shall look back and thank the pioneers in physics, electricity, radiology, and general medical pedagogy who made equipment practicable and who encouraged physicians to specialize in the field of X-ray diagnosis and treatment.

GENERAL CONSIDERATIONS

To appreciate the importance of X-rays it is desirable that certain basic facts be kept in mind. These rays are penetrating radiations corresponding to light rays but having much shorter wavelengths. They may be used in a manner similar to light rays for the inspection of some materials and, by virtue of their peculiar properties, for the analysis of others. Gross inspection methods include simple roentgenography (or X-ray "photography") and roentgenoscopy (or X-ray fluoroscopy); detailed inspection methods include various other means such as microradiography, Roentgen spectroscopy, Roentgen diffraction, and so forth. In practice, X-rays usually are generated by allowing a stream of high-speed electrons to impinge upon a metal target. They have wavelengths of from 10.0 to 0.01 angstroms, and effect a sensitized film in a manner similar to that of light rays. They also cause certain substances to fluoresce. The materials through which they pass are ionized and give rise to scattered X-rays. Because of this ionization, the rays are of use in the treatment of certain medical conditions. X-rays can be reflected, refracted, and polarized by special means (including the use of crystals).

The principal use of X-rays lies in their ability to penetrate opaque objects. Such objects arrest the rays approximately in direct proportion to their densities. Substances of low atomic weight such as cotton, gauze, and aluminum, are traversed readily by the rays, while other substances such as bone and heavy metals are opaque, and cast a dense shadow on a sensitized film. Some materials are transparent to light rays but opaque to X-rays (for example, a plate of lead glass).

In the radiographic examination of materials (both animate and inanimate) it is important to remember that the delineation of an object depends on its differing in density from its surroundings. Unless such difference exists, the outline of the object cannot be shown on ordinary roentgenograms. A simple example of this is the demonstrability of the heart in X-rays of the chest. Surrounded as it is by air-filled lungs, the heart is readily visible in chest films. However, if nature had placed it in the middle of the liver, no distinct shadow would be cast as the liver is of approximately the same density.

Under ordinary circumstances, X-rays are not directly visible and require a specially prepared surface for their detection (a fluoroscopic screen or sensitized film). We use the adjective "ordinary" because you actually can see X-rays with a little training and practice. Unfortunately, if you look at them sufficiently long, you will lose your eyelashes, and probably your eyebrows, if not most of your hair. This is because of the destructive effect of large amounts of X-rays on the hair follicles and other living tissues. However, it is safe to gaze at the rays for a few minutes, using a small beam (perhaps 1-inch diameter). One must sit in total darkness for some 30 minutes before he can appreciate the faint fluorescence produced by the rays on the human retina; one is then able to see small lead objects placed between the X-ray tube and the human eye, and, if one has an opaque lens (cataract) or cornea, he can ascertain whether or not the optic nerve is intact. The method is used occasionally by radiologists, at the request of eye specialists, to assure that the patient has an intact retina and nerve before surgical procedures on the cornea or lens are performed. It is to be noted that objects will seem upside down, since the focusing power of the human lens will be ineffective with X-rays.

The action of X-rays on photographic film is similar to that of light rays. Ordinary X-ray films are coated on both sides with a silver halide emulsion, especially sensitive to the violet range of the spectrum, because they are used mostly with double intensifying screens which glow with that color. These screens consist of thin pieces of cardboard coated with calcium tungstate and a protective transparent film. They are placed in a special bakelite or aluminum-fronted frame, and for satisfactory results must make perfect contact with the film. Thin lead screens may be used with industrial film for very high voltage radiography. Special non-screen films may be used for improved detail, but are from 5 to 10 times slower than screen films. The modern film has a cellulose-acetate base (with no greater fire hazard than paper). The finished roentgenogram is a negative image and is studied in a flashed opal glass illuminator.

The fluoroscopic screen usually is made with zinc sulfide because it must carry an image to be viewed directly and this chemical fluoresces in the color range to which the eye is quite sensitive (yellow-green). Roentgen's original screen was made of barium platino-cyanide, which was much less efficient than the present type. All fluoroscopic screens must be covered with lead glass to protect the operator from exposure to X-rays. Except when using specially amplified beams, the operator must "adapt" his eyes prior to examination by remaining in a darkened room for several minutes or by wearing special goggles before beginning the work.

A beam of X-rays consists of electromagnetic radiations of various wavelengths. If of very short wavelength they are of high penetrating power; if of very long wavelength they may penetrate only a few millimeters of tissue. The quality of a beam of rays may be measured by various methods, the most convenient one in ordinary practice being the determination of their absorption by some material such as copper or aluminum. A spectrometer can be employed, but is too time-consuming and troublesome for routine use. The quality is expressed as the thickness of an absorber which reduces the intensity of a given beam to one-half its initial value, and the resulting figure is known as the half-value layer for that beam. For low-voltage rays (up to 20 kilovolt) cellophane may be used as the absorber; between 20 and 120 kilovolt, aluminum; between 120 and 400 kilovolt, copper; and for more than 400 kilovolt, lead or tin. A refinement of the method is to record a second half-value layer, the ratio of the second to the first being used as an index of homogeneity. It is to be noted that the expression half-value layer is only part of the description of the quality of a given beam; for scientific purposes one also must specify the nature of the target material, the tube wall, and the generator wave form.

The quantity of X-rays in a given beam at a given point may be measured by recording the ionization in a fixed volume of air or gas at that point. The "roentgen" is the unit of X-ray quantity and was defined as "that quantity of X or gamma radiation such that the associated corpuscular emission per 0.001293 gram of air produces, in air, ions carrying one electrostatic unit of electricity of either sign." The mass of 1 cubic centimeter of air at 0° centigrade and 760 millimeters of mercury is 0.001293 gram. The rays usually are measured by an electroscope attached to a small thimble chamber composed of a special light plastic material. The unit of absorbed X-ray dose is the rad, which is equal to 100 ergs per gram.

X-RAYS IN SCIENCE

The importance of X-rays to science in general is so great that a volume would be necessary to describe it. However, a few of the more interesting applications of X-rays will be mentioned in this article and an attempt made to give a clue to their true value. For the sake of brevity the sciences will be grouped into a few general categories.

Anatomy and physiology. — The importance of X-rays to anatomy, comparative anatomy, paleontology, and associated sciences is now well appreciated. However, it is not realized generally that the modern method of teaching anatomy to medical and other students involves the use of roentgenological demonstration of the skeleton and its various associated soft parts, both in the cadaver and in the living subject. In this manner the appearance and behavior of bony and other structures in the living is demonstrated in a way never before possible. The study of the skeletal development in vertebrate embryos is facilitated enormously by Roentgen methods. The anatomy of small and large animals is revealed in zoological work. The status and often the diseases of mummies may be determined without opening the wrappings or even the sarcophagi. Genetics has been furthered by studying the behavior

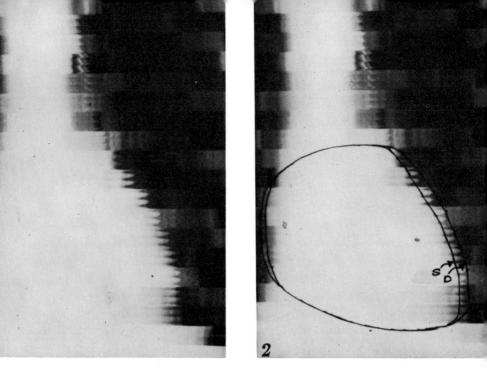

ILLUS. 35—ROENTGENKYMOGRAM OF THE HEART OF AN ADULT MALE.

1. Three contractions of the heart are visible in each of the frames with the tip or peak of each wave representing maximum expansion and the base or valley maximum contraction of the heart (diastole and systole, respectively). The contractions are of normal amplitude and shape. (Exposure time, 2 seconds.)

2. Same case as figure 1, illustrating method of tracing the outline of the heart shadow in contraction (S) and expansion (D). In this way the output of the heart is ascertained.

of many species, notably *Drosophila melanogaster* (the common fruit fly) following exposure to specific quantities of X-rays (with the production of subsequent mutations of certain types).

Physiology is greatly indebted to roentgenologic methods, notably in connection with the study of the alimentary tract, the circulation of the blood, and the functioning of moving parts, especially joints. X-ray "movies" as well as fluoroscopy and "still" films have been used extensively in this field. As an example of their value in one small department the X-ray (kymographic) determination of cardiac output can be cited.

An X-ray film is made of the subject's chest, in the erect position, at a measured distance (say 5 or 6 feet), using a lead grid between the patient and the film. The exposure takes about 2 seconds' time and the film is moved slowly downward a distance of 12 millimeters during the exposure. When the film is dried, the outline of the heart appears as a serrated border, the "peaks" representing the shadow in maximum expansion and the "valleys" in maximum contraction. The peaks are joined by one line, the valleys by another. The rest of the heart shadow is completed as shown in Illustration 35, figure 2. The area in these two phases then is measured with a planimeter and the figures corrected for distortion. The corrected figures then are converted into volumes according to a table established from experimental and cadaver work. The difference in volume between expansion and contraction gives the output per beat. In many normal subjects the average stroke output per ventricle is 60 cubic centimeters; a person with a rapid pulse tends to have a smaller, and one with a slow pulse a correspondingly larger output. Therefore, it is more informative to speak of the output per minute than the output per stroke; this in turn varies with body size, which may be expressed fairly simply in terms of total body surface. The number of liters of blood pumped per minute per square meter of body surface is termed the cardiac index. This index may be found by using this particular X-ray method. (Needless to say, there are other methods of determining this index, but the roentgenkymographic one is a simple and reliable one when correctly used.)

Our knowledge of the functions and behavior of the alimentary tract in health and disease is largely dependent on the use of Roentgen methods of examination. Some of the earliest investigators in this field have been American physiologists who did their original work on cats (to whom they fed bismuth in milk, and so forth). Food also may be used, provided it is opaque to the rays. On an early morning walk near San Francisco several years ago, I came across a plump horned toad. Having a little time to spare that day, I brought the toad into my fluoroscopic room and placed it on the table. I then captured a common house fly and dusted it with barium sulphate. After setting the tasty meal beside the toad I turned on the X-rays and watched the inevitable and fascinating sequence of events. The barium cast just as good a shadow in the toad's stomach as it does in the human, and the progress of the meal could be studied easily.

Physics and chemistry. — The use of X-rays in the sciences of physics and chemistry and all their innumerable ramifications is an ever-expanding chapter in X-ray history. The gross analysis of many materials may be performed in part by roentgenoscopy or roentgenography, and the detailed analysis by methods such as Roentgen diffraction, crystallography, or electron microscopy. The diffraction method of measuring small objects is well established. The principle depends on the fact that a beam of light or X-rays which has traversed a collection of small objects is seen surrounded by a series of rings or diffraction spectra, from the diameter or pattern of which the size of the object can be calculated. A familiar example is the ring visible around lights on a misty night, the diameter of which is determined by the mean diameter of the mist particles. The interpretation of X-ray diffraction patterns in terms of the ultimate structure of crystals and solids has its foundations in crystallography. By such methods it is found that rubbers, plastics, and fibers, although superficially different, are intrinsically similar materials. X-ray studies also have assisted greatly in analyzing the structure of the higher polymers. The essential features of such diffraction apparatus are:

1. A source of X-rays.
2. A device to limit the rays to a beam of minimum divergence.
3. A holder to support the test specimen in the beam.
4. A means for recording the X-rays diffracted from the sample of critical angles (determined by the crystal structure of the samples).

A former issue of Electrical Engineering included a description of a method of X-ray analysis of unknown chemical substances by employing a photoelectric roentgen intensimeter. The meter is so delicate that if the X-rays are passed through a pile of 100 sheets of paper, the difference in absorption caused by adding or subtracting a single sheet can be recorded.

As a direct result of investigations in physics and chemistry there are numerous industrial and commercial X-ray developments which include the following:

1. The examination of various complicated appliances, such as radio-tubes, without the necessity of breaking open the tubes.

2. The examination of castings and welds.
3. The examination of packages and, under special circumstances, personnel for concealed materials.
4. The examination of edible materials (such as candy bars and oranges) for defects or impurities.
5. The behavior of solids and liquids under projectile bombardment (such as high-speed roentgenography of bullets).

The roentgenographic examination of metal parts in connection with the airplane industry is said to have used up more film per month during the last few months of World War II than was used in all medical procedures in the United States during the same period. Currently they are extensively used for the examination of honeycomb metal structures. The importance of skilled interpretation of these roentgenograms and of adequate protection for the employees operating the X-ray equipment obviously is great.

Since the early days of X-ray development, packages, clothing, and even personnel have been inspected for contraband and other illegally possessed materials. Packages and similar objects may be inspected without harm, provided they do not contain unprocessed film or other sensitized material. Individuals may be examined only under extraordinary conditions, as exposure of large amounts of the body to X-rays, especially if repeated, is fraught with ultimate danger to the individual; possibly resulting later in skin damage, anemia, or genetic damage.

It is to be recollected that metals and other materials may be radiographed either with X-rays or radium rays. It is therefore appropriate to consider a few aspects of radioactive substances, as many of them have properties analogous to those of X-rays. Radium rays are of three general types:

1. Alpha rays, which are positively charged particles of very low penetrating power, being stopped by a sheet of ordinary paper.
2. Beta rays, which are negative electrons, of moderate penetrating power, stopped by a thin metal filter (2 millimeters of brass or 0.5 millimeter platinum or their equivalent).
3. Gamma rays, which are electromagnetic radiations (photons) of considerable penetrating power, the hardest ones traversing several centimeters of lead.

Because of their different charges, these three types of rays can be separated in a magnetic field. The alpha rays are deflected slightly in one direction, the beta more strongly in the opposite direction, and the gamma not at all. Radium disintegrates slowly, its half period being 1,590 years. For medical purposes it usually is kept in small containers in the form of a radium salt. Many of these containers can be placed together and the group then used like an X-ray tube. Radioactive cobalt sources may be similarly used.

Since the work of Rutherford, in 1919, we have been able to produce artificially radioactive substances. One method of doing this is to use the cyclotron, by means of which the nuclei of atoms are transformed into new unstable substances.* High-speed protons, deuterons, and neutrons have been used to transform most elements. The resultant radiations are of many types (alpha, beta, gamma, neutron, and positron). Many biologically useful radio elements are produced by deuteron bombardment and include radiophosphorus, radiosodium, radioiron, radioiodine, radiocobalt, and radiostrontium. These substances can be administered to patients and their exact method of localization and storage in the human body studied by means of Geiger counters and similar apparatus. In this manner the metabolism of certain living tissues, in both health and disease, can be studied more completely than ever before. For example, totally new information concerning the need for and method of use of iron in the human body, in conditions like anemia, has been obtained.

An indirect development of high-voltage tubes in physics is the electron microscope which permits much higher magnifications of minute objects than are feasible with optical microscopes. With this instrument the image of the object is either viewed on a fluorescent screen or is recorded on a photographic film. Recent developments include modifications by which the instrument may be used either as a diffraction camera or a microscope. Stereoscopic electron micrographs can be made. The usual electron microscope operates at about 60 kilovolts, but there is a small table model operating at 30 kilovolts. The structure and behavior of viruses has been studied for the first time, and the detailed structure of bacteria has been revealed. Chromosomes, the tiny rodlike particles that bear the major responsibility for inherited characteristics, may

* See article on Radioisotopes, by Paul C. Aebersold, in this volume. — ED.

be examined, and by means of ingenious methods the actual location of certain specific genes in a number of chromosomes has been determined.

Biology. — X-rays have been used in most of the various biological sciences, notably in botany and zoology. The architecture of many forms of plant life has been studied by macroradiography as well as microradiography. Mutations have been produced by bombardment of seedlings and rootlings with X-ray, and new hybrids successfully developed. In fact, one physician insists that a special type of begonia he grows is a direct result of irradiation of a former plant. He gives no credit to Mendel's cosmic ray but, unfortunately, I am not sufficiently familiar with botany to know whether or not he is correct.

In zoology, several types of animal life have been studied with X-rays. With the larger type of animal one naturally has to make segmental studies. About a generation ago an ailing elephant at the London zoo was subjected to X-ray examination. The tired pachyderm lay on her side and had her torso marked with chalk into a series of rectangles, each a little less than 14 by 17 inches in size. These then were numbered in sequence and a series of roentgenograms made. We cannot vouch for the quality of the films made through the thicker parts, but those of the extremities which we saw were quite good. Race horses, greyhounds, parrots, and other domestic pets frequently are subjected to examination in connection with injuries, foreign bodies, and certain diseases. Before the development of shockproof apparatus, cats were particularly difficult to X-ray as they have a strong dislike for the hair-raising qualities of the corona from exposed high-voltage wires.

Miscellaneous. — One of the less-known but more valuable uses of X-rays is in connection with art. Many pigments contain lead and other radio-opaque salts, and the roentgenogram of a canvas often reveals shadows different from those on the visible painting. Areas of overpainting, alterations, and erasures can be detected. The authenticity of some old masters has been proved and of others disproved by such means. A recent refinement includes sectional radiography of the canvas in which, by keeping the tube and film in motion, a very fine layer of the painting can be registered to the exclusion of other layers.

TABLE I.—THE ELECTROMAGNETIC SPECTRUM

Type of radiation	Range of wavelengths	Range of frequencies
Electrical waves	1,000,000 to 20 kilometers	10^{-1} to 10^4
Radio waves	20 to 0.01 meters	10^4 to 10^{11}
Infrared rays	120,000 to 7,700 angstroms*	10^{11} to 10^{15}
Visible rays	7,700 to 3,900 angstroms	
Ultraviolet rays	3,900 to 1,800 angstroms	
X-rays	10 to 0.01 angstroms	
Gamma rays	0.1 to 0.02 angstrom	
Cosmic rays	$0.00001 \pm$ angstrom	

* 1 angstrom $= 10^{-8}$ centimeter; 100,000,000 angstroms $= 1$ centimeter.

X-RAYS IN MEDICINE

The importance of roentgenologic methods in medicine, dentistry, and allied sciences is increasing continually. They permit the examination of parts of the body hitherto inaccessible to study and the detection of disease at a stage when it may be cured readily. They extend the physician's eye to an incalculable distance. They are also of use in the prevention of disease and in its treatment. (A small precancerous skin nodule, keratosis, may be cured before it develops into a malignancy; established, localized, accessible cancer can be destroyed.) Our knowledge of many diseases such as stomach ulcer, lung tuberculosis, and bone cancer has been entirely revolutionized and reoriented since the discovery of X-rays. They have provided an impetus to investigation and research in preventive medicine such as no other weapon ever placed at the disposal of the doctor.

One might arrange this section according to the various medical specialties, but I think it will be of more interest to nonmedical readers to consider the importance of the rays according to each of the various systems of the human body. However, it is timely at this point to acknowledge the debt of roentgenology to members of the specialties outside of its own field, physicians who have contributed greatly to the refinements of many techniques in diagnosis as well as treatment. The reader should know that there are now "national qualifying boards for specialists." These boards examine eligible graduate physicians and certify those who pass successfully. At the present time the specialty boards include the following branches of medicine:

1. Anesthesiology.
2. Dermatology and syphilology.
3. Internal medicine.
4. Neurological surgery.
5. Obstetrics and gynecology.
6. Ophthalmology.
7. Orthopedic surgery.

8. Otolaryngology.
9. Pathology.
10. Pediatrics.
11. Plastic surgery.
12. Psychiatry and neurology.
13. Radiology.
14. Surgery.
15. Neurology.

X-ray diagnostic methods involve first and foremost intelligent use: one case may be diagnosed quickest without X-rays at all; the next may need only fluoroscopy; the third, fluoroscopy, roentgenograms, and special-section techniques; the fourth may require repeated roentgenograms. Only a trained physician knows the correct answer to these questions: only a trained physician can be economic in the exposure of your tissues to a radiation known to be noxious. The wise layman selects his physician-radiologist according to his experience or ability, and not according to the newness or extent of his equipment. In assessing the value of a roentgenogram it is important to remember that it is just a shadowgraph and not a true photograph and as such is subject to erroneous interpretation. Furthermore, the roentgenogram is a projection on a flat surface of everything on every plane between the X-ray tube and the film. Thus it is desirable that the interpreter familiarize himself with the projected appearance of normal structures of various shapes. Multiple views, preferably at right angles, usually are essential; stereoscopic roentgenograms frequently are necessary. The examination of moving parts such as the stomach, heart, or diaphragm frequently requires fluoroscopy as well as multiple films.

There are many shadows in roentgenograms of healthy persons which cause errors in interpretation. These include the normal epiphyseal or growth line in bones (often mistaken for a fracture), the overlapping of a bony margin, or the slender canal of the artery to the bone. The existence of a congenital fissure or cleft also may be mistaken for a fracture. Calcium deposits are fairly common in various tissues; they are normal findings in rib cartilages, laryngeal cartilages, and certain other areas, but occasionally they are mistaken for tuberculosis lesions, foreign bodies, and so on. This is one of the reasons why a consultant roentgenologist may require stereoscopic or other additional projections even though you present yourself with a perfectly good film made elsewhere only a few days before. A small wart on the back may be projected on a film in a manner identical with that of a kidney stone or gall stone. Visual examination of the undressed patient or stereoscopic projections should prevent an error being made. In general, it is advisable for persons to be undressed when having X-rays taken, since objects such as earrings have been mistaken for misplaced toothroot fragments, buttons for gallstones, and the edge of folded clothing for fractures. Faulty darkroom technique sometimes results in undeveloped or fogged areas of films which can suggest (in chest films) pneumonia or (in films of the limbs) diseased bone, even to the initiated.

The use of X-ray methods in medical diagnosis may be outlined in relation to the various systems of the body.

Alimentary system. — X-ray examination of the alimentary system permits the early diagnosis of a vast number of common disease conditions, ranging from adhesions to volvulus. Both fluoroscopic and film examinations are usually essential. The fluoroscopic examination discloses facts regarding the mobility and function of organs which cannot be obtained from films alone; the films in turn reveal detail of structure which cannot be appreciated on the fluoroscopic screen. The value of either method depends on the skill, patience, and experience of the examiner. When it is a question of a condition such as early stomach cancer, the examination may have to be repeated two or three times before a reliable opinion can be rendered. For the upper part of the system (the gullet, stomach, and small intestine) it is necessary for the patient to come fasting. He is given a drink of barium sulfate suspended in water and the appearance of these portions of the tract is studied under the fluoroscope. Patients often complain of the chalky taste of the bariumized water. The reason that flavoring agents are not used is that in some persons they stimulate large amounts of gastric secretion which dilutes the test meal undesirably. In the early days of roentgenology the barium or bismuth used to be given in flavored preparations. However, if these contained much milk or cream, stomach emptying would be (physiologically) delayed. If they contained much sugar, stomach emptying would be hastened. These conditions often resulted in erroneous conclusions as to the presence of gastric stasis. In the average case 4 ounces of barium sulfate (by weight) are given in about 8 ounces of water. This eventually mixes with the other contents of the intestinal tract and does not require laxation for its natural ejection.

The lower portion of the alimentary system normally is examined by barium enema. Sixteen ounces of barium sulfate are suspended in 2 quarts of warm water, with the addition of some medium such as acacia solution to maintain suspension during the procedure. After fluoroscopic and roentgenographic examinations the patient evacuates the suspension.

Conditions diagnosable by X-ray include varicose veins in the gullet, ulcers, and tumors in the stomach or duodenum. Before the days of X-ray, duodenal ulcer was considered a rarity; a person with severe and prolonged indigestion was usually diagnosed stomach ulcer. Since the development of Roentgen methods it has been found that most such cases are actually due to duodenal ulcer, the latter being over 20 times as common as gastric ulcer. This was one of numerous revolutionary findings during the first two decades of this century.

Gastric cancer is one of the most common and serious malignant tumors in man; unfortunately it tends to be asymptomatic in its early stages and therefore its presence is not manifested until it is pretty well advanced. Persistent disturbance of digestion in men over 40 renders X-ray examination of the stomach advisable. The growth shows as a small intrusion on the barium shadow or as a small zone of immobility of the stomach wall.

The normal appendix usually is visible at some time during X-ray examination of the intestinal tract. It may be seen to fill and empty but if it does remain filled for some days this finding alone is not of grave importance. The X-ray evidence of acute disease in the appendix consists of marked local tenderness, absence of or incomplete filling, delay in the passage of the barium in the adjacent terminal inches of small bowel, and, occasionally, a local inflammatory mass. However, the diagnosis of acute appendicitis is more reliable when made by methods other than radiological ones.

X-ray examination is invaluable in the study and elucidation of the various diseases of the colon.

The liver and spleen are normally visible in most abdominal roentgenograms. Their visibility may be enhanced by intravenous injection of thorium dioxide sol (thorotrast), a drug which has the property of depositing itself in the small cells lining certain portions of the liver and spleen (the reticuloendothelial cells). The thorium is opaque and aids in the diagnosis of certain tumorous and cystic diseases of these organs. After 7 years, thorium degenerates into a mildly radioactive product, and therefore this medium is used principally in patients whose life expectancy is less than this period of time. Another area of the alimentary tract which may be examined by selective methods is the gall bladder. If you ingest a suitable iodine preparation, the material will be excreted in your bile and will be concentrated in the gall bladder; provided the duct between the liver and gall bladder is not blocked and you remain fasting. This test is a valuable method for the detection of nonopaque cholesterin stones in the gall bladder; indeed, it is the only method by which such may be diagnosed preoperaitvely.

Cardiovascular system. — The accurate determination of heart size in the living human being can be made only by roentgenological methods. It is to be noted, in passing, that this is not always a very important factor, since cardiac function rather than size governs most healthy lives, and function can be assessed by many means much more accurate than roentgenologic ones. However, the problem of heart size does come up in some individuals and Roentgen methods are then invaluable. Correction should always be made for the amount of magnification present, the phase of respiration in which the patient happens to be during the exposure, and similar items. As in the case of the alimentary tract, complete examination of the cardiovascular system involves both fluoroscopy and roentgenography. In recent years the use of opaque substances has permitted the outlining of the individual heart

chambers in the roentgenogram and the study of the circulation
in a manner one could scarcely have even dreamed of 50 years
ago. Besides giving information concerning the size, shape, position, and mobility of the heart, Roentgen methods also may disclose the presence or absence of coronary disease and its sequelae.
Records of the beating heart may be obtained on a single film by
means of kymographic apparatus, and deductions as to the presence of localized areas of heart-muscle disease may be made there-
from. The condition of the arteries and veins in the extremities can
be studied by means of both plain films and films made with contrast media, and the presence of varicose veins in the deep venous
circulation of the leg can be detected and unnecessary operations
avoided.

Central nervous system. — Medical advances in the diagnosis and
treatment of diseases of the brain, spinal cord, and peripheral
nerves form one of the most interesting chapters in modern science.
The normal brain casts no distinguishing shadow in the routine
roentgenogram. However, by very simple methods, its outlines can
be revealed. These consist of performing a spinal puncture (in the
lower portion of the back), withdrawing several cubic centimeters
of cerebrospinal fluid, and injecting in its place a corresponding
amount of air. Upon placement of the patient in an erect position
this gas will ascend into the cerebrospinal fluid pathways around,
between, and in the various lobes of the brain. Several plain or
stereoscopic roentgenograms then are made from various angles,
with the patient both erect and horizontal. The air absorbs during
the next few days and is replaced by normal fluid. By this method
various types of brain injury, brain disease, and tumors may be
detected. Considerable experience is desirable in interpreting these
pneumo-encephalograms.

The spinal cord may be studied by similar methods, or by the
injection of radio-opaque contrast media into various portions of
the spinal canal. The media most commonly used at the present
time are preparations containing iodine (iodized poppy-seed oil
and ethyl iodophenylundecylate). About 3 cubic centimeters of
the opaque oil are injected in the lower lumbar area and the patient is fluoroscoped on a special table. By tilting the body up and
down, the lake of opaque oil can be made to traverse the spinal

canal. Indentations and certain other alterations of its shadow will disclose the presence of ruptured disks, tumors, and so forth.

Genito-urinary system. — It is now possible to examine the outlines of virtually every portion of the genito-urinary system. One can determine the function of each kidney following intravenous injection of an iodine salt selectively excreted by the kidneys. The seminal vesicles and ducts may be outlines by contrast media. Similarly, the cavity of the uterus and the slender canals of the fallopian tubes can be shown. In this manner an extraordinary variety of conditions, normal as well as abnormal, may be detected. The number, size, and approximate age of infants in utero may be told. The placenta has been studied by arteriographic injection of opaque media and valuable information as to the uniovular or multiovular nature of twins ascertained. Abnormal gestations have been diagnosed correctly in time to save the mother an unnecessarily prolonged pregnancy or labor. These cases are some of the most tragic incidents that a radiologist encounters. The normal fetal skeleton does not contain sufficient calcium to cast a clear shadow in routine roentgenograms before a gestation period of 12 weeks. With increasing accuracy after that time the fetal parts may be shown. Attempts have been made to determine the sex of the fetus by X-ray methods, but no practical method has yet been found. Extensive studies have been made on the influence of the shape as well as the size of the female pelvis on spontaneous delivery. Female pelves are classified into four general types, based on their shape. By careful Roentgen examination, the probability of easy or difficult labor can be prognosed with considerable accuracy in selected cases.

Osseous system (bones and joints). — The first use of X-rays was in the examination of cases of suspected fracture. From that day its uses have been extended to include the study of bone growth, bone tumors, joints, tendons, bursae, and adjacent structures. In the correct diagnosis of all bone conditions, and in the treatment of many of them, X-rays are essential.

The detection of a gross fracture in an ordinary roentgenogram is a simple matter; the detection of fine or fissure fractures is often extremely difficult. An important example of this is in injuries involving the wrist, probably the most commonly injured area in the

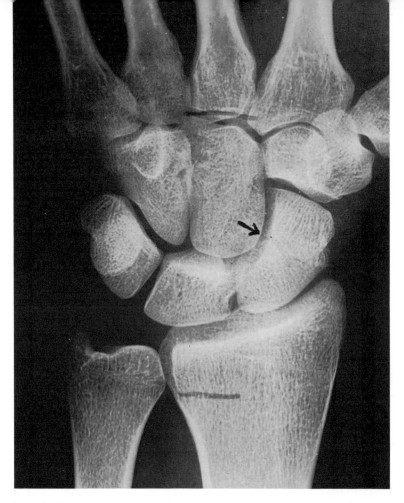

ILLUS. 36—

    1. *Left wrist of adult male showing faint fracture line in one of the small bones (the scaphoid). Fracture is indicated by arrow.*

body (see Illus. 36, fig. 1). One type of "sprain injury" results in fracture of the scaphoid or navicular bone, a small bone in the wrist joint. This bone has a very critical blood supply. If injured, healing requires immediate and complete immobilization for many weeks. Fractures of this bone are often difficult to detect except in films of the highest technical quality; three or four views may be necessary before the crack can be confirmed or excluded. If overlooked, and the wrist is not immobilized, most of these cases re-

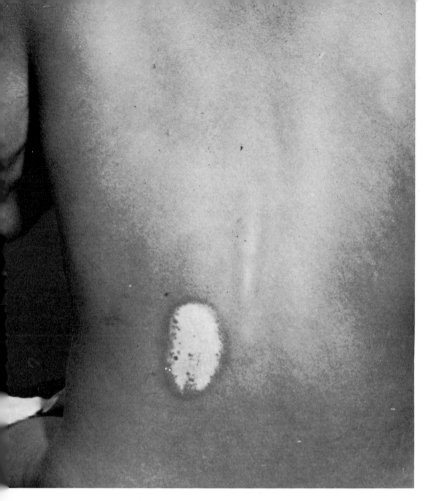

2. *Localized bleaching of the skin of the lower back of an adult male as a result of excessive Roentgen irradiation (healed X-ray burn). Oval area of pallor surrounded by brown pigmentation is the effect of a second-degree burn suffered some months before when the patient underwent X-ray examination of his stomach by an untrained worker.*

sult in nonunion and chronic arthritis in the wrist joint, a serious source of disablement in laborers. Attempts have been made to restore the function of the joint by removing the two broken pieces of scaphoid and replacing them with a synthetic bone (made of a biologically tolerable metal such as vitallium) but these results have not been conspicuously successful. The only method of assuring safety is early X-ray diagnosis and complete immobilization.

Fractures of the ribs are quite common and usually unimpor-

tant injuries and the vast majority of them heal without any particular treatment. However, compensation and legal considerations
often require a decision as to whether or not a fracture is present
in a given case of alleged chest injury. In at least 10 percent of
actual fracture cases, the fracture line is not immediately demon-
strable by ordinary X-ray methods. It is concealed by its obliquity
or by overlapping parts. Therefore, your physician may tell you in
such a case that there is "no X-ray evidence of fracture" rather
than "there is no fracture." If it should be of legal importance to
confirm a suspected fracture in such a case, reexamination at the
end of 4 weeks' time usually will provide the answer. By that time
a little "fuzz" of new bone will be present in the fracture site and
will be visible in the roentgenograms.

Roentgen methods are also invaluable in the detection of various
types of bone disease due to infection, tumor, and so forth. However, the shadows cast often are not characteristic of one particular
infection. For example, a bone that has been disused for several
weeks (perhaps in the foot, when a patient is wearing an extensive plaster splint for fracture of the upper leg) may cast a shadow
identical with that of one extensively diseased. Therefore, it is
necessary for the roentgenologist to have some of the clinical facts
or history of a given case before rendering an interpretation of a
film. The film is not misleading; our deductions, in the absence of
clinical data, may be misleading.

Some diseases cause fairly characteristic changes in bone, but
these are in the minority. The more experience the observer has
the more he realizes that a host of different conditions can produce
identical pathological and, therefore, identical radiological changes.
A good example of this is leprosy. Many years ago an author reported "characteristic" atrophy of the terminal phalanges as a fairly early sign of this disease. On studying cases of nerve disease of
other types, and of obliterative or spastic vascular diseases of various types, it was found that quite identical changes occurred in
many of them. Phosphorus poisoning causes changes in the jaw
bone similar to those of infection and of radium poisoning. Thus,
it is important to maintain reserve in accepting reports of new or
"characteristic" findings in disease.

One interesting finding in roentgenograms of children's extremities is that seen in lead poisoning. Children who have licked the paint off of their toys or pens sometimes develop signs of joint disease or leg weakness. If they have been following this dietary indiscretion for some time, the growing ends of long bones will show dense lines due to actual deposit of lead salts therein.

The roentgenologist is required to have a general knowledge of the development, anatomy, and pathology of the teeth. Satisfactory examination of the teeth requires careful technique and even more careful interpretation. Without the latter, early abscesses at the roots of the teeth, early areas of caries or decay in the crowns, and similar processes may be overlooked.

The value of a consultant specialist is almost nowhere better seen than in certain cases of dental radiography. The dentist or family doctor is apt to look at such films with his thoughts concentrated purely on the dental structures and innocently may neglect a malignant growth in the adjacent bony mandible, a lesion which an expert in the field of X-ray interpretation would be apt to detect readily. It is not suggested that ability in such interpretation is confined exclusively to the roentgenologist. Any person, professional or otherwise, can learn how to interpret films of certain parts of the body after a fairly short period of training. However, the human tendency is to concentrate on the matters in which one is most interested and to overlook other data, even though such are quite apparent in retrospect.

Normal joint cartilage casts no distinguishing shadow in roentgenograms, so routine Roentgen methods are not of much value in the early diagnosis of many types of joint disease. However, "soft-tissue" films of joints, and films made following intra-articular injection of air do provide valuable diagnostic information in many cases. Roentgenograms are of considerable value in the differential diagnosis of established cases of joint disease (chronic rheumatism, gout, specific infection). Bleeding in and about joint areas, such as occurs in hemophiliacs, presents fairly characteristic changes.

Respiratory system. — If roentgenology had made no other contribution to medicine than the ability to study the shadows cast by the lungs in living individuals it would have conferred a tremendous boon. But in considering this portion of the system, let us

commence at the upper portion of the respiratory tract, namely
the nose and nasal accessory sinuses. The cartilages, bones, and
even the skin of the nose can be radiographed with simplicity,·
and various injuries and other conditions accurately diagnosed.
The nasal accessory sinuses, nasal passages, and adjacent areas
can be recorded and various conditions ranging from sinusitis to
cancer detected. The air passages leading from the nose to the
lungs can be portrayed and the true and false vocal cords may be
studied both fluoroscopically and radiographically. A special technique known as body-section roentgenography (laminography or
tomography) permits the obtaining of films of such areas as the
cords relatively free from underlying or overlying shadows. In this
method the tube and film are moved synchronously but in opposite directions about a fulcrum, the location of which depends on
the height above the X-ray table of the area to be studied.

All types and varieties of diseases of the lungs and pleura are
amenable to X-ray diagnosis, and many require such examination
for their elucidation. Communicable diseases such as active lung
tuberculosis provide an excellent example. In recent years the
training of increased numbers of physicians in radiology plus the
development of special X-ray apparatus has permitted mass surveys of hundreds of thousands of individuals. The best method involves the use of standard (14- by 17-inch) films. A slightly less
expensive and currently popular method is the photofluorographic
one, in which the fluoroscopic image is photographed on small or
roll film (35-millimeter, 70-millimeter, or 100-millimeter widths,
depending on the type of equipment). The film comes in rolls of
from 35 to 100 frames, permitting a like number of exposures.
Some of the newer units have built-in photoelectric cells by which
the X-ray exposures are timed automatically. This strip film is
processed in special developer, then dried and viewed either in a
magnifying transilluminator or by means of a projection unit. The
detail in the films is naturally not as great as in the conventional
14- by 17-inch film but it is sufficiently good to permit screening
of lungs for significant lesions. The prime object in the method is
to detect cases of open pulmonary tuberculosis, that is, patients
with cavities or other lesions from which they cough bacilli and so
innocently infect their fellow citizens. Miniature films permit the

detection of most such lesions. Only about one previously unsuspected case of active pulmonary tuberculosis is discovered per 5,000 persons currently examined.

LOCALIZATION OF FOREIGN BODIES

X-rays are essential for the detection and accurate localization of most foreign bodies in the tissues. These bodies may be divided into two general types, nonopaque to the X-rays and opaque. Surprising as it seems, nonopaque foreign bodies frequently may be localized, with considerable accuracy, by careful examination. For example, a peanut lodged in one of the bronchial tubes will itself cast no shadow; however, it will produce partial or complete obstruction of the bronchus. As a result the involved lobe of the lung will show either persistent distention with air on expiration, or gradual collapse. Nonopaque foreign bodies in the alimentary tract often may be located by giving the patient small barium-soaked cotton pledgets or swallows of barium cream. Nonopaque foreign bodies in other parts of the body sometimes are located by injecting radio-opaque liquids into draining sinus tracts.

Opaque foreign bodies, common in war time, may be found and localized by various methods. The simplest is by roentgenoscopic and roentgenographic examination in two planes at right angles to each other. Other methods include parallax and triangulation. The detection and localization of small metallic bodies in the eye may be performed with the aid of special apparatus. The procedure most generally employed involves examining the patient's eye in accurate relationship to two fixed objects placed at a known distance from the cornea. The data obtained from two films made at different angles are transferred to a special ruled chart, and the position of the body indicated in three different planes with an accuracy of less than one millimeter.

Protection against unnecessary or excessive exposure to X-rays or radium rays is of the utmost importance for patient, operating personnel, and radiologist. Protection against excessive exposure from the direct beam is now well established in responsible offices and departments by methods which include careful calibration of the apparatus, adequate distance between tube and patient's skin, use of lead-protected shockproof tubes, suitable diaphragms, and filters.

Protection against radiation scattered from the patient or the X-ray table is often more difficult but, unfortunately, sometimes is overlooked. The best way to achieve this protection is to use as small a beam as possible in examining patients, to work as expeditiously as is consistent with thoroughness, and to stay at the maximum distance or behind the safest barrier available. Protective barriers usually are made of lead or concrete. If workers are not safeguarded properly they may develop injury to the blood or reproductive system with consequent dangers of anemia, leukemia, or sterility. Permissible doses of radiant energy and detailed rules for protection are available in the numerous special handbooks of the National Bureau of Standards (Washington 25, D.C.).

X-RAYS IN TREATMENT

X-rays are of considerable significance in the treatment of a large number of diseases, ranging from simple infections such as ringworm of the scalp to serious processes such as cancer. The physician performing Roentgen therapy must strive to be as careful in the calibration and handling of his apparatus as a physicist, and as accurate in the application of his rays as a surgeon is when applying his knife. The therapist has at his disposal a wide variety of equipment supplying low-voltage beams for superficial treatment (40 to 100 kilovolt), intermediate voltage for more deeply seated lesions (120 to 150 kilovolt), high voltage for deep-seated lesions (180 to 220 kilovolt) and, finally, extra-high voltage for a few selected conditions or for biological research (400 to 70,000 kilovolt). He must select a filter suited to the procedure desired, varying from less than 1 millimeter of aluminum up to as much as 5 millimeters of lead. He calculates his dose in roentgens, and delivers small doses to most inflammatory or benign conditions, and very high doses to certain localized malignant lesions. A small dose ranges from 10 to 100 roentgens and may need to be repeated at intervals for weeks or even months. For example, generalized acne vulgaris may require weekly doses of 100 roentgens for three months. On the other hand a small localized cancer may require from 3 to 6 thousand roentgens delivered either at one session or, depending on the amount of associated infection and similar complications, in several sessions. The essential effect of X and gamma rays on the tissues is a destructive one. Cancer cells are slightly more sensitive to such radiations than are normal cells, and for this reason it is possible to destroy some cancers without permanent injury to the normal surrounding tissues.

The following is a partial list of conditions in which X-rays or gamma rays are of value: Inflammatory diseases of the skin and adjacent tissues; certain thickenings of the skin (plantar warts, keratoses); disturbed function of certain glands such as salivary and thyroid (hyperthyroidism); many benign and malignant tumor conditions.

Just as the mere possession of a knife does not make you a surgeon, so the possession of X-ray apparatus or radium does not make you a radiation therapist. The safe and efficient application of radiation methods in disease requires as much skill and even more training than many types of surgery. It also requires recognition of the fact that there are many conditions far better treated by nonradiological methods and a few which actually are rendered worse by Roentgen treatment.

The rays may be applied to human tissues by a variety of methods including external application of the beam, internal (intracavitary) application, interstitial application (that is, direct insertion of radium or radon seeds into the tissues), and various combinations of these methods, all designed to deliver the involved tissues a specific planned radiation dose.

FUTURE DEVELOPMENTS

The world has seen tremendous advances in the X-ray field during the past 65 years but there still are numerous developments, both in apparatus and technique, to which physicists and physicians are looking forward. These include the following:

1. More efficient recording media, including improved film emulsions, processing equipment, and fluorescent screens.
2. Improved simplified exposure meters and automatic timers.
3. Finer focal-spot diagnostic tubes.
4. Greatly improved fluoroscopes, perhaps an electron fluoroscope, and, as a result, better, safer X-ray motion pictures.
5. More widespread use of X-rays in teaching and in preventive medicine (including the installation of X-ray units in morgues to aid in research and routine autopsy work).
6. Improved methods of calculating the size and depth of tumors, so that radiation beams may be still more accurately aimed.
7. Improved selection of patients for both diagnosis and treatment (to reduce unnecessary expense and unnecessary exposure of human tissues — especially the reproductive organs — to X-rays or gamma rays).
8. Finally, and most important of all, the training of more and better radiologists, medical physicians specializing in X-ray diagnosis and treatment.

The value of X-rays to science in general and to medicine in particular is immense and ever increasing. They have provided us with a weapon by which we may search out the structure of matter, as well as the hidden components of the body. The diagnosis of innumerable disease conditions is dependent largely or entirely on X-ray examinations and the treatment of several types of disease likewise requires Roentgen irradiation. The debt of mankind to Roentgen and his fellow workers in the field of physics and engineering cannot easily be repaid.

W. F. G. SWANN

The Story of Cosmic Rays

[FROM THE SMITHSONIAN REPORT FOR 1956*]

THE STORY *of X-rays discussed in the two previous articles has a refreshing simplicity compared with the complexity of cosmic-ray investigation. This highly penetrating radiation, arriving at the earth from all directions, was first observed more than 50 years ago, but in spite of intensive study by many leading physicists, its origin is still not definitely established.*

The author of the present summary of present-day opinion regarding cosmic rays is Dr. W. F. G. Swann, Director Emeritus of the Bartol Research Foundation of the Franklin Institute, previously professor of physics at several leading American universities, a former president of the American Physical Society, and an officer at various times of American and British scientific societies. It might be in order to warn readers that a careful perusal of this article will involve rather strenuous intellectual exercise, for the subject has become highly involved. It has been learned that what we observe is not the primary radiation coming in from outer space, but in part the debris of atomic particles resulting from the bombardment of atoms in our atmosphere by the cosmic rays. The subject is further complicated by the bending and reflection of the

* Revised as of December 1959 by insertion of addendum at end of article.

primary radiation by the magnetic fields of stars and galaxies. But the entire subject is of such elemental importance and potential usefulness to mankind that its understanding is well worth considerable effort.

T HE ATMOSPHERE is, to an extremely small extent, a conductor of electricity, and we know that such a condition results from the presence of charged atoms called ions, with positive and negative charges. These occur in practically equal numbers. The positive ions are those atoms that have lost a negatively charged particle — an electron — and the negative ions are those that have acquired the negative charges lost by other atoms. As a result of mutual attraction, the negative ions are continually returning their negative charges to atoms that have lost such charges, so that if the continued existence of a "state of ionization" is to be maintained, there must be present some agency that continually detaches electrons from atoms. Such agencies are, in part, the radiations that are emitted by the normal radioactive contamination of the atmosphere. However, such agencies are confined to low altitudes, so that to account for ionization at high altitudes, where, indeed, it is greater than at low altitudes, we must invoke some other agency. This agency is the cosmic radiation which, at first, was assumed to be a single kind of radiation coming into our atmosphere from above.

The simple concept of a single type of radiation entering the atmosphere and being responsible for the phenomena observed had to be modified as time progressed. The situation, as we have it today, is much more complicated. We have been led to believe that there is a "primary radiation" consisting for the most part of positively charged hydrogen atoms, and that the radiation, on entering our atmosphere, bombards the atoms of the atmosphere with the resulting emission of all sorts of other atomic particles which, in their totality, constitute what we *observe* as the cosmic radiation.

ATOMS AND ELEMENTARY PARTICLES

Atoms and their parts. — An atom of matter consists, essentially, of two parts — an inner core, composed of positively charged particles called protons, and uncharged particles called neutrons. Around this core we have a cloud of negative electrons.

Hydrogen, the lightest of the atoms, has in its normal state only one proton in its core or nucleus, and attendant upon this is a single electron. Helium has two protons and two neutrons in its core. Uranium, until recently the heaviest element known, has, in its nucleus, 92 protons. In the case of one kind of radium there are 143 neutrons, while in another kind there are 146 neutrons. It is the number of *protons* that determines the *chemical* nature of the element. Atoms having the same number of protons but different numbers of neutrons are called isotopes of one another.

Subsidiary elementary particles. — Although neutrons, protons, and negative electrons form the only permanent constituents of the atom, other particles come into existence during periods of drastic perturbation such as occur when a primary cosmic ray or one of its descendants strikes an atom of air.

First, we have a particle called the positron, which is the counterpart of the negative electron, having the same mass, but carrying an electric charge equal and opposite to that of the negative electron. Sometimes it is called a positive electron.

Other important particles are the mesotrons. The mesotrons are peculiar in the sense that they have but a finite life and die in due course without the intervention of any external agency.

When the mesotrons were first discovered, it was thought that they were all of one kind, but as knowledge has advanced, it now appears that there are several kinds, which are in part related to one another like child and parent, or brother and sister. When a proton of high energy enters our atmosphere, collisions with the atoms of the air result in the proton's disintegration and the formation of mesotrons which are, as it were, born from its ashes. When a heavy atom enters the atmosphere, its individual protons suffer a similar fate, with the resulting production of mesotrons. The neutrons of the atomic nuclei seem to be preserved from a like fate, but they are not completely immune, because a neutron freed from its home in an atomic nucleus sacrifices its right of permanent existence and dies after a period of about 20 minutes.

On page 226 we shall return to a fuller discussion of the individuals of the mesotron family.

In phenomena of the kind we are discussing, another particle has entered the picture, the neutrino. Its presence has only been inferred, but never observed in the ordinary sense of the word. As is well known, physicists place great faith in the conservation of energy and momentum in atomic processes. However, it appears that in some of these processes, adding up all the contributions of the various particles to the energy after the occurrence in question gives a sum less than that obtained by adding up the various contributions before the occurrence. And so the concept of the neutrino was invented to play the role of the thief who stole the energy.

Photons. — The term "photon" is used to characterize all of those particles that are associated with wavelike properties. In particular, it comprises ordinary light rays, ultraviolet rays, X-rays, and the so-called gamma rays from radium.

There was a time when these radiations were thought to be of a wave nature, the wave concerned spreading out into space from the place of origin with ever-decreasing intensity.

Early in the present century, radiations of this type began to present a great puzzle to the student of physics. In some respects the radiations acted like waves, as already stated, but in others they acted like particles.

The concept of spreading waves is inevitably bound up with diminution of the wave's intensity with distance from the point of its origin. On the other hand, the radiations we have classed as photons, while exhibiting wavelike characteristics in certain phenomena, masquerade in other instances like bullets shot from a gun. Apart from effects resulting from the resistance of the medium, such a bullet is just as potent after traveling 100 yards as it is after 1 yard. In the case of a battery of such guns firing in all directions from a fort, the chance of getting hit would diminish with the distance from the fort. But if one did get hit, he would be

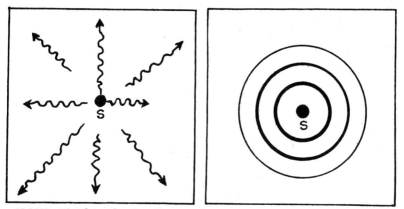

ILLUS. 37—*These sketches illustrate the two concepts of the nature of light:*
At the right, waves diminish in intensity as they spread from a
source; at the left, wavelike particles retain their energy as they
travel outward.

just as dead if hit at half a mile as he would be if hit at 100 feet.

The mathematical physicist has formulated his ideas and theories in such a manner that he is not disturbed by the apparent paradox in the coexistence of the bulletlike properties and wavelike properties, but he has not succeeded in presenting them in such a form as to give contentment to the layman. Fortunately for our purpose, these matters need not cause us serious trouble. It will suffice for us to think of these radiations, which in the aggregate we have called photons, as particle-like in nature; they differ in energy, however, not by the normal differences of velocity, but by some other characteristics customarily associated with definite frequencies of vibration. In other words, their velocities are all the same (in a vacuum), and their frequency of vibration determines their energy content.

FURTHER PROPERTIES OF THE
FUNDAMENTAL PARTICLES

Ionization — Consider the behavior of a charged particle in creating ions as it passes through a gas. It detaches electrons from the atoms which it approaches sufficiently closely, and these electrons form the basis for the creation of ions, as we discussed on page 220. If the charged particle is moving very rapidly, with a speed comparable with but not too nearly equal to the velocity of light, and if it carries the equivalent of one electronic charge, it detaches from atoms about 30 electrons per centimeter of path at atmospheric pressure.

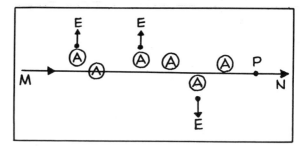

ILLUS. 38—P *is a high-energy charged particle pursuing the line of flight MN. It affects atoms along its path and frees the electrons, E.*

By this act, the particle loses energy as it progresses through the gas, and the more energy it has lost the more rapidly does it spend that which remains.

Particles moving more nearly with the speed of light, that is, faster than those that begin by detaching about 30 electrons per centimeter of path, are even more active. Thus, the charged particle spends its energy freely when it is very rich (moving nearly with the speed of light) and when it is very poor (near the end of its path). It is most conservative in its expenditures when it is moderately rich.

The ionization produced by a particle per centimeter of its path depends to a first approximation only upon its velocity and its charge. Doubling the charge increases the ionization per centimeter of path by a factor of four.

Pair production. — A phenomenon more drastic than ionization occurs when very rapidly moving charged particles collide with atoms, and associated with it is a phenomenon resulting from the collision of high-energy photons with atoms. The charged particles concerned in this matter are almost exclusively electrons, for although, in principle, heavier particles can operate in an analogous manner, the effect is so much more prominent in the case of the lighter electron that we can ignore it in the other cases.

Start with a high-energy photon which finds itself directed toward an atom. This photon possesses the characteristic of becoming mathematically irritated when it comes into the vicinity of the atom. Existence as a photon becomes mathematically intolerable, but nature has provided for it the option of changing its state of existence by allowing it to materialize into two oppositely charged electrons; these share the energy of the photon between them, but not necessarily in equal amount.

Each of the pair of electrons thus produced pursues its course, and if either has sufficient energy, when entering the domain of another atom it will jerk that atom in such a manner as to give rise to a new photon. This photon, if of sufficient energy, will repeat the history of its ancestors, giving rise to two more charged particles. The process would go on and on were it not for the fact that each of these progeny has only a small share of the energy of the original photon; and when the energy of a particle falls below about 10 million electron volts, the chance of its reproducing itself in this manner becomes infinitesimal. (An electron volt is the energy gained by an electron in falling through a drop of potential of one volt.)

Once the energy of an electron has fallen below the value necessary to carry on the process of photon emission and pair production, its remaining energy is gradually drained away from it by ionization and it loses the characteristics of a high-energy ray.

In the light of the foregoing, it may be expected that if a high-energy photon or electron enters our atmosphere, or comes into existence in the upper atmosphere as a result of the primary cosmic rays, this electron or photon will initiate the phenomenon of pair production. As we descend into the atmosphere, the number of electrons passing through a unit area will at first increase, attaining finally a maximum, after which it will decrease. This is because there is a birth rate of electrons resulting from the pair production and a death rate resulting from electrons falling to an energy at which they are no longer able to perpetuate the process. Highest in the atmosphere is a region where the birth rate exceeds the death rate; below that the two are equal and the number of rays is a maximum; further descent takes us to regions where the death rate exceeds the birth rate and the number of electrons diminishes.

As we proceed in the study of cosmic rays, we shall find that pair production plays a significant role in the phenomena observed.

Properties of mesotrons. — The need for the existence of a charged particle intermediate in mass between the electron and the photon was first sensed by the Japanese physicist Yukawa, as a result of efforts to understand the nature of the forces that bind the particles of an atomic nucleus together. From purely theoretical considerations, Yukawa was able to calculate the mass and mean life of the particle in question: about 300 times the mass of the electron and a mean life of the order of $\frac{1}{100}$ of a microsecond (a microsecond is a millionth of a second).

Not long after Yukawa's calculations were made, it was found that the principal constituents that we observe as cosmic rays at sea level are charged particles having a mass of the general order of magnitude of that of Yukawa's predictions, but these particles have a mean life of the order of 100 times that predicted by him.

Of course, the discrepancy of 100 times in the mean life was embarrassing to the logic of the subject, but physicists were happy to have experimental verification of Yukawa's work to the extent of the actual existence of any kind of particle intermediate in mass between the electron and the proton, and having any kind of finite life expectancy. It was hoped that time would clear up the discrepancy, possibly by modifications of the theory.

Time did, indeed, clear up the discrepancy, but not quite in the way anticipated. The particle found in cosmic rays was not Yukawa's mesotron, but rather a child of that mesotron. Before very long, experiment revealed that there did indeed exist in nature a particle, now called the *pi-mesotron* (π-mesotron), of mass about 300 times the electron's mass and with a mean life of the order of a hundred millionth of a second, as predicted by Yukawa. The pimesotrons are usually brought into existence as the result of the bombardment of atomic nuclei by high-energy charged particles such as the primary cosmic rays which enter our atmosphere from outer space. This kind of mesotron can have either a positive or negative charge.

Experiment has further revealed the existence of uncharged mesotrons of mass about 300 electron units; these are also called pi-
mesotrons. They are produced by bombardment of atomic nuclei
by high-energy particles, and have a life expectancy of the order
of 10^{-13} second. A neutral pi-mesotron decays into two photons of
high energy — gamma rays.

The child of the pi-mesotron is called a *mu-mesotron* (μ-meso-
tron), and it is the result of the death of a pi-mesotron, which is
thought to be accompanied also by the emission of a neutrino. The
mu-mesotron plays the most important role in cosmic-ray phenomena. Being a charged particle, it, of course, ionizes like any other
charged particle. However, it has a rest mass 210 times as great as
that of the electron, and so an energy 210 times that of the electron for the same velocity. Moreover, on account of its large mass,

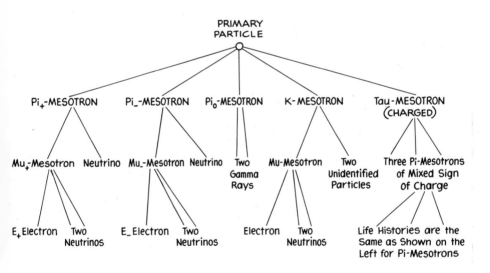

ILLUS. 39—*The descendants of a high-energy particle may include those
shown here. Any one such primary particle does not, in general,
give rise to all the types of mesotrons in the second stage.*

it is relieved of the duty of pair production and loses energy only by ionization phenomena. As a result of this, the mu-mesotron can travel very much farther through matter than can an electron of the same energy.

The mu-mesotron, when traveling with a velocity small compared with that of light, has an average life of only about 2.3 microseconds. Even if it traveled with the velocity of light and had only this average lifetime, it could not go more than about 700 meters before death overtook it. However, it results that the theory of relativity demands and experiment confirms that the lifetime of the particle shall increase with its energy. As a result of this, many cosmic-ray mesotrons have lives hundreds or thousands of times 2.3 microseconds, so that, so far as life is concerned, they could travel right through the atmosphere and to distances far below.

ELEMENTARY PARTICLES OF MATTER

Particle	Mass in electron masses	Average lifetime against spontaneous decay	Products of spontaneous decay°
Electron	1	Stable	
Proton	1,845	Stable	
Neutron	1,848	18.5 ± 3.6 minutes	Proton and electron
Positron	1	Stable	
Positive mu-mesotron	210	2.3×10^{-6} sec.	Electron and two neutrinos
Negative mu-mesotron	210	2.3×10^{-6} sec.	Electron and two neutrinos
Positive pi-mesotron	276	About 10^{-8} sec.	Mu-mesotron and neutrino
Negative pi-mesotron	276	About 10^{-8} sec.	Mu-mesotron and neutrino
Neutral pi-mesotron	264	Less than 10^{-13} sec.	Two photons
K-particle	About 1,100	About 10^{-9} sec.	One mu-mesotron and two neutral particles
Tau-particle	977	Greater than 10^{-9} sec.	Three pi-mesotrons
Chi-mesotron†	900–1,500	Greater than 10^{-9} sec.	Pi-mesotron and one neutral particle
Kappa-mesotron†	Less than 1,400	Greater than 10^{-9} sec.	Mu-mesotron
Zeta-particle	537	Greater than 10^{-10} sec.	Two pi-mesotrons
Positive V-particle†	Uncertain	Less than 10^{-9} sec.	Uncertain
Negative V-particle†	Uncertain	Less than 10^{-9} sec.	Uncertain
Neutral V-particle	Uncertain	Less than 10^{-10} sec.	Probably mesotrons and protons
Photon	0	Stable	None
Neutrino	0	Stable	None

° In general, these products are accompanied with release of energy in kinetic form and in amount sufficient to conserve mass.

† It is uncertain how far the positive and negative V-particles are distinct from the chi- and the kappa-particles.

The death of a mu-mesotron is accompanied by birth of an electron — positive or negative — and two neutrinos.

Finally, in the realm of cosmic-ray particles there have appeared the *K-mesotron*, of around 1,100 electron mass units, and another heavy particle, the *tau-mesotron* (τ-mesotron) of about 900 electron mass units. The tau-mesotron is unstable and is believed to decay into three pi-mesotrons.

It is of interest to observe that even the neutron, when in free space, is unstable and has a life expectancy of only about 18½ minutes, after which it changes to a proton by ejecting an electron in the mysterious process of dividing nothing into two halves, throwing out the negative half (a negative electron) and retaining the positive half (a proton).

Of the various mesotrons, only the mu-mesotron plays a significant part in the phenomena observed in cosmic rays. However, from the standpoint of what one may call cosmic-ray genealogy, a recognition and understanding of the other particles is necessary.

COSMIC RAYS IN THE ATMOSPHERE

The primary cosmic radiation. — The primary cosmic rays appear to contain samples of every kind of nonradioactive atom in the universe. The chief constituent is the proton, the nucleus of the hydrogen atom. The percentages of the elements vary according to different observers, but from representative data they are in the ratio of 4,000 particles of hydrogen to 1,000 of helium, to 35 of carbon, nitrogen, and oxygen, to 10 of all nuclei with atomic numbers greater than 10.

There can be no mesotrons in the primary radiation, for the mean life of the mu-mesotron, the longest-lived of the mesotron family, is only 2.3 microseconds when the particle is at rest, and even with energies as great as 100 billion electron volts, the mean life is only $\frac{2}{1000}$ of a second. There is no place from which the mesotrons could have come, for the nearest body that could reasonably be a candidate for supplying them is the sun, and a particle traveling with the velocity of light itself would take more than 8 minutes to reach us from the sun.

Lifetime considerations rule out even neutrons as possible components of the primary radiation, since neutrons have a mean life of the order of 18.5 minutes. The sun is the only body from which they could reach us, and if they came from the sun in appreciable amount, there would be a much larger change in their intensity from day to night than experiment reveals. Unlike charged particles, whose paths can be bent by the earth's magnetic field, neutrons could not reach the side of the earth opposite their point of origin.

The production of mesotrons. — When the protons of the primary radiation enter our atmosphere, they very rapidly disintegrate into mesotrons, as the result of collisions with the nuclei of atoms. The protons disappear so rapidly by this process that only about a third of them remain at an altitude where the pressure is $\frac{1}{10}$ of an atmosphere.

Even in the case of the heavier atoms contained in cosmic rays, it is the protons in their nuclei that are responsible for giving birth to mesotrons; and since mesotrons are the most important constituent of the rays that we observe at lower altitudes, a helium atom, containing two protons, is twice as effective in producing mesotrons as is a single proton. An atom like iron, with 26 protons in its nucleus, is 26 times as effective as is the proton itself. If iron atoms, for example, were only 1 percent as numerous as free protons, they would nevertheless contribute about one-third as many mesotrons as do the free protons. Thus, despite the relatively small percentage of atoms of high atomic weight, it turns out that 50 percent of the mesotrons produced in the atmosphere come from primaries that are heavier than protons.

When a proton, either free or in combination in a nucleus, enters the atmosphere and collides with the nucleus of an atom of air, it is probable that, in the first instance, pi-mesotrons are produced, as shown in the genealogical chart on page 227. A slowly moving pi-mesotron with a mean life of 10^{-8} second would travel only a meter or so before disintegrating to form a mu-mesotron. A slow mu-mesotron, with a mean life of the order of 2.3 microseconds, would go less than 700 meters before disintegrating into an electron.

Mesotrons of higher energy live longer and penetrate farther, so that a mesotron of 10 billion electron volts would live for about $\frac{2}{10000}$ of a second and in that time could travel 60 kilometers. Thus, from mean-life considerations alone it would have no difficulty in penetrating the whole atmosphere. As a matter of fact, only about 1.3 billion volts of its energy are necessary to allow for all the ionization it would cause on such a journey, so that neither ionization loss of energy nor mean-life considerations would prevent such a mesotron from reaching the earth's surface. Indeed, some of the mesotrons are produced with such high energies that they can penetrate far more than the thickness of the earth's atmosphere, and cosmic-ray intensity has a measurable value at depths below the earth's surface comparable with 250 meters of water.

Starting in the outer regions of the atmosphere, we have only the primaries. These decrease rapidly with descent, by the production of mesotrons, so that the mesotron intensity rises as we descend into the atmosphere until, at a depth of about $\frac{1}{10}$ of the whole atmosphere, the rate of production of mesotrons balances the rate of decay and there is a maximum in the mesotron intensity. Below this point, the disappearance of mesotrons (as a result of mean-life considerations enhanced by energy loss) exceeds the rate of formation, and the mesotron intensity declines and continues to decline with further descent. The high-energy mesotrons penetrate far, while the low-energy mesotrons, either by decay or by coming to rest as a result of energy loss, travel only shorter distances.

The production of electrons. — How does the number of electrons change with height? Near the extreme upper limits of the atmosphere cosmic-ray electrons are very few, because the mesotrons that breed them have not yet been produced by the primaries in sufficient number. The mu-mesotrons that are produced with low energy in the first tenth of the atmosphere die very near the places where they are born, giving rise to electrons. Higher-energy mesotrons, which can travel farther, do not die as rapidly and therefore do not produce electrons as copiously as do the low-energy mesotrons. Therefore, many more electrons will be formed in the higher regions of the atmosphere than in the lower.

Each electron that is produced, however, goes through the process of pair production (discussed earlier, on pages 224–225) and gives rise to progeny which increase in numbers as we descend from the point where the original parents were formed. The increase continues until it becomes balanced by the loss of electrons, when the ionization that they produce reduces their energy below the point at which the electrons can reproduce themselves. Thus, each electron formed has its own little genealogical history involving rise in progeny to a maximum with descent, followed by a decline in numbers with further descent. A combination of the life histories of all the parent electrons produced near the top of the atmosphere thus results in a rise of the electron intensity as we descend, a maximum being reached at a depth corresponding to about $\frac{1}{10}$ of the atmosphere, after which the electron intensity diminishes rapidly with further descent.

The situation is such that practically none of the parent electrons produced in the higher regions of the atmosphere can succeed in having any progeny at the earth's surface. In fact, a parent electron would have to have an energy of some 10 trillion electron volts in the outer regions of the atmosphere to have a single offspring at the earth's surface!

Such electrons as we find in the lower atmosphere come partly from the relatively rare deaths of fast-moving mesotrons and from the deaths of mesotrons that have been slowed down by ionization energy losses. Another source of electrons is closely related to ionization itself: If a mesotron passes sufficiently near an electron in an atom, it may hurl that electron out with an energy very high compared with the normal energy given to electrons by mesotrons in ordinary ionization. Electrons shot out of atoms with high energy in this manner are referred to as *knock-on electrons*, and they contribute appreciably to the electron component of the radiation measured, particularly at low altitudes.

Neutrons. — It is of importance to observe that disintegration of the protons in a primary incident atom leaves free neutrons, which should therefore be fairly plentiful in the places where proton disintegration occurs. Experiment, indeed, reveals the fact that neutrons do exist in the atmosphere, and their intensity mounts very rapidly as high altitudes are approached. It is not at present known whether the neutrons in high-energy atoms disintegrate on collision as protons do, but even if such is the case, we may expect to find some neutrons that have escaped destruction of this kind by becoming reduced in energy in the collision process to the point at which they no longer invite destruction by such a process.

Extensive showers. — The phenomena above are the main contributions to what we measure as the cosmic radiation. However, there are other comparatively rare but very interesting phenomena. In extensive showers, some of the rays observed at sea level arrive so close together in time, in spite of wide separation in their places of arrival, as to suggest that they have a common origin, probably in one very high-energy primary particle. P. Auger, who has studied these matters intensively, states that such showers of rays may correspond to more than a million particles arriving simultaneously over an area of 25 acres. If we should imagine these particles to originate through pair production from a single high-energy electron, it would be necessary to assume for that electron an energy between 10^{15} and 10^{16} electron volts. Taking all losses into consideration, as high as 10^{18} electron volts for the parent particle has been estimated as necessary to account for some of the phenomena observed.

Nuclear disintegration caused by cosmic rays. — Another matter of great interest in nuclear physics, although possibly of subsidiary interest to cosmic-ray students, is nuclear disintegration produced by the rays. The neutrons in the upper atmosphere doubtless play a significant role in promoting such nuclear disintegrations.

It has been customary to classify the events observed according to the number of prongs which emanate from the centers of collision of the rays with the nuclei of the atmospheric atoms, as seen in sensitive films. Study of these tracks, their angular spread, their ranges in matter, combined with the fundamental principles of the conservation of energy and momentum during collision, serve to enhance our knowledge in that most mysterious realm of nuclear theory that involves the nature of nuclear forces.

THE EFFECT OF TERRESTRIAL, SOLAR, AND
GALACTIC MAGNETIC FIELDS

The primary cosmic rays appear to come toward our earth uniformly from all directions, or nearly so. The earth is a huge magnet, with a magnetic field of small intensity but large extent, so
that the paths of charged particles approaching the earth are bent.
Consideration of the influence of the magnetic field leads to the
following conclusion: Particles of the same charge and momentum
(relativistic mass times velocity) are indistinguishable as regards
the effect of the magnetic field upon them.

While the student of cosmic rays usually speaks of particles in
terms of their momenta, the kinetic energy is a quantity more famil-
liar to the layman. It is, however, less simply related to the bending effect in a magnetic field. Thus, for a given energy, heavy particles are bent less in their paths than are light particles.

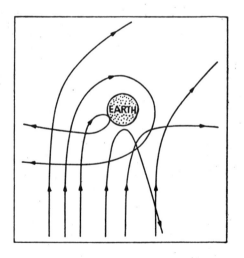

*ILLUS. 40—Paths of primary cosmic rays (in this case protons with 15 billion
electron volts energy) as they are deflected by the earth's magnetic
field. The paths are drawn in the plane of the earth's magnetic
equator, with the north pole upward from the paper.*

Any charged particle, such as a proton, has to have a certain minimum energy before it can reach the earth's vicinity at all without being bent back into space by the magnetic field. That minimum energy amounts to 14 billion electron volts for a proton entering vertically at the magnetic equator. It gets less and less as we proceed toward the magnetic poles until, theoretically, at the poles themselves particles with infinitesimal energy could reach the outer bounds of the atmosphere.

At any given geomagnetic latitude (we shall henceforth call this simply *latitude*), the minimum energy for entry of positive particles into the atmosphere varies as the direction of entry varies. It is greatest for the east and least for the west, the value for the vertical being intermediate in amount.

There was a time when a strong belief existed that the primary particles were photons and not charged particles at all. J. C. Clay's discovery of the variation of cosmic-ray intensity with latitude, a discovery confirmed by a series of worldwide measurements by A. H. Compton and his associates, first led to the conclusion that there were at least some charged particles in the primary radiation. Later, as the matter was more deeply studied in connection with intensities from different directions, it appeared that there was no room for anything else but charged particles and, further, that the particles were positively charged.

Of course, the latitude effect is greatly complicated by the fact that our observations are made in the atmosphere itself. Suppose that observations could be made at an altitude so high that a negligible amount of air existed above. Then we might expect that the intensity of the radiation would mount continually as we passed from the magnetic equator to the magnetic pole and included in our measurements more and more of the less energetic radiation that can reach the atmosphere at higher latitudes. But if we should observe at a depth in the atmosphere, and even if we could be sure that we were measuring only the primary cosmic rays, we should expect that the increase of intensity with latitude would continue only until a latitude was reached at which the low-energy rays, deflected away by the magnetic field below that latitude, would still be unable to reach us because they were stopped by the atmosphere.

From this viewpoint the variation with latitude of, let us say, the vertical intensity of the primary cosmic rays might take the form shown in the accompanying simple diagram (Illus. 41). The curve *ABC* would hold at very high altitudes; *ABD* would apply at a place where there is an appreciable amount of the at-

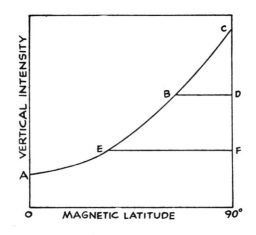

ILLUS. 41—The effect of absorption by the atmosphere on the intensity of cosmic rays at various latitudes.

mosphere above; *AEF*, where there is more of the atmosphere above, and so on. We might thus expect that the knee of the latitude curve — the place where the horizontal portion starts — would occur at a latitude which was greater the greater the altitude.

Now the simplicity of the foregoing picture is disturbed by the fact that the knee does not seem to vary with latitude as the altitude is varied, but seems to occur around 50° latitude for all altitudes. This led to the view that the origin of the knee was not to be explained by the absorption of low-energy rays by the atmosphere, but by something outside the atmosphere, something that creates, for the energy spectrum, a lower limit of energy which is nevertheless sufficiently great to permit penetration of the whole atmosphere. Under such conditions, the intensity-versus-latitude curve would show, at all altitudes, a knee corresponding to this energy.

To solve this paradox, it was suggested that the knee of the latitude curve owed its origin to the sun's magnetic field. The bending of the paths of the rays near the earth, that is, within a few earth radii, is caused mainly by the earth's magnetic field, which is here considerably stronger than the field of the sun. At greater distances from the earth, however, the sun's magnetic field could predominate.

Consider a sphere containing the earth's orbit and centered at the sun. Then, neglecting the influence of the earth's magnetic field, we can ask what energy a cosmic ray of assigned type must have to enter that sphere at all in the vicinity of the earth's orbit, which orbit lies roughly in the plane of the sun's magnetic equator. No rays of energy less than this amount could reach the earth's orbit at all. If this energy is enough to penetrate the atmosphere, we would expect, as found, that the cosmic rays falling upon the earth would increase in intensity with increase of latitude from the equator only to the point at which all the rays permitted access to the earth's orbit by the sun had been received by the earth. Increase of latitude beyond this point would yield no further rays because there would be no more rays. The knee of the latitude curve would occur at a definite latitude which would be the same for all altitudes.

The foregoing considerations become complicated by what happens to the primary cosmic rays as they enter our atmosphere. However, a fairly clean-cut story appears if observations are made so high in the atmosphere that down to that depth nothing in particular has happened to the primary rays. At such altitudes, and for the case where the primary radiation contains rays of all degrees of smallness in energy, we should expect the intensity to show a continual increase with latitude right up to the poles. (However, the matter is not quite as simple as here stated because even the small amount of atmosphere above the apparatus at high altitudes, and indeed the absorbing material in the apparatus itself, places a lower limit on the energy of the rays that can be observed.)

If the intensity of the magnetic field of the sun at its magnetic pole is known, we can calculate its value at the earth's orbit, and we can calculate the energy below which no rays are to be found striking the earth's atmosphere. We can then compute the corres- ponding latitude on the earth at which further increase of latitude would yield no additional rays, as these would have energies lower than those permitted by the sun to be present.

The magnitude of the sun's magnetic field has been debated for a long time, and particularly within recent years. Optical measure- ments of the Zeeman effect led, about 40 years ago, to the con- clusion that the sun had a field of about 50 gauss at its pole. If the sun acted like an ordinary magnet, the corresponding field in the earth's vicinity would prevent protons reaching us if they had less energy than 3 billion electron volts, which is the energy for entry through the earth's magnetic field at the latitude of 50° geo- magnetic. Consequently, on this basis, we should expect that even at the outer limits of the atmosphere there would be no increase of intensity with latitude from 50° to the pole.

However, recent experiments by M. A. Pomerantz, under the auspices of the Bartol Research Foundation, the Office of Naval Research, and the National Geographic Society, have shown that over the range of latitude from 52° to 69° there is an increase of 46 percent in the vertical primary cosmic radiation intensity. Also, this radiation is composed of rays of such small energies that they could not possibly have come to us from outer space through the sun's magnetic field if it had more than 6 percent of the strength originally assumed from the Zeeman effect.

This argument should be accepted with reservation. There is in- creasing evidence that some primary rays may come to us from the sun itself, and such rays might reach us in spite of the sun's magnetic field because their short journey to us would not permit enough bending in their paths to keep them away from us. At the present time, the whole question of the magnitude of the sun's magnetic field and its bearing upon the primary cosmic rays calls for further elucidation.

Astronomers have come to doubt the existence of a solar mag- netic field as high as 25 or 50 gauss at the poles of the sun. Indeed, G. Thiessen, who was originally one of the strongest supporters of the earlier value for the sun's field, concluded in 1949 that a strict analysis of the original data, while not denying the existence of the larger field, does not support such a field with any certainty. Moreover, his recent careful observations by improved methods, and those of others, using the new solar magnetograph, have led to a solar value of only about one gauss, and in the opposite direction to that formerly found.

On the other hand, observations of the solar field at one time do not necessarily guarantee its value at another. This warning is important, for some stars are known with certainty to possess variable magnetic fields. H. W. Babcock found in 1948 that the star HD 125248 has a magnetic field of 6,000 gauss at its pole, a field that reverses itself to a comparable value of opposite sign in a period of about 10 days. In *Sky and Telescope* for March 1950, Otto Struve presented a detailed discussion of "Stars as Magnets."

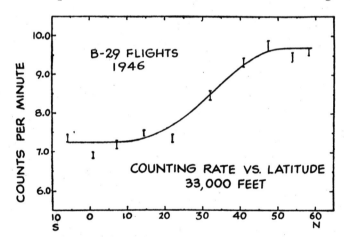

ILLUS. 42—*How cosmic-ray intensity varies with latitude is shown by these measurements made under the author's direction in 1946 with airborne Geiger counter trains. As the number of counts per minute varies, each measured intensity has a statistical uncertainty, indicated by the length of the vertical line representing it. Note the leveling off of the curve at about 50° latitude.*

Finally, in connection with cosmic magnetic fields, it has been suggested that the great galaxies of space may be the seats of magnetic fields. The magnetic fields in question are extremely small, of the order of 10^{-5} gauss, but their great extent makes them potent influences on the paths of the cosmic rays within the galaxy.

Theoretical considerations show that a charged particle coming to the boundaries of such a region would be turned back into the galaxy as though the latter were provided with a reflecting wall, and similar considerations operate to prevent any cosmic ray that is outside the galaxy from entering it. Thus, on such an assumption, the cosmic rays within the galaxy would remain imprisoned within it forever or until destruction through collision with atoms or with other material in the galaxy, such as the stars, terminated their existence.

THE ORIGIN OF THE PRIMARY COSMIC RADIATION

Early students of the primary cosmic radiation pictured it as distributed with equal intensity over the whole of galactic and intergalactic space. Such an idea is attended with considerable difficulty. Thus, R. D. Richtmyer and E. Teller have pointed out that on such a view the total energy carried by all cosmic-ray particles is much more than all the energy ever emitted by stars, together with their kinetic energy. In fact, it would be an energy less by only a few orders of magnitude than the total energy ($E = mc^2$) represented by all the matter in the universe.

Difficulties also arise as to how the supply of cosmic-ray particles can be maintained, since it is necessary to allow for a continual loss as a result of their collisions with atoms in space.

Such considerations have led to the general concept of an extensive magnetic field confining cosmic radiation to a definite region, a galaxy for example, as just mentioned above. Such a theory removes the necessity of extending the rays to the whole of intergalactic space, and avoids the enormous amount of energy that such extension would impute to cosmic rays in the universe as a whole.

There are three general possibilities to account for the enormous energies of the rays themselves, from 10^{10} to as high as 10^{17} electron volts:

1. The particles may receive energy by relatively small forces acting over great distances.

2. They may receive energy in single acts associated with enormous forces.

3. The particles, with their energies, might be considered to have been born with the universe, their properties depending upon the circumstances associated with that event.

The third possibility, first propounded by the Canon Lemaitre, cannot very well be proved or disproved. At the time of the supposed origin of the universe, conditions may have been so drastically different from what they are now that in our ignorance we may assume almost anything to form a basis for the origin of the high energies.

The second category is deemed unlikely because we now know that the cosmic radiation contains particles much heavier than protons. Quantum theory demands that a process that could give them their energy in a single act would disintegrate them.

The first category, therefore, presents the natural field for explanation in terms of our present knowledge. This category may be divided into two classes, in one of which the energies are acquired little by little by processes that are primarily mechanical, while in the second the forces are primarily electrical. Of course, mechanical forces are usually electromagnetic in the last analysis, but it is convenient to distinguish between the processes that are very clearly the result of electromagnetic forces and those in which any electromagnetic feature is involved in more subtle form.

Mechanical methods. — Thus, in the mechanical realm we have effects of the pressure of light. For instance, L. Spitzer, Jr., has considered the acceleration of small particles under the influence of radiation pressure in the tremendous energy outburst of a supernova. He calculates that such particles can receive from a supernova outburst from 0.01 to 1.0 billion electron volts per nucleon (proton or neutron) of each particle, within an interval of a few hours to a few weeks.

It is also postulated that the particles are held within the galaxy by an extensive magnetic field. As a result of collisions with atomic nuclei in the galaxy, the particles which have escaped collisions with stellar bodies break up ultimately into nucleons. The neutrons soon change to protons because of their finite life expectancy, and the protons are lost finally by encounters with atomic nuclei or by striking large bodies like the earth. An equilibrium condition is set up in which the number of high-energy nucleons contributed to the galaxy per unit time is equal to the number lost by the aforesaid processes. By this means, a cosmic-ray intensity between 0.0001 and 0.01 of the measured intensity is predicted, depending upon assumptions as to the frequency of nuclear collisions in the galaxy.

E. Fermi, in 1949, suggested an intriguing mechanism which may be pictured in elementary fashion by thinking of a room containing gas molecules and many hard steel spheres flying about and rebounding from one another and from the walls of the room. It will be convenient to eliminate gravity temporarily during our meditations.

According to well-understood principles of thermodynamics, the spheres will, in the last analysis, lose their energies to the gas molecules and will finally come to a state of equilibrium in which the average translational energy of each sphere will be the same as that of a gas molecule. If the spheres are sizable, let us say 10 centimeters in radius, their average velocity will then be very small compared with that of the molecules. If, however, the spheres and the walls of the room are perfectly elastic, and if the spheres have considerable velocities initially, it will be a very long time before they get to this final state of equilibrium.

Meanwhile, the spheres will seek another quasi-stationary equilibrium in which they have a velocity distribution among themselves which is like that of the gas molecules, but with an average kinetic energy of each sphere enormous compared with that of one of the molecules. This kinetic energy will be approximately equal to the total original energy of the spheres divided by their number. In other words, the spheres will have a kind of macroscopic temperature of enormous amount which diminishes extremely slowly to the final temperature representative of the true equilibrium of both spheres and gas molecules.

The quasi-equilibrium of the spheres is not an accidental phenomenon, but is an inevitable consequence of the laws of dynamics as applied to the collisions between the spheres.

Suppose now that we imagine the molecules to be reduced in number so that the chances of molecules colliding with one an-

ILLUS. 43—A cosmic-ray cascade of 10 billion electron volts.

other are very much less than their chances of colliding with the
spheres. The molecules may become "ambitious" and seek, through
their collisions, to accommodate themselves to the kinetic energy
of the spheres, acquiring velocities much greater than those of the
spheres. This ambition, though at first sight fantastic, is not indeed
illogical under the specialized conditions we have assumed — dynamical laws require it.

In the Fermi mechanism our steel spheres are replaced by
bounded magnetic fields, associated with moving masses of gas in
the galaxies. A magnetic field of this kind is representative of a hard
elastic body, because an electric particle entering it is turned back
to the region from which it came, without any loss of energy as
measured in the frame of reference in which the magnetic field
is at rest.

However, there are certain difficulties in the Fermi mechanism.
A fast-moving charged particle loses energy by ionizing the other
atoms in its path; and while the density of matter in space is very
small, the loss of energy by this process more than offsets the
Fermi gain for low energies, where the ionization probability is
greater. Only when a particle has attained the lower range of
cosmic-ray energies is the Fermi mechanism capable of taking hold
to increase further the energy of the particle. In this matter, heavy
particles are at a disadvantage with respect to light particles.
Thus, the Fermi mechanism requires a kind of injector process to
get it started, such as the suggestion of Spitzer already cited.

Then, since the average energy gained by the mechanism is only
about 10 electron volts per collision, and since each particle would
have only about one collision per year, about 60 million years
would be necessary for a particle to acquire cosmic-ray energy.
During this period, it would have opportunities for collision with
the nucleus of some particle in the surrounding space, and such
a collision, as we know from the evidence presented by protons
entering our atmosphere, would result in destruction of the particle and its conversion into mesotrons, which disappear because
of their finite life.

As our quantitative knowledge becomes more complete, the
strength of the evidence against the Fermi mechanism increases
also, one of the most potent difficulties arising from the time

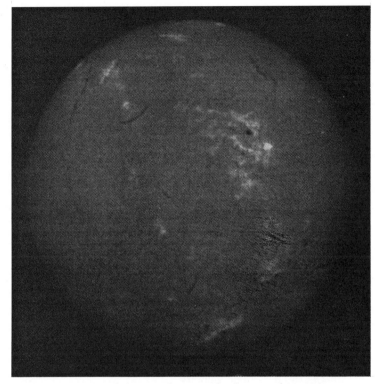

ILLUS. 44—Hα spectroheliogram showing solar flare, April 26, 1946.

necessary for the particle to acquire cosmic-ray energies and the chance of its destruction during that time.

Electromagnetic methods. — The science of electricity and magnetism suggests many processes by which cosmic-ray energies can be realized. Phenomena and quantities that are of negligible importance in experiments on a laboratory scale can grow to very fundamental significance in the scale of the cosmos. We can only briefly sketch some of the suggestions that have been made in this connection.

First, we could view the planets or other cosmic bodies as electrically charged to very high potentials, so that charged particles coming to them from space could acquire great energies in reaching them. It is with some comfort that one finds a fairly general method of dismissing this naive suggestion. While interstellar space

contains only about one atom per cubic centimeter, there is reason to think that it is a comparatively good conductor of electricity
for small electric fields. A large portion of interstellar atoms is
ionized by ultraviolet starlight, and the mean free path of the ions
is large because of the low density. Therefore, on a simple view
of the matter, the electrical conductivity of interstellar space
should be comparable with that of a completely ionized gas at atmospheric pressure and should amount, in fact, to two percent of
the conductivity of copper. Under such conditions, any electro-
statically charged body in the galaxy would become rapidly discharged.

A rotating, magnetized, conducting sphere experiences electro-
dynamic forces resulting from the rotation of its substance in its
own magnetic field. Such a rotating sphere develops a potential
difference between its axis and its equator. A star the size of our
sun, possessing a magnetic field like that attributed to the sun
until recently, would acquire a potential difference of about three
billion electron volts when rotating in a nonconducting medium.
For a magnetic star, such as was cited by H. W. Babcock, with a
field of some 6,000 gauss at the pole and twice the sun's radius,
the potential difference would be of the order of a thousand billion
volts for the same angular velocity.

These potential differences would not be completely annulled
by the electrical conductivity of interstellar space since they would
be continually rejuvenated by the rotation of the star. They would
be modified depending upon the ratio of the conductivity of space
to the conductivity of the star itself. Under suitable conditions,
such a rotating star could shoot out from one of its poles charged
particles which at great distances would show cosmic-ray energies.

Recognizing the existence of violent magnetic disturbances on
stars, akin to the growth of sunspots with their accompanying
magnetic fields, the writer, some 20 years ago, suggested that such
phenomena might result in cosmic-ray energies. The mechanism is
quite analogous to that of an ordinary electrical transformer,
where we have a changing magnetic field threading through a
wire circuit and inducing therein an electromotive force which
drives the current through the circuit. The actual circuit itself is
not necessary for the realization of the electromotive forces, and

if there be charged particles in the vicinity of the changing magnetic field, they will be whirled around by the electromagnetic forces even though they do not form part of a material circuit. It seems that cosmic-ray energies can readily be acquired by processes of this kind.

Recently, the foregoing mechanism has been extended to galaxies, where magnetic fields of the order of 7×10^{-6} gauss are recognized as existing. On the supposition that these magnetic fields have grown from zero, it appears that a charged particle that had zero energy when the field was zero would acquire energy continually, and could attain an energy greater than 10^{19} electron volts by the time the field had risen to 7×10^{-6} gauss. The complete story of the possibilities in this matter involves the lifetime of a cosmic ray, and the conditions pertaining to the case where the magnetic field has already attained a finite value at the time the particle, as a result of becoming charged, starts to acquire energy.

It is also known that if an electrical conductor in a magnetic field is removed from the field, the conductor will tend to carry the magnetic field with it. What really happens is that the change of magnetic flux that would occur in the conductor, if it simply left the magnetic field behind, introduces electromotive forces and so current. This forms a new magnetic field which just replaces the loss of magnetic flux that would otherwise have resulted from the departure of the conductor from the original field. A. Unsöld has called attention to the fact that, in those huge solar cataclysms in which a mass of matter is seen to be hurled from one portion of the sun's surface and to fall back upon another, we have a condition favorable for changing magnetic fields. If such a mass of matter is conducting and starts from a place where there is a magnetic field, it will pursue its course in the cataclysm, carrying the magnetic field with it until it eventually splashes once more into the sun, resulting in the annihilation or the dispersal of the magnetic field that it carried. The rapid change in magnetic flux through the regions of space in which the cataclysm occurs provides for the birth of electrical forces that can give cosmic-ray energies to charged particles.

Another method of accelerating charged particles has been suggested by D. H. Menzel and W. W. Salisbury and has been further developed by E. M. McMillan. It depends upon energy that is electromagnetic in nature, but with very low frequencies of only a few cycles per second and existing only in the extreme outer portion of the solar corona. Such low-frequency waves may arise from large magnetic disturbances initiated by solar flares and propagated through the corona. Sparsely distributed ions in the space around the sun (and other flare-type stars) might be accelerated to cosmic-ray energies if a mechanism of this kind actually exists.

But if the general cosmic radiation originates in stellar flares, why does it come nearly uniformly from all directions? This difficulty attends any theory that involves the stars as the origin of cosmic rays. Therefore, it has become customary to postulate an extensive magnetic field extending throughout the whole galaxy. This field is supposed to be weak but sufficiently extensive to curl up the paths of the cosmic-ray particles in such fashion as to prevent their escape from the galaxy, and at the same time to provide, as the result of successive reflections at the boundaries of the galaxy, for a condition in which an observer on our earth, for example, receives rays with approximately equal intensity from all directions.

If cosmic rays are purely stellar in origin, however, we might expect cosmic radiation from the sun to outweigh that from the other stars by something like the extent to which sunlight exceeds starlight. This is not the case, and radio noise from the stars in general seems to outweigh that from our sun; therefore, Unsöld is driven to assume that the sun is not typical in these matters and that the cosmic-ray activity of many stars may be very much larger than that of the sun.

An alternative not inconsistent with the possibilities is to attribute practically the whole observed cosmic radiation to the sun itself. For this, the magnetic field of the space around the sun would have to confine cosmic rays to the general vicinity of the solar system, with boundary reflections producing the observed near-uniformity from all directions. It is a fact that unusual solar activity is accompanied by variations in measured cosmic radiation. Thus, for example, in July of 1946 an exceptionally large flare developed on the sun, and during this period a change of as much as 20 percent in cosmic-ray intensity was observed by stations of the Carnegie Institution of Washington distributed in various localities.

Abundances of the elements. — Suppose that, regardless of the methods of origin and places of origin of the rays, different substances contributed to the rays in proportion to the amounts of the substances present. If the rays came directly to us from their places of origin, the proportions of atoms of different kinds in the primary rays should reflect the abundances of the different kinds of atoms in the universe.

If, however, the rays are confined by the boundaries of a magnetic field co-extensive with the galaxy, like fish kept in a gigantic pool, they will increase in numbers without limit. But each fish will die eventually, and a state of equilibrium will finally be reached in which the density of fish is such that the number that die per year will equal the number thrown into the pool. For a given rate of supply to the pool, the ultimate density will be greater, the greater the life of the fish. If fish of different kinds have different lives, their ultimate relative numbers will reflect their relative lifetimes as well as the rate at which they are thrown into the pool.

Death occurs to a cosmic ray when, in its wanderings through the galaxy, it strikes another atomic particle and disintegrates into mesotrons, and these in due course decay into electrons and neutrinos. The chances of collision are small; a cosmic ray may travel for many millions of years without hitting another atomic nucleus and dying. However, a larger atom will collide more frequently than a smaller one, and so lifetime considerations will tend to favor the lighter particles.

From the researches of astronomers, physicists and chemists, we have found the observed relative abundances to be:

Element	Cosmic rays	Sun, stars, interstellar matter
H	100,000	100,000
He	25,000	10,000
C, N, O	900	130
Heavier elements	10	15

This table does not favor the light elements in relation to heavy ones, although carbon, nitrogen, and oxygen appear to be relatively more abundant in cosmic rays than in the universe as a whole. However, the mechanisms of acceleration may act more strongly on one atom than on another, and there is, after all, very little reason to suppose that the atoms of different elements have an equal chance of receiving cosmic-ray energies.

Nevertheless, one cannot doubt the importance of obtaining further more definite knowledge of the relative abundances of elements in the primary cosmic rays, and of the relative energies acquired by the different kinds of particles. From data of this kind, combined with further studies of such phenomena in the cosmos as a whole, we may hope some day to understand in greater detail all the processes involved in the life histories of these rays from the time of their creation from ordinary matter to their entry into our atmosphere.

ADDENDUM, DECEMBER 1959

Since this article was originally written, much has happened in relation to cosmic rays and allied phenomena. We have the continued discovery of new particles of the mesotron type. We have the discovery of the anti-proton with all its implications as regards cosmological phenomena, and we have discoveries which lead us to conclude that, at any rate during the present period — the period of the International Geophysical Year, with its exceptionally large sun activity — the story of cosmic rays, particularly as regards the sun's contribution to such rays, is much more complicated than had been formerly supposed.

Solar Phenomena. — The correlation of solar activity and magnetic storms with cosmic-ray phenomena entered the picture as a matter for major study when S. E. Forbush discovered, at sea level, a change of the cosmic-ray intensity of the order of 16 percent during the period of a magnetic storm. About the same time, observations carried out, under the writer's direction, on the latitude effect at 30,000 feet altitude showed, on one particular day, considerable abnormalities which were absent on other days. Since that time, an exhaustive series of measurements, co-ordinating solar activity with cosmic-ray measurements, have been carried out at high altitudes by M. A. Pomerantz and others, using balloon-borne equipment. These experiments have verified a conclusion tentatively reported earlier by Pomerantz to the effect that during periods of solar activity, low-energy heavy particles from the sun reached the earth's atmosphere. The arrival of such particles is also, in many cases, accompanied by ionization in the upper atmosphere of sufficient amount to influence radio transmission. An interesting feature of these particles is that some of them arrive with energies below that necessary for entry through the earth's magnetic field. The inference is that other magnetic fields between the earth and the sun have co-operated to provide channels of easy passage to the earth.

The Van Allen Radiation Belt. — Recent measurements performed with apparatus carried in satellites Explorers I and III, under the direction of James Van Allen, have revealed two belts of intense radiation encircling the earth around the magnetic axis. The inner belt occurs in the vicinity of one earth's radius from the earth's surface; and in it, a Geiger counter showed a 6,000-fold increase in counting rate over the normal counting rate on the earth's surface. The outer zone, extending for about two or three earth's diameters above the surface, and arcing along the lines of geomagnetic force to points above the polar regions, shows a counting rate nearly 10,000 times the earth's surface value.

It is believed that the zones are caused by charged particles trapped by the earth's magnetic field. Such particles would spiral along the lines of force, being reflected back and forth between regions to which the lines converge and regions from which they diverge.

Primary Radiation Intensity of Heavy Particles. — The primary radiation intensity due to heavy particles, which cannot penetrate appreciably into the atmosphere, can be obtained from sea-level measurements of the neutrons to which they give rise and which *can* penetrate to sea level. This method, devised by John A. Simpson, has been applied in measurements aboard a ship which traveled over a wide range of latitude and longitude, the observations being carried out according to a program planned by M. A. Pomerantz and D. C. Rose. A similar monitor is in service in Thule, Greenland and another monitor is being established in Antarctica. Such measurements, with the inferences to be drawn from them, provide a useful means of studying the earth's magnetic field in the regions around the earth where the magnetic field controls the motion of the primary particles.

Air Showers. — Measurements of cosmic-ray air showers which have been responsible for the discovery of particles of unusually high energy have been intensified and extended by use, instead of Geiger counters, of large plastic scintillators covering wide areas. The scintillators emit light quanta when charged particles pass through them, and the light quanta are detected by the photoelectric effect which they produce in suitably designed apparatus (in photomultipliers).

W. F. G. SWANN

PIERRE CURIE

Radium

[FROM THE SMITHSONIAN REPORT FOR 1903*]

THE DISCOVERY *of radium as an element by Professor and Madame Curie is another of the spectacular scientific events that took place around the turn of the last century. The record of that discovery and of the brilliant investigations of the properties of radium are given here in the words of M. Curie, who at that time was a professor on the faculty of science of the University of Paris. For the pioneering work of M. and Mme. Curie on the properties of radium they were awarded the Davy medal of the Royal Society, London, in 1903, and, in the same year, the Nobel prize for physics jointly with Henri Becquerel, discoverer of radioactivity. Some of the Curies' conclusions regarding the emanations of radium are startlingly prophetic, taking into consideration the fact that radiations of any kind had then only very recently been discovered.*

That the Curies were able to isolate radium at all was in itself a remarkable feat in the state of chemistry a half century ago. To obtain only one-tenth of a gram of the pure element required the chemical reduction of a ton of pitchblende. Yet they persisted, and were able to prove that their reasoned belief in a new powerfully

* Translated from a lecture delivered by Professor Curie before the Royal Institution of London, as printed in the *Revue Scientifique,* February 13, 1904.

radioactive element was justified. The work of the Curie family won them world renown, and in their honor the internationally adopted unit of the rate of radioactive decay is named the curie. It is today defined as the quantity of any radioactive material giving 37 billion disintegrations per second.

I.

M. BECQUEREL discovered in 1896 that uranium and its products emit spontaneously radiations which, like the Roentgen rays, are photographically active, augment the electrical conductivity of the air through which they pass, traverse black paper and thin sheets of metal freely, but can neither be reflected nor refracted.

Compounds of thorium emit radiations analogous in their properties, and of comparable intensity. The radiations thus spontaneously emitted by certain substances received the name "Becquerel rays," and we are accustomed to speak of the substances emitting them as radioactive.

Madame Curie and myself have discovered new radioactive substances existing in minute quantities in certain minerals, but possessing the property of radioactivity in a very high degree. We have separated the radioactive substance polonium, analogous to bismuth in its chemical reactions, and radium which more resembles barium. M. Debierne has since separated actinium, which is a radioactive substance to be classed chemically with the rare earths.

Polonium, radium, and actinium emit radiations of an order of intensity a million times higher than those emitted by uranium and thorium, and have enabled physicists to conduct many investigations of the phenomena of radioactivity within the past few years. The present paper is confined to the description of radium, which we have proved to be a new element, and have succeeded in isolating in the form of a pure salt. This is the substance which has been most widely used in researches on radioactivity.

II.

The radiations of radium produce photographic impressions very quickly, and are able to penetrate any screen whatsoever. Bodies differ in transparency, but no screen is absolutely opaque to radium waves.

The radiations of radium excite phosphorescence in a great number of bodies, including, among others, the following: Alkaline salts, alkaline earths, organic substances, the skin, glass, paper, salts of uranium, etc., while diamond, platino-cyanide of barium, and the phosphorescent sulphide of zinc of Sidot are particularly sensitive. The luminescence of phosphorescent sulphide of zinc persists for some time after the removal of the radium which excites it.

Radium emits its rays with equal intensity whether immersed in liquid air at $-180°$ C. or at ordinary temperatures. When a bit of radium salt is placed with a little screen of platino-cyanide of barium in a test tube and the whole plunged into liquid air, the screen appears to glow at least as strongly as before. Under the same circumstances a screen of sulphide of zinc loses some of its luminosity, but this is due to the diminished phosphorescent power of this substance at low temperatures.

Little by little phosphorescent substances are altered under the prolonged action of radium and become less readily excited and less luminous.

The salts of radium are spontaneously luminous, and it may be presumed that they render themselves phosphorescent by their own radioactivity. Radium chloride and radium bromide are the most intensely luminous of these salts, and may even appear visibly bright in open daylight. In these circumstances the light emitted by the radium recalls to mind the color of that given by the firefly or glowworm. The luminosity of radium salts diminishes with lapse of time, but never wholly disappears, and salts at first uncolored become at length tinged with gray, yellow, or violet.

III.

The radiations of radium impart electrical conductivity to the air through which they pass. When a fragment of radium salt is brought near a charged electroscope the latter is immediately discharged. If the electroscope is inclosed by a thick, solid wall the discharge still takes place, though more slowly. Lead and platinum are strongly absorbent, but aluminum is the most transparent of the metals, and organic substances absorb relatively little of the Becquerel rays.

Nonconducting liquids, such as petroleum ether, sulphide of carbon, benzine, and liquid air are rendered conducting under the influence of radium.

Under certain conditions the radiations of radium facilitate the passage of sparks between two conductors placed in air. This is illustrated by the apparatus shown in Illustration 45 consisting

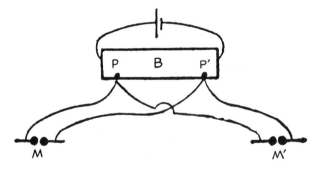

ILLUS. 45—Conductivity of air augmented by radium.

of an induction coil, B, from the poles, P and P', of which two metallic circuits are led to micrometric sparking devices, M and M', at considerable distance apart, and offering two distinct paths of equal resistance to the passage of sparks. The micrometers are adjusted so that each transmits equally an abundance of sparks between their terminals. Upon bringing a fragment of radium near one of the micrometers the sparks cease to pass at the other.

It appears to be the most penetrating rays which are most effective in promoting electrical conductivity, for the efficiency of the rays for this purpose is not greatly reduced by interposing a lead screen 2 centimeters thick, although the larger portion of the rays is arrested by such a screen.

IV.

The radiations of radium can be neither reflected nor refracted. They form a heterogeneous mixture, separable into three groups, which following the nomenclature of Rutherford we will designate by the Greek letters α, β, and γ. These groups may be discriminated by the aid of the magnetic field; for in an intense magnetic

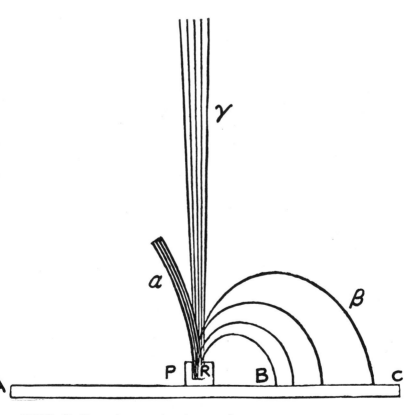

ILLUS. 46—Magnetic separation of a, β, and γ rays.

field the α rays are slightly deviated from a rectilinear course in
the same manner as the "canal rays" in vacuum tubes, while the
β rays are deviated like the cathode rays, and the γ rays, like
those of Roentgen, are not deviated at all.

A bit of radium, R, Illustration 46, is placed within a small
cavity in a block of lead. In the absence of all magnetic action the
radiation escapes from the block as a rectilinear pencil, but in a
uniform magnetic field normal to the plane of the figure, and
directed toward the rear of this plane, the β rays are strongly deflected toward the right and caused to follow a circular trajectory;
the α rays are slightly deviated toward the left, while the γ rays,
which are by far the least abundant, continue in a straight line.

The α rays are of slight penetrating power. A sheet of aluminum only a few hundredths of a millimeter in thickness absorbs
them. To exhibit their deviation a very intense magnetic field is
required, and the actual demonstration requires a far more delicate
method than that indicated in Illustration 46, which is merely a
diagram given in general illustration.

The α rays may be compared to projectiles of atomic dimensions charged with positive electricity and shot off with great
velocities. Apart from their behavior in a magnetic field, the α
rays may be recognized by their manner of absorption in a succession of thin screens. In traversing successively a series of screens
the α rays become less and less penetrating, whereas residual
Roentgen rays under these circumstances become more and more
penetrating. It appears that the energy of each projectile becomes
less with each screen that it passes.

It is the α rays which appear to be active in the beautiful experiment exhibited by the spinthariscope of Sir William Crookes. In
this apparatus a small fragment of radium salt (only a fraction of
a milligram) is suspended by a metallic wire at a small distance
(one-half millimeter) from a screen of phosphorescent sulphide
of zinc. When the face of the screen which is turned toward the
radium is examined in darkness by the aid of a magnifying glass,
it appears studded with sparkling points, reminding one of the
stars in the sky, except that these luminous points are appearing
and disappearing continually. It may be supposed that each bright
point which appears is the result of the impact of a projectile, and

thus for the first time there has been discovered a means of distinguishing an individual action of an atom.

The β rays are analogous to the cathode rays and behave similarly in the magnetic field. They comport themselves as projectiles charged negatively and escaping from the radium with high velocity. These projectiles (electrons) appear to have a mass about one thousand times smaller than the hydrogen atom. By means of the following experiment the magnetic deviation of the β rays may be demonstrated. A tiny phial holding a little radium, R, is placed at one end of a thick-walled lead tube, AB, as shown in section in Illustration 47. An electroscope is placed somewhat beyond the other end of the tube, so that the pencil of rays emerging from the tube tends to discharge the electroscope. The lead tube is situated between the poles of an electromagnet, E E, and at right

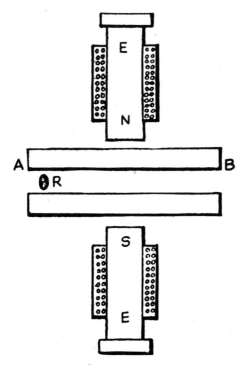

ILLUS. 47—Magnetic deviation of β rays.

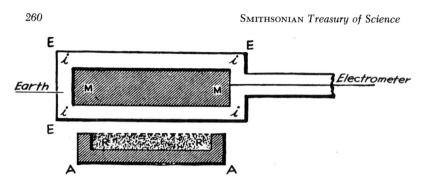

ILLUS. 48—Negative electrical charges transported by β rays.

angles to the line of poles, N S. When the current is flowing in the coils of the electromagnet the β rays are thrown upon the walls of the lead tube, and do not escape to discharge the electroscope as before, so that it now discharges more slowly. When the current is cut off, the electroscope is again rapidly discharged.

It may be shown that the β rays transport negative electricity, which is in harmony with the hypothesis that they are electrically charged projectiles. For this experiment the apparatus illustrated in Illustration 48 may be employed, in which R R represents the radium emitting the β rays. Those among them which are directed toward the upper part of the figure traverse successively a thin sheet of aluminum, E E E E, in electrical contact with the earth, and supporting an insulating block of paraffin, $i i i i$. They are finally absorbed by a lead block, M M, which is connected to an electrometer by an insulated wire. It is found that the electrometer is continually charged negatively. In this experiment the α rays are absorbed by the sheet of aluminum which is connected to earth. The layer of paraffin is required to insulate the lead block M M, for the insulation of this block would be defective if there was only air between it and the aluminum, on account of the air being rendered conducting by the presence of the rays, so that it would then be impossible to detect at the electrometer the charging of the lead block.

An experiment the inverse of this may be performed. The metallic trough A A, Illustration 49, containing radium, R, is connected with the electrometer and surrounded by paraffin, $i i i i$, inclosed in the metallic envelope E E E E, which is connected to earth.

Curie: Radium 261

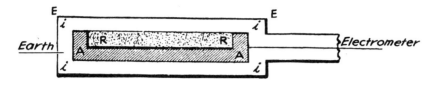

ILLUS. 49—Negative charges carried by β rays.

Since the α rays are but feebly penetrating they cannot escape, but the β rays traverse the paraffin and carry off negative electricity, so that the trough A A becomes positively charged.

A sealed glass test tube containing radium salt becomes spontaneously charged with electricity, as if it were a Leyden jar. If, after a sufficient time, a line is traced by a glass cutter on the wall of the test tube, a spark may pass at the point where the wall is thinned by the scratch, and at the same time the operator receives a feeble shock in his fingers by the passage of the discharge.

The group of β rays is made up of a variety of rays differing in their penetrating power. Some β rays are absorbed by a thickness of one one-hundredth millimeter of aluminum, while others are able to traverse, before complete absorption, a layer of lead several millimeters in thickness. Another method of distinguishing the varieties of β rays is by the curvature of their path in a magnetic field. In the experiment represented in Illustration 46 the β rays deviated by the magnetic field would darken a photographic plate all the way from B to C. The least deviated rays would be distinguished at C and those most deviated at B. Thus there would appear the photograph of a sort of spectrum produced by the influence of the magnetic field on the β rays. By interposing a thin sheet of metal in the path of the rays, it may be shown that the rays most deviated are suppressed, so that it appears that the most penetrating rays are least deviated.

According to the ballistic theory, it may be assumed that the β rays are composed of electrons projected with different velocities. The most penetrating rays have the highest velocity. Kaufmann's researches, interpreted in the light of the theory of electrons as given by M. Abraham, lead to very important general conclusions. Certain very penetrating β rays may consist of electrons impressed with a velocity nine-tenths of that of light. The property of mass in electrons, and perhaps in all bodies, may be a consequence of electromagnetic reactions. The energy required to impress higher and higher velocities upon an electrically charged body approaches infinity when the velocity of the body approaches the velocity of light.

The γ rays, which are not deviable in a magnetic field, and which are analogous to X-rays, form but a small part of the total radiation. Certain γ rays are extremely penetrating, and are able to traverse a thickness of several centimeters of lead.

Becquerel rays may be utilized to make radiographs without special apparatus. A small glass test tube containing some hundredths of a gram of radium salt replaces the Crookes tube. Both β and γ rays are employed, but such radiographs lack sharpness on account of the diffusion of the β rays by the bodies through which they pass. Sharp radiographs are obtained by deflecting the β rays with a magnetic field, so that only the γ rays remain; but the γ rays are so feeble that several days' exposure must then be employed.

V.

Radium salts continually give off heat. The evolution of heat is so great that it may be shown in a rough experiment made with two ordinary mercury thermometers. Two similar vacuum-jacketed receptacles, A and A', Illustration 50, are employed. In one of them, A, let us suppose, is placed a test tube containing 0.7 gram of pure radium bromide, and in the second, A', is a similar tube of inactive substance such as chloride of barium. The temperature of each inclosure is indicated by a thermometer whose bulb is close to the test tube. The top of each vessel is closed by a wad of cotton. In these conditions the thermometer t, which is placed in the same vessel with the radium, continually indicates a temperature about 3° higher than that of the other thermometer t'.

A determination of the amount of heat emitted by the radium may be made with the aid of the ice calorimeter of Bunsen. When a tube of radium is placed in the calorimeter, there is observed a

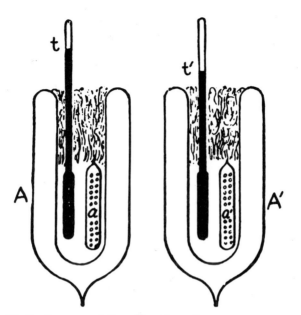

ILLUS. 50—Continuous evolution of heat by radium.

continual evolution of heat, which ceases when the radium is withdrawn. Measurements made with a sample of radium which had been prepared a long time previously indicated that each gram of radium gives off about 80 small calories per hour. Thus radium gives off sufficient heat in an hour to melt its own weight of ice. This evolution of heat produces no change in the appearance of the salt, nor can any ordinary chemical reaction be pointed out as the source of the heat evolved.

It has been shown that a radium salt when first prepared gives off comparatively little heat, and that the heating increases steadily toward a maximum amount, which is not fully attained at the end of a month.

When a salt of radium is dissolved in water and the solution is placed in a sealed tube, the quantity of heat evolved by the solution is at first feeble, but increases and tends toward a constant value, which is attained after about a month. When this constant state is reached, the salt in solution evolves the same amount of heat which it would give if in a solid state.

The amount of heat given out by radium at different temperatures may be determined by causing it to boil a liquefied gas, and measuring the volume of gas evolved. This experiment may be performed with methyl chloride (at −21° C.). Professor Dewar and M. Curie have conducted such experiments with liquid oxygen (at −180° C.) and liquid hydrogen (at −292° C.). This last liquid serves the purpose particularly well. A tube A, Illustration 51, (closed at the lower end and inclosed by a vacuum heat insulator of Dewar) contains a little liquid hydrogen H. A tube tt′ serves to convey the gas to be collected over water in the inverted graduate E. The tube A and its insulator are plunged into a bath of hydrogen H′. In these conditions no evolution of gas is produced in A. But when a tube containing 0.7 gram of radium bromide is placed in the hydrogen in the tube A, the gas is continually evolved at the rate of 73 cubic centimeters per minute.

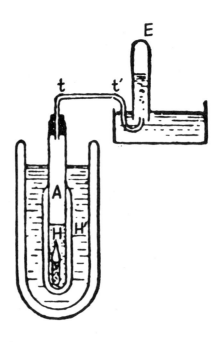

ILLUS. 51—Boiling liquid hydrogen by radium.

VI.

The radiations of radium provoke many chemical reactions. They act upon the substances employed in photography in the same manner as light. Glass is tinged violet or brown, and salts of the alkalies are colored yellow, violet, blue, or green. Under the action of the rays paraffin, paper, and celluloid turn yellow, paper becomes brittle, and ordinary phosphorus is transformed into the red variety. In general, bodies phosphorescent under the action of radium rays undergo a transformation, and at the same time their phosphorescence tends to disappear. Finally it has been shown that the presence of radium salts promotes the formation of ozone in the air.

VII.

The radiations of radium produce various physiological effects.

A salt of radium contained in an opaque tube of metal or pasteboard produces a sensation of light upon the eye. This may be shown by placing the tube of radium before the closed eye or against the temple. The eye then becomes phosphorescently luminous under the influence of the rays and light is perceived within the eye itself.

Radium acts upon the skin so that if one holds a tube of radium in the hand for some minutes, though no particular sensation is felt at the time, after 15 or 20 days an inflammation is produced and then the skin sloughs off at the place where the radium was applied. If the action of radium is continued long enough a sore is formed which may take months to heal. The action of radium rays on the skin is analogous to that of the Roentgen rays. It has been attempted to utilize it in the treatment of lupus and cancer.

The action of radium rays on nervous centers may result in paralysis or death. They seem to act with particular intensity on living tissues in the process of growth.

VIII.

When any solid body is placed near a salt of radium it acquires the radiant properties of radium, or in other words becomes radio-active. This induced radioactivity persists for some time after the body is removed from the presence of the radium, but it becomes steadily feebler and diminishes about half in each half hour till it disappears. This phenomenon is produced in a particularly intense and regular fashion if the solid body is placed with the radium salt in a closed vessel, and it is advantageous to employ a solution of radium salt rather than the salt in the solid form.

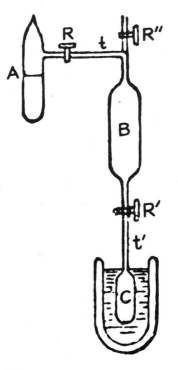

ILLUS. 52—Induced radioactivity.

A salt of radium is placed at A, Illustration 52, in a glass reservoir which communicates by tubes t and t' with two other glass reservoirs B and C, from which air may be exhausted. It may be shown that the walls of the reservoirs B and C become radioactive and emit Becquerel rays analogous to those emitted ordinarily by radium itself, while on the contrary the solution of radium emits very little radiation, so that the radioactivity becomes, as it were, exteriorized.

This phenomenon is well exhibited in other gases than air, and is independent of the presence of the gas. The radioactivity is communicated from one place to another by a sort of conduction through the gas, and may even be propagated from one reservoir to another through a capillary tube. Gas which has been in contact with radium, therefore, acquires the property of imparting radioactivity to solids. The gas is itself radioactive, but does not emit rays which are very penetrating. Rays emitted by gases are not transmitted through the walls of a glass receiver.

When the gas thus modified is removed far from the radium it retains its properties for a long time, and continues to emit Becquerel rays of slight penetration and to impart radioactivity to solids. But its activity from either point of view diminishes by half in each four days till it disappears.

Rutherford supposes that radium continually emits a radioactive gaseous substance which diffuses in space and provokes the induced radioactivity. He gives to this hypothetical substance the name of radium emanation and believes that it is to be found in a mixed condition in gases in the vicinity of radium. Without necessarily admitting the material nature of the emanation, this expression may be employed to designate the special radioactive energy stored in the gas.

Air charged with the emanation provokes phosphorescence in bodies which are immersed in it. Glass (especially Thuringian glass) gives a beautiful white or green phosphorescence. Sidot's sulphide of zinc becomes excessively brilliant under the action of the emanation. This experiment may be tried with the apparatus shown in Illustration 52. The cock R being closed, the radioactive emanation which is emitted by the solution in A saturates the air above the solution. When the emanation has accumulated in A for some days the reservoirs B and C, whose inner walls are coated with zinc sulphite, are exhausted. The cock R″ is then closed and R opened, so that the air charged with the emanation expands suddenly into the reservoirs B and C, which immediately become luminous.

Radium emanation comports itself as a gas from many points of view. Thus it is shared in the same proportions as a gas would be by two communicating reservoirs. It diffuses in air according to the law of diffusion of gases, and has a coefficient of diffusion not far from that of carbonic acid gas in air.

Messrs. Rutherford and Soddy discovered that the emanation has the property of condensing at the temperature of liquid air. The effects of such condensation may be shown with the apparatus pictured in Illustration 52. The cock R″ being closed, and the emanation being diffused throughout the apparatus, as at the conclusion of the experiment last described, the reservoirs B and C (which are covered within with phosphorescent zinc sulphide) are luminous. On closing the cock R and plunging the reservoir C in liquid air, at the end of a half hour, it is seen that the reservoir B has lost its luminosity, while the reservoir C is still bright. Thus it is seen that the emanation has quitted the reservoir B and become condensed in the cooled portion of the reservoir C. However, the luminosity of C is not very intense, since the phosphorescence of sulphide of zinc is more feeble at the temperature of liquid air than at ordinary temperatures; but by closing the cock R′, which interrupts communication between the two reservoirs, and again bringing C to the temperature of the surroundings, it becomes again brilliantly illuminated, while B remains dark. Thus the emanation which at first filled the two reservoirs is now all contained in C.

The preceding experiments tend to convince us that the emanation is analogous to ordinary gases, but up to the present time the hypothesis of the existence of such a gas rests wholly on the manifestations of radioactivity. It may be remarked that, contrary to the behavior of ordinary gases, the emanation spontaneously disappears when contained for a sufficient time in a sealed tube.

IX.

Having briefly enumerated the principal properties of radium, it is proper to recall in a few words the origin of its discovery, in which Mme. Curie has had a very great share.

Experiments with the substances separated from uranium and thorium had shown that the radioactivity is an atomic property which always accompanies the atoms of these simple substances. The radioactivity of a complex substance is generally greater the larger the proportion of the radioactive metal contained in the compound. Certain ores of uranium, as pitchblende, chalcolite, and carnotite, have, however, a radioactivity superior to that of metallic uranium. We therefore questioned whether these minerals might not contain in minute proportion some substances still unrecognized and far more radioactive than uranium, and we searched by chemical methods for the hypothetical substances, always guided by the radioactivity of the substance treated.

Our anticipations were verified by the results. Pitchblende contains new radioactive substances, but in an excessively minute proportion. A ton of pitchblende, for example, contains a quantity of radium on the order of one-tenth of a gram. In these conditions the preparation of radium salts is very tedious and costly. A ton of ore furnishes some kilograms of radiferous barium bromide, from which the radium is extracted by a series of fractionations.

During the separation of radium, Demarçay, whose recent death is much deplored, was so good as to examine spectroscopically the products which we prepared. This cooperation was most valuable to us, for at the conclusion of our research the spectrum analysis confirmed our anticipations and furnished the proof that the radioactive barium which we had separated from pitchblende contained a new element. Demarcay made the first investigation of the spectrum of radium.

Radium has a very sensitive spectrum reaction — indeed, quite as sensitive as that of barium. The presence of radium may be detected spectroscopically in radiferous barium containing only one ten-thousandth of radium; but the radioactivity of radium gives a reaction 10,000 times as sensitive still. An electrometer ordinarily well insulated enables the observer to detect readily the presence of radium when contained in a mixture of inactive substance in the proportion of 1 to 100,000,000.

Radium is a higher homologue of barium in the series of alkaline earth metals. Its atomic weight has been determined by Madame Curie to be 226.

While thus a near neighbor to barium, it is not found, even as a trace, in the ordinary mineral sources of barium, and only accompanies it in the uranium ores, which fact is of great theoretical importance.

X.

Radium therefore gives us an example of a body which, while remaining in the same state, evolves continuously a considerable amount of energy. This fact is apparently in contradiction to the fundamental principles of energetics, and various hypotheses have been put forward to avoid this contradiction.

Among these hypotheses we may consider two which were made at the beginning of the studies of radioactivity.

In the first hypothesis it is assumed that radium is an element in process of evolution. It must then be admitted that the evolution is extremely slow, so that no appreciable change of state is discernable in the course of several years, for the energy which is disengaged in the course of a year corresponds with an insignificant transformation of matter. It would appear natural to suppose that the quantity of energy put in play in the transformation of atoms is considerable.

The second hypothesis assumes the existence in space of radiations still unknown and inaccessible to our senses. Radium might be assumed to be capable of absorbing the energy of these hypothetical rays and transforming it into radioactive energy.

The two hypotheses which we have mentioned seem not incompatible.

Since the delivery of this lecture there was made (June 19, 1903) a discovery of great importance by Messrs. Ramsay and Soddy.

They found that the emanation of radium as it disappears gives place to the production of helium gas, whose presence can be recognized by spectrum analysis. It seems, then, that we are here brought face to face for the first time with the formation of an element. It is possible that radium is an unstable chemical element, and that helium is produced as one of the products of its disaggregation.

KARL K. DARROW

Nuclear Fission

[FROM THE SMITHSONIAN REPORT FOR 1940]

HERE IS *presented, with conciseness and clarity, the story of the scientific discovery that can mean either the destruction of our civilization or its vast enrichment, a choice to be made by man himself. The story was written just before the urgency of World War II had resulted in a "crash program" to develop the atomic bomb. Since that time great strides have been taken to develop nuclear weapons of vastly greater destructive power, as well as to promote the peaceful uses of nuclear fission such as the production of power and medically useful radioisotopes.*

Karl K. Darrow, physicist with the Bell Telephone Laboratories and author of books and many technical articles on various aspects of theoretical physics, here outlines the six stages in the history of the transmutation of elements, beginning with the discovery of the art in Rutherford's laboratory in 1919 and ending with the actual fission of a uranium nucleus by the impact of a slow neutron. At the time Darrow wrote this article, it was not yet known whether a chain reaction could be produced, with the accompanying enormous release of energy.

In 1940 the art of transmutation came to its majority; that is to say, 21 years had passed since the day it was born in Rutherford's laboratory. Infancy and adolescence for this art have been marked by more stages than we generally count for human children; I propose to distinguish six. Here follows a table of six great events in the story of transmutation, beginning with birth and ending with fission, which, by the way, bears a name that in biology means a certain sort of birth. Each of them lifted the art to a higher level with a broader scope. It is only the sixth and latest which is my topic, but all the others lead up to it, as I will show immediately with the table for my text.

Table of Great Events in History of Transmutation

1919. First success with helium nuclei (energy of activation derived from radium, etc.).

1932. First success with hydrogen nuclei (energy of activation derived from voltage).

1932. Recognition of the liberated neutron.

1934. Recognition of radioactive bodies resulting from transmutation.

1934. Slow neutrons used to produce transmutation, this resulting in radioactive bodies.

1939. Recognition of fission.

Be it said that, in general, transmutation takes place when two nuclei meet and enter into a reaction with each other. They are made to meet by projecting one against the other, and accordingly we speak of one as the projectile and of the other as the target. Transmutation does not occur whenever a projectile comes into the neighborhood of a target nucleus, but only on rare occasions which I will call "lucky hits." There are four principal kinds of projectiles in use for transmutation: Helium nuclei — hydrogen nuclei of two sorts, the light and the heavy — and neutrons. Three stages of my chronology have been marked with their names. The phenomena of fission are produced with neutrons as the projectiles and uranium* as the target, and they therefore belong in the fifth stage of the chronology. But they also depend on the first and the second stages, for neutrons are always obtained by bombarding various targets with projectiles of the first three kinds; and of course they depend on the third, because if the neutron had not been recognized it would hardly now be in use as a tool. Moreover, they depend upon the fourth; the phenomena of fission were first detected because the new-born elements resulting from it are radioactive, and to this day they are often, though not always, observed through this radioactivity. Next it will be noticed that instead of putting fission into the fifth stage, I gave it a line and a stage to itself, and said "recognition of fission" instead of "discovery of fission." This was not in order to compose a three-word poem, but because the phenomena were detected about 4 years before they were properly analyzed; a strange and interesting story, for which, however, there is not space.

Now I make final use of the table in speaking about energy. Everyone has heard so much about the gigantic energies and the huge voltages required for transmutation, that anyone may be pardoned for thinking that transmutation is a process which swallows up enormous quantities of energy — which is strongly endothermic, to use the chemical word. Well, there are many transmutations that swallow energy up without restoring it, but many of them give back much more than they receive. I mean by this simply that whenever a projectile makes a "lucky" hit on a target the total energy of motion of the new-born nuclei is greater than that of the projectile. On balance the experimenter does spend much more energy than is released, because of the amount which he is obliged to squander on projectiles which never make lucky hits; but if one considers only those which do transmute, then their energy may well be smaller and even very much smaller than that which appears on the new-born nuclei. This is what I mean to suggest by using the name "energy of activation" for the energy which hydrogen or helium nuclei must have in order to make them

---

* The lecture on which this article was based was confined to the fission of uranium by slow neutrons. "Fast" neutrons (of energies amounting to a million or millions of electron-volts) produce fission of a different isotope of uranium, and also of thorium and of protactinium.

efficient projectiles. It is, however, the release of energy which is one of the spectacular features of fission.

This release of energy is indeed amazing. When the process occurs in any single nucleus there is released — in the form of kinetic energy of the new-born particles — the appalling amount of 175,000,000 electron-volts. To get a notion of what this figure means, remember that in the synthesis of hydrogen and oxygen into water — perhaps the most terrific explosion of all of chemistry — there is released between two and three electron-volts for each pair of reacting molecules; and in the notorious explosives of industry and war, such as TNT and nitroglycerine, not even so much as that.

Now I have said that fission occurs when a slow neutron impinges on a uranium nucleus, and that an enormous amount of energy is released, and that the resulting new-born elements are radioactive; but I have not yet said what these new-born elements are. This is the second of the astonishing features of fission. All other transmutations have resulted in changing the target element to some other not more than two steps away from it in the periodic table of the elements. In this periodic table, uranium stands at the ninety-second and last place; but the no fewer than 16 different elements thus far identified among the "fission-products" (as they are called) stand in places ranging from the thirty-fifth to the fifty-seventh! What happens in fission is therefore something never before observed — the division of a massive nucleus into two nearly equal fragments. In ordinary transmutations of heavy nuclei, a particle small in both charge and mass pops into a nucleus, and another particle small in charge and mass pops out. In this kind of transmutation a particle of small mass and no charge at all wanders into a uranium nucleus, and the nucleus promptly bursts apart into two pieces not exactly alike indeed but not very different from one another. Fission in biology is the division of a cell into two which are very much alike in size, and this is the source of the name.

As for the fact that fission results in so many different types of nucleus instead of just two, that probably has a double meaning. Many of the radioactive bodies which are observed during and after fission are clearly not the original fragments of the explosions, for after the neutron influx is suspended they increase for a while in amount instead of diminishing. It is clear that these are descendants of the original fission fragments, and the question as to which are really the original ones is at present a very live one. Theory suggests that the initial fragment-pair need not always be the same. One nucleus, on being entered by a neutron, may burst into barium and krypton, another into xenon and strontium, another perhaps into caesium and rubidium. (Note that the members of these element-pairs are so chosen that their atomic numbers add up to 92, which is a way of saying that the entire positive charge of the uranium nucleus must be found upon the two initial fragments immediately after the explosion.) Whatever the initial fragment-pair may be, one at least of its members must be the parent of a long chain of radioactive bodies, and probably both are. This sufficiently accounts for the fact that the fission process produces radioactive elements in a profusion and variety beyond any other which is known.

I have saved the most sensational item for the last. Not only is fission caused by slow neutrons, but it produces fresh neutrons among its many products. Could these fresh neutrons produce fission in their turn? Presumably they could; we know of nothing to differentiate them from other neutrons. Could they produce new fissions and these in turn new fissions and so onward in geometrical progression, so that a whole massive piece of uranium might blow up in sudden explosion of unparalleled fury touched off by so seemingly innocent an event as the entry of a single neutron?

This is perhaps the most important of the unsolved questions of physics. Let us begin by asking after a certain necessary though not sufficient condition. The fissions cannot proceed in geometrical progression, the explosion of the whole mass cannot occur, unless each fission results (on the average) in more than one free neutron to replace the one neutron which is consumed in producing it. Is it so? Well, the few people whose opinions are worth taking agree that it is. They do not agree well as to how many fresh neutrons there are over and above one, but they do agree that there is an excess.

With this as a basis, let us turn the question around. Why has not the great explosion happened as yet, since there are neutrons enough to achieve it?

One reason, apparently, is that the fresh neutrons are moving with the wrong speeds when they are released. Fission is performed mainly by very slow neutrons, while the new-born ones are very rapid. But if the piece of uranium were very large, even the fresh neutrons would be slowed down by their repeated collisions with nuclei; and therefore those who are trying to make the explosion, or trying to approach it without quite making it, are heaping up great masses of uranium. If, however, the uranium is mixed with other elements — as in nature it always has been — the neutrons are liable to be captured and rendered harmless by the nuclei of these others. Therefore, the next step is to purify the uranium. This would be easy enough were it not that "purity" in this connection means something more stringent than even chemical purity. Within the last few weeks it has been proved that only one isotope of uranium is sensitive to slow neutrons, and this is a rare one — fortunately, I feel like saying. One must perform a process of isotope-separation in which the two isotopes differ in mass by less than 2 percent, and one is more than a hundred times as abundant as the other. Probably this will take a long time in the doing. If and when it is done, shall we find that human artifice has succeeded in removing or relaxing the last brake provided by nature to impede the slide toward catastrophe? Perhaps not even then, for the rare isotope of uranium may have ways of its own for capturing neutrons and rendering them harmless before the most of them achieve fissions. Perhaps on the other hand the brakes are easier to relax than the foregoing words imply. Possibly they can be relaxed just a little without letting go altogether, and then there may be available a potent source of power. But at this point I depart from the traditional detachment of the scientist, and express the fervent hope that the mastery of this process, if ever to be achieved at all, will not be achieved until the world is ready to use it wisely.

ALBERT EINSTEIN

Isaac Newton

[FROM THE SMITHSONIAN REPORT FOR 1927]

NEWTON AND EINSTEIN — *two of the greatest intellects the world has ever known — are here brought together in a single article. In 1927, on the occasion of the two hundredth anniversary of Newton's death, Einstein published this eulogy in the* Manchester Guardian. *These two men, seldom, if ever, equaled in their capacity for abstract thought, are alike in that each broke through the barriers of the known and advanced entirely new concepts that revolutionized the theories of the physical universe.*

Although Newton's name is most commonly thought of in association with the laws of gravitation and the motions of planets, moons, and comets, Einstein points out that the greater significance of his achievements is that they formed the basis of practically all the progress in physical research for nearly 200 years. Einstein even considered that his own revolutionary theory of relativity was an organic development of Newton's thought.

THE two-hundredth anniversary of the death of Newton falls at this time. One's thoughts cannot but turn to this shining spirit, who pointed out, as none before or after him did, the path of Western thought and research and practical construction. He was not only an inventor of genius in respect of particular guiding methods; he also showed a unique mastery of the empirical material known in his time, and he was marvelously inventive in special mathematical and physical demonstrations. For all these reasons he deserves our deep veneration. He is, however, a yet more significant figure than his own mastery makes him, since he was placed by fate at a turning point in the world's intellectual development. This is brought home vividly to us when we recall that before Newton there was no comprehensive system of physical causality which could in any way render the deeper characters of the world of concrete experienc~

The great materialists of ancient Greek civilization had indeed postulated the reference of all material phenomena to a process of atomic movements controlled by rigid laws, without appealing to the will of living creatures as an independent cause. Descartes, in his own fashion, had revived this ultimate conception. But it remained a bold postulate, the problematic ideal of a school of philosophy. In the way of actual justification of our confidence in the existence of an entirely physical causality, virtually nothing had been achieved before Newton.

NEWTON'S AIM

Newton's aim was to find an answer to the question: Does there exist a simple rule by which the motion of the heavenly bodies of our planetary system can be completely calculated, if the state of motion of all these bodies at a single moment is known? Kepler's empirical laws of the motion of the planets, based on Tycho Brahe's observations, were already enunciated, and demanded an interpretation.* These laws gave a complete answer to the question how the planets moved round the sun (elliptical orbit, equal areas described by the radius vector in equal periods, relation between

---

* Everyone knows today what gigantic efforts were needed to discover these laws from the empirically ascertained orbits of the planets. But few reflect on the genius of the method by which Kepler ascertained the true orbits from the apparent ones; i.e., their directions as observed from the earth.

semi-major axis and period of revolution). But these rules do not satisfy the requirement of causality. The three rules are logically independent of one another, and show no sign of any interconnection. The third law cannot be extended numerically as it stands, from the sun to another central body; there is, for instance, no relation between a planet's period of revolution round the sun and the period of revolution of a moon round its planet.

But the principal thing is that these laws have reference to motion as a whole, and not to the question how there is developed from one condition of motion of a system that which immediately follows it in time. They are, in our phraseology of today, integral laws and not differential laws.

The differential law is the form which alone entirely satisfies the modern physicist's requirement of causality. The clear conception of the differential law is one of the greatest of Newton's intellectual achievements. What was needed was not only the idea but a formal mathematical method which was, indeed, extant in rudiment but had still to gain a systematic shape. This also Newton found in the differential and integral calculus. It is unnecessary to consider whether Leibnitz arrived at these same mathematical methods independently of Newton or not; in any case, their development was a necessity for Newton, as they were required in order to give Newton the means of expressing his thought.

THE STEP FROM GALILEO TO NEWTON

Galileo had already made a significant first step in the recognition of the law of motion. He discovered the law of inertia and the law of free falling in the earth's field of gravitation: A mass (or, more accurately, a material point) uninfluenced by other masses moves uniformly in a straight line; the vertical velocity of a free body increases in the field of gravity in proportion to the time. It may seem to us today to be only a small step from Galileo's observations to Newton's laws of motion. But it has to be observed that the two propositions above, in the form in which they are given, relate to motion as a whole, while Newton's law of motion gives an answer to the question: How does the condition of motion of a point-mass change in an infinitely small period under the influence of an external force? Only after proceeding to consider the phenomenon during an infinitely short period (differential law) does Newton arrive at a formula which is applicable to all motions. He takes the conception of force from the already highly developed theory of statics. He is only able to connect force with acceleration by introducing the new conception of mass, which, indeed, is supported curiously enough by an apparent definition. Today we are so accustomed to forming conceptions which correspond to differential quotients that we can hardly realize any longer how great a capacity for abstraction was needed to pass across a double barrier to the general differential laws of motion, with the further need to evolve the conception of mass.

But this was still a long way from the causal comprehension of the phenomena of motion. For the motion was only determined by the equation of motion if the force was given. Newton had the idea, to which he was probably led by the laws of the planetary motions, that the force acting on a mass is determined by the position of all masses at a sufficiently small distance from the mass in question. Not until this connection was realized was a completely causal comprehension of the phenomena of motion obtained. How Newton, proceeding from Kepler's laws of the motion of planets, solved this problem for gravitation and so discovered the identity of the nature of gravity with the motive forces acting on the stars is common knowledge. It is only the combination of —

$$(\text{Law of motion}) + (\text{Law of attraction})$$

through which is constituted that wonderful thought-structure which enables the earlier and later conditions of a system to be calculated from the conditions ruling at one particular time, in so far as the phenomena occur under the sole influence of the forces of gravitation. The logical completeness of Newton's system of ideas lay in the fact that the sole causes of the acceleration of the masses of a system prove to be the masses themselves.

On the basis sketched Newton succeeded in explaining the motions of the planets, moons, comets, down to fine details, as well as the ebb and flow of the tides and the precessional movement of the earth — this last a deductive achievement of peculiar brilliance. It was, no doubt, especially impressive to learn that the cause of the movements of the heavenly bodies is identical with the force of gravity, so familiar to us from everyday experience.

SIGNIFICANCE OF NEWTON'S ACHIEVEMENT

The significance, however, of Newton's achievement lay not only in its provision of a serviceable and logically satisfactory basis for mechanics proper; up to the end of the nineteenth century it formed the program of all theoretical physical research. All physical phenomena were to be referred to masses subject to Newton's law of motion. Only the law of force had to be amplified and adapted to the type of phenomena which was being considered. Newton himself tried to apply this program in optics, on the hypothesis that light consisted of inert corpuscles. The optics of the undulatory theory also made use of Newton's law of motion, the law being applied to continuously diffused masses. The kinetic theory of heat rested solely on Newton's formulae of motion; and this theory not only prepared people's minds for the recognition of the law of the conservation of energy, but also supplied a theory of gases confirmed in its smallest details, and a deepened conception of the nature of the second law of thermodynamics. The theory of electricity and magnetism also developed down to modern times entirely under the guidance of Newton's basic ideas (electric and magnetic substance, forces at a distance). Even Faraday and Maxwell's revolution in electrodynamics and optics, which was the first great advance in the fundamental principles of theoretical physics since Newton, was still achieved entirely under the guidance of Newton's ideas. Maxwell, Boltzmann, and Lord Kelvin never tired of trying again and again to reduce electromagnetic fields and their dynamical reciprocal action to mechanical processes occurring in continuously distributed hypothetical masses. But owing to the barrenness, or at least unfruitfulness, of these efforts there gradually occurred, after the end of the nineteenth century, a revulsion in fundamental conceptions; theoretical physics outgrew Newton's framework, which had for nearly two centuries provided fixity and intellectual guidance for science.

NEWTON ON ITS LIMITATIONS

Newton's basic principles were so satisfying from a logical stand-point that the impulse to fresh departures could only come from the pressure of the facts of experience. Before I enter into this I must emphasize that Newton himself was better aware of the weak sides of his thought-structure than the succeeding generations of students. This fact has always excited my reverent admiration; I should like, therefore, to dwell a little on it.

1. Although everyone has remarked how Newton strove to repre-sent his thought-system as necessarily subject to the confirmation of experience, and to introduce the minimum of conceptions not directly referable to matters of experience, he makes use of the conceptions of absolute space and absolute time. In our own day he has often been criticized for this. But it is in this very point that Newton is particularly consistent. He had recognized that the ob-servable geometrical magnitudes (distances of material points from one another) and their change in process of time do not completely determine movements in a physical sense. He shows this in the famous bucket experiment. There is, therefore, in addition to masses and their distances, varying with time, something else, which determines what happens; this "something" he conceives as the re-lation to "absolute space." He recognizes that space must possess a sort of physical reality if his laws of motion are to have a mean-ing, a reality of the same sort as the material points and their distances.

This clear recognition shows both Newton's wisdom and a weak side of his theory. For a logical construction of the theory would certainly be more satisfactory without this shadowy conception; only those objects (point-masses, distances) would then come into the laws whose relation to our perceptions is perfectly clear.

2. The introduction of direct, instantaneously acting forces at a distance into the exposition of the effects of gravitation does not correspond to the character of most of the phenomena which are familiar to us in our daily experience. Newton meets this objec-tion by pointing out that his law of reciprocal gravitation is not to

be taken as an ultimate explanation, but as a rule induced from experience.

3. Newton's theory offered no explanation of the very remarkable fact that the weight and inertia of a body are determined by the same magnitude (the mass). The remarkable nature of this fact struck Newton also.

None of these three points can rank as a logical objection against the theory. They form, as it were, merely unsatisfied needs of the scientific spirit in its effort to penetrate the processes of nature by a complete and unified set of ideas.

THE THEORY OF THE ELECTROMAGNETIC FIELD

Newton's theory of motion, considered as a program for the whole field of theoretical physics, suffered its first shock from Maxwell's theory of electricity. It was found that the reciprocal action between bodies through electrical and magnetic bodies does not take place through instantaneously acting forces at a distance, but through processes which are transmitted with finite velocity through space. Alongside the point-mass and its movements there arose, in Faraday's conception, a new sort of physically real thing, the "field." It was first sought to conceive this, with the aid of mechanical modes of thought, as a mechanical condition (of movement or strain) of a hypothetical space-filling medium (the ether). When, however, in spite of the most obstinate efforts, this mechanical interpretation refused to work, students slowly accustomed themselves to the conception of the "electromagnetic field" as the ultimate irreducible foundation stone of physical reality. We owe to H. Hertz the deliberate liberation of the conception of the field from all the scaffolding of the conceptions of mechanics, and to H. A. Lorentz the liberation of the conception of the field from a material bearer; according to Lorentz the physical empty space (or ether) alone figured as bearer of the field; in Newton's mechanics, indeed, space had not been devoid of all physical functions. When this development had been completed, no one any longer believed in directly acting instantaneous forces at a distance, even in connection with gravitation, though a field theory for gravitation, for lack of sufficient known facts, was not unmistakably indicated. The development of the theory of the electromagnetic field also led, after Newton's hypothesis of action at a distance had been abandoned, to the attempt to find an electromagnetic explanation for Newton's law of motion, or to replace that law by a more accurate law based on the field theory. These efforts were not crowned with full success, but the mechanical basic conceptions ceased to be regarded as foundation stones of the physical conception of the universe.

The Maxwell-Lorentz theory led inevitably to the special theory of relativity, which, by destroying the conception of absolute simultaneity, negatived the existence of forces at a distance. Under this theory mass is not an unalterable magnitude, but a magnitude dependent on (and, indeed, identical with) the amount of energy. The theory also showed that Newton's law of motion can only be considered as a limiting law valid only for small velocities, and substituted for it a new law of motion, in which the velocity of light in a vacuum appears as the limiting velocity.

THE GENERAL THEORY OF RELATIVITY

The last step in the development of the program of the field theory was the general theory of relativity. Quantitatively it made little modification in Newton's theory, but qualitatively a deep-seated one. Inertia, gravitation, and the metrical behavior of bodies and clocks were reduced to the single quality of a field, and this field in turn was made dependent on the bodies (generalization of Newton's law of gravitation or of the corresponding field law, as formulated by Poisson). Space and time were so divested, not of their reality, but of their causal absoluteness (absoluteness — influencing, that is, not influenced), which Newton was compelled to attribute to them in order to be able to give expression to the laws then known. The generalized law of inertia takes over the role of Newton's law of motion. From this short characterization it will be clear how the elements of Newton's theory passed over into the general theory of relativity, the three defects above mentioned being at the same time overcome. It appears that within the framework of the general theory of relativity the law of motion can be deduced from the law of the field, which corresponds to Newton's law of force. Only when this aim has been fully attained can we speak of a pure theory of fields.

Newton's mechanics prepared the way for the theory of fields in a yet more formal sense. The application of Newton's mechanics to continuously distributed masses led necessarily to the discovery and application of partial differential equations, which in turn supplied the language in which alone the laws of the theory of fields could be expressed. In this formal connection also Newton's conception of the differential law forms the first decisive step to the subsequent development.

The whole development of our ideas concerning natural phenomena, which has been described above, may be conceived as an organic development of Newton's thought. But while the construction of the theory of fields was still actively in progress, the facts of heat radiation, spectra, radioactivity, and so on, revealed a limit to the employment of the whole system of thought, which, in spite of gigantic successes in detail, seems to us today completely insurmountable. Many physicists maintain, not without weighty arguments, that in face of these facts not only the differential law but the law of causality itself — hitherto the ultimate basic postulate of all natural science — fails.

The very possibility of a spatio-temporal construction which can be clearly brought into consonance with physical experience is denied. That a mechanical system should permanently admit only discrete values of energy or discrete states — as experience, so to say, directly shows — seems at first hardly deducible from a theory of fields working with differential equations. The method of De Broglie and Schrödinger, which has, in a certain sense, the character of a theory of fields, does deduce, on the basis of differential equations, from a sort 'of considerations of resonance the existence of purely discrete states and their transition into one another in amazing agreement with the facts of experience; but it has to dispense with a localization of the mass-particles and with strictly causal laws. Who would be so venturesome as to decide today the question whether causal law and differential law, these ultimate premises of Newton's treatment of nature must be definitely abandoned?

G. MARCONI

Wireless Telegraphy

[FROM THE SMITHSONIAN REPORT FOR 1901]

UP TO THIS POINT, *we have been dealing largely with basic research in astronomy and physics, conducted with little or no thought for any practical application. In this article Marconi sets forth the actual beginning of a new art derived directly from such basic researches. Pure-science investigations have been likened to a reservoir from which practical applications may be drained off. Should the reservoir shrink or dry up, applications for the use of man likewise dwindle.*

Marconi's wireless telegraphy, and our present-day radio and television, trace their origins directly to Maxwell's theory of the electromagnetic field and ether waves, followed by Hertz's experimental proof of the theory. Although wireless communication as revealed here in its earliest stages appears crude and feeble, it actually developed very rapidly. In 1899 communication across the English Channel was achieved, and, only two years later, across the Atlantic from England to Newfoundland. Marconi's work won him the Nobel prize for physics, as well as innumerable honors in his homeland and abroad.

(The Bettman Archive)

ILLUS. 53—Signor G. Marconi, M. Inst. C. E.

W HEN Ampère threw out the suggestion that the theory of a universal ether, possessed of merely mechanical properties, might supply the means for explaining electrical facts, which view was upheld by Joseph Henry and Faraday, the veil of mystery which had enveloped electricity began to lift. When Maxwell published, in 1864, his splendid dynamical theory of the electromagnetic field, and worked out mathematically the theory of ether waves, and Hertz had proved experimentally the correctness of Maxwell's hypothesis, we obtained, if I may use the words of Professor Fleming, "the greatest insight into the hidden mechanisms of nature which has yet been made by the intellect of man."

A century of progress such as this has made wireless telegraphy possible. Its basic principles are established in the very nature of electricity itself. Its evolution has placed another great force of nature at our disposal.

We cannot pay too high a tribute to the genius of Heinrich Hertz, who worked patiently and persistently in a new field of experimental physics, and made what has been called the greatest discovery in electrical science in the latter half of the nineteenth century. He not only brought about a great triumph in the field of theoretical physics, but, by proving Maxwell's mathematical hypothesis, he accomplished a great triumph in the progress of our knowledge of physical agents and physical laws.

I cannot forbear saying one word as to the eminent electrician who was placed in his last home only a very short time ago, for it is manifest that several years ago Professor Hughes was on the verge of a great discovery, and, if he had persevered in his experiments, it seems probable that his name would have been closely connected with wireless telegraphy as it is with so many branches of electrical work, in which he gained so much renown and such great distinction.

The experimental proof by Hertz in the year 1887 of the identity of light and electricity, and the knowledge of how to produce and how to detect these ether waves, the existence of which had been so far unknown, made possible true wireless telegraphy. I think I may be justified in saying that for several years the full importance of the discovery of Hertz was realized by but very few, and for this reason the early development of its practical application was slow.

The practical application of wireless telegraphy at the present time is many times as great as the predictions of five years ago led us to expect in so short a time. The development of the art during the past three or four years and its present state of progress may perhaps justify the interest which is now taken in the subject. Yet only a beginning has been made and the possibilities of the future can as yet be only incompletely appreciated. All of you know that the idea of communicating intelligence without visible means of connection is almost as old as mankind. Wireless telegraphy by means of Hertzian waves is, however, very young. I hope that if I pass over the story of the growth of this new art, as I have watched it, or do not attempt to prove questions of priority, no one will take it for granted that nothing is to be said on these subjects or that all that has been said is entirely correct.

The time allowed for this discourse is too short to permit me to recount all the steps that have led up to the practical applications of today. I believe it will probably interest you more to hear of the problems which have lately been solved, and the very interesting developments which have occurred during the last few months.

I find that a great element of the success of wireless telegraphy is dependent upon the use of a coherer such I have adopted. It has been my experience, and that of other workers, that a coherer as previously constructed — that is, a tube several inches long partially filled with filings inclosed by corks — was far too untrustworthy to fulfill its purpose. I found, however, that if specially prepared filings were confined in a very small gap (about 1 mm.) between flat plugs of silver, the coherer, if properly constructed, became absolutely trustworthy. In its normal condition the resistance of a good coherer is infinite, but when influenced by electric waves the coherer instantly becomes a conductor, its resistance falling to 100 or 500 ohms. This conductivity is maintained until the tube is shaken or tapped.

I noticed that by employing similar vertical and insulated rods at both stations it was possible to detect the effects of electric waves of high frequency, and in that way convey the intelligible alphabetical signals over distances far greater than had been believed to be possible a few years ago.

I had formerly ascertained that the distance over which it is possible to signal with a given amount of energy varies approximately with the square of the height of the vertical wire, and with the square root of the capacity of a plate, drum, or other form of capacity area which may be placed at the top of the wires.

The law governing the relation of height and distance has already been proved correct up to a distance of 85 miles. Many months ago it was found possible to communicate from the North Haven, Poole, to Alum Bay, Isle of Wight, with a height of 75 feet, the distance being 18 miles. Later on, two installations with vertical wires of double that length, i.e., 150 feet, were erected at a distance of 85 miles apart, and signals were easily obtained between them. According to a rigorous application of the law, 72 miles ought to have been obtained instead of 85; but as I have previously stated, the law has been proved only to be approximately correct, the tendency being always on what I might call the right side; thus we obtain a greater distance than the application of the law would lead us to believe. There is a remarkable circumstance to be noted in the case of the 85 miles signaling. At the Alum Bay station the mast is on the cliff, and there is no curvature of the earth intervening between the two stations; that is to say, a straight line between the base of the Haven and Alum Bay stations would clear the surface of the sea. But in the case of the 85 miles the two stations were located on the sea level, and between them exists a hill of water, owing to the earth's curvature, amounting to over 1,000 feet. If those waves traveled only in straight lines, or the effect was noticeable only across open space, in a direct line, the signals would not have been received except with a vertical wire 1,000 feet high at both stations.

While carrying out some experiments nearly three years ago at Salisbury, Captain Kennedy, R.E., and I tried numerous forms of induction coils wound in the ordinary way, that is, with a great number of turns of wire on the secondary circuit, with the object of increasing, if possible, the distance or range of transmission; but in every case we observed a very marked decrease in the distance obtainable with the given amount of energy and height. Similar results were obtained some months later, I am informed, in experiments carried out by the general postoffice engineers at Dover.

In all our above-mentioned experiments the coils used were those in which the primary consisted of a smaller or larger number of turns of comparatively thick wire, and the secondary of several layers of thinner wire. I believe I am right in saying that hundreds of these coils were tried, the result always being that by their employment the possible distance of signaling was considerably diminished instead of being increased. We eventually found an entirely new form of induction coil that would work satisfactorily, and that began to increase the distance of signaling.

The results given by some of the new form of induction coils have been remarkable. During the naval maneuvers I had an opportunity of testing how much they increased the range of signaling with a given amount of energy and height. When working between the cruisers *Juno* and *Europa*, I ascertained that when the induction coil was omitted from the receiver, the limit distance obtainable was 7 miles, but with an improved form of induction coil included, a distance of over 60 miles could be obtained with certainty. This demonstrated that the coils I used at that time increased the possible distance nearly tenfold. I have now adopted these induction coils, or transformers, at all our permanent stations.

A number of experiments have been carried out to test how far the Wehnelt brake was applicable in substitution for the ordinary make and brake of the induction coil at the transmitting station; but although some excellent results have been obtained over a distance of 40 miles of land, the amount of current used and the liability of the brake getting fatigued or out of order have been obstacles which have so far prevented its general adoption.

As is probably known to most of you, the system has been in practical daily operation between the East Goodwin lightship and the South Foreland lighthouse since December 24, 1898, and I have good reason for believing that the officials of Trinity House are convinced of its great utility in connection with lightships and lighthouses. It may be interesting to you to know that, as specially arranged by the authorities of Trinity House, although we maintain a skilled assistant on the lightship, he is not allowed to work on the telegraph. The work is invariably done by one of the seamen on the lightship, many of whom have been instructed in the use of the instrument by one of my assistants. On five occasions assistance has been called for by the men on board the ship, and help obtained in time to avoid loss of life and property. Of these five calls for assistance, three were for vessels run ashore on the sands near the lightship, one because the lightship herself had been run into by a steamer, and one to call a boat to take off a member of the crew who was seriously ill.

In the case of a French steamer which went ashore off the Goodwins, we have evidence, given in the admiralty court, that by means of one short wireless message property to the amount of £52,588 was saved; and of this amount, I am glad to say, the owners and crews of the lifeboats and tugs received £3,000. This one saving alone is probably sufficient in amount to equip all the lightships round England with wireless telegraph apparatus more than ten times over. The system has also been in constant use for the official communication between the Trinity House and the ship, and is also used daily by the men for private communication with their families, etc.

It is difficult to believe that any person who knows that wireless telegraphy has been in use between this lightship and the South Foreland day and night, in storm and sunshine, in fog and in gales of wind, without breaking down on any single occasion, can believe or be justified in saying that wireless telegraphy is untrustworthy or uncertain in operation. The lightship installation is, be it remembered, in a small damp ship, and under conditions which try the system to the utmost. I hope that before long the necessary funds will be at the disposal of the Trinity House authorities, in order that communication may be established between other lightships and lighthouses and the shore, by which millions of pounds' worth of property and thousands of lives may be saved.

At the end of March, 1899, by arrangement with the French Government, communication was established between the South Foreland lighthouse and Wimereux, near Boulogne, over a distance of 30 miles, and various interesting tests were made between these stations and French warships. The maximum distance obtained at that time, with a height of about 100 feet on the ships, was 42 miles. The commission of French naval and military officers who were appointed to supervise these experiments, and report to their Government, were in almost daily attendance on the one coast or the other for several weeks. They became intensely interested in the operations, and I have good reasons to know made satisfactory reports to their Government. I cannot allow this opportunity to pass without bearing willing testimony to the courtesy and attention which characterized all the dealings of these French gentlemen with myself and staff.

The most interesting and complete tests of the system at sea were, however, made during the British naval maneuvers. Three ships of the "B" fleet were fitted up — the flagship *Alexandra* and the cruisers *Juno* and *Europa*. I do not consider myself quite at liberty to describe all the various tests to which the system was put, but I believe that never before were Hertzian waves given a more difficult or responsible task. During these maneuvers I had the pleasure of being on board the *Juno,* my friend, Captain Jackson, R.N., who had done some very good work on the subject of wireless telegraphy before I had the pleasure of meeting him, being in command. With the *Juno* there was usually a small squadron of cruisers, and all orders and communications were transmitted to the *Juno* from the flagship, the *Juno* repeating them to the ships around her. This enabled evolutions to be carried out even when the flagship was out of sight. This would have been impossible by means of flags or semaphores. The wireless installations on these battleships were kept going night and day, most important maneuvers being carried out and valuable information telegraphed to the admiral when necessary.

The greatest distance at which service messages were sent was 60 nautical miles, between the *Europa* and the *Juno,* and 45 miles, between the *Juno* and the *Alexandra*. This was not the maximum distance actually obtained, but the distance at which, under all circumstances and conditions, the system could be relied upon for certain and regular transmission of service messages. During tests messages were obtained at no less than 74 nautical miles (85 land miles).

As to the opinion which naval experts have arrived at concerning this new method of communication, I need only refer to the letters published by naval officers and experts in the columns of The Times during and after the period of the autumn maneuvers, and to the fact that the admiralty are taking steps to introduce the system into general use in the navy.

As you will probably remember, victory was gained by the "B" fleet, and perhaps I may venture to suggest that the facility which Admiral Sir Compton Domville had of using the wireless telegraph in all weathers, both by day and night, contributed to the success of his operations.

Commander Statham, R.N., has published a very concise description of the results obtained in the Army and Navy, illustrated, and I think it will be interesting if I read a short extract from the admirable description he has published:

"When the reserve fleet first assembled at Tor Bay, the *Juno* was sent out day by day to communicate at various distances with the flagship, and the range was speedily increased to over 30 miles, ultimately reaching something like 50 miles. At Milford Haven the *Europa* was fitted out, the first step being the securing to the main topmast head of a hastily prepared spar carrying a small gaff or sprit, to which was attached a wire, which was brought down to the starboard side of the quarter-deck through an insulator and into a roomy deck house on the lower afterbridge which contained the various instruments.

"When hostilities commenced, the *Europa* was leading ship of a squadron of 7 cruisers dispatched to look for the convoy at the rendezvous. The *Juno* was detached to act as a link when necessary and to scout for the enemy, and the flagship of course remained with the slower battle squadron. The *Europa* was in direct communication with the flagship long after leaving Milford Haven, the gap between reaching to 30 or 40 miles before she lost touch while steaming ahead at a fast speed. (This difference between the ranges of communication on these ships was owing to the *Juno* having a higher mast than the *Alexandra*.)

"Reaching the convoy at 4 o'clock one afternoon, and leaving it and the several cruisers in charge of the senior captain, the *Europa* hastened back toward another rendezvous, where the admiral had intended remaining until he should hear whether the enemy had found and captured the convoy; but scarcely had she got well ahead of the slow ships when the *Juno* called her up and announced the admiral coming to meet the convoy. The *Juno* was at this time fully 60 miles distant from the *Europa*.

"Now imagine," says Commander Statham, "a chain of vessels 60

miles apart. Only five would be necessary to communicate some
vital piece of intelligence a distance of 300 miles, receive in return their instructions, and act immediately all in the course of
half an hour or less. This is possible already. Doubtless a vast
deal more will be done in a year or two or less, and meanwhile
the authorities should be making all necessary arrangements for
the universal application of wireless telegraphy in the navy."

The most important results, from a technical point of view, obtained during the maneuvers were the proof of the great increase
of distance obtained by employing the transformer in the receiver,
as already explained, and also that the curvature of the earth
which intervened, however great the distance attained, was apparently no obstacle to the transmission. The maximum height of
the top of the wire attached to the instruments above the water
did not on any occasion exceed 170 feet, but it would have been
geometrically necessary to have had masts 700 feet high on each
ship in order that a straight line between their tops should clear
the curved surface of the sea when the ships were 60 nautical
miles apart. This shows that the Hertzian waves had either to go
over or round the dome of water 530 feet higher than the tops of
the masts, or to pass through it, which latter course I believe
would be impossible.

Some time after the naval maneuvers, with a view to showing
the feasibility of communicating over considerable distances on
land, it was decided to erect two stations, one at Chelmsford and
another at Harwich, the distance between them being 40 miles.
These installations have been working regularly since last September, and my experiments and improvements are continually being
carried out at Chelmsford, Harwich, Alum Bay, and North Haven,
Poole.

In the month of September last, during the meetings of the
British Association in Dover and of the Association Française pour
l'Avancement de Science in Boulogne, a temporary installation was
fixed in the Dover town hall, in order that members present should
see the practical working of the system between England and
France. Messages were exchanged with ease between Wimereux,
near Boulogne, and Dover town hall. In this way it was possible
for the members of the two associations to converse across the
channel, over a distance of 30 miles.

During Professor Fleming's lecture on the Centenary of the Electric Current, messages were transmitted direct to and received from France, and via the South Foreland lighthouse to the East Goodwin lightship. An interesting point was that it was demonstrated that the great masses of the Castle Rock and South Foreland cliffs lying between the town hall, Dover, and the lighthouse did not in the least degree interfere with the transmission of signals. The result was, however, by no means new. It only confirmed the results of many previous experiments, all of them showing that rock masses of very considerable size intervening between two stations do not in the least affect the freedom of communication by ether wave telegraphy.

It was during these tests that it was found possible to communicate direct from Wimereux to Harwich or Chelmsford, the intervening distance being 85 miles. This result was published in a letter from Professor Fleming addressed to the Electrician on September 29. The distance from Wimereux to Harwich is approximately 85 miles, and from Wimereux to Chelmsford also 85 miles, of which 30 miles are over sea and 55 over land. The height of the poles at these stations was 150 feet, but if it had been necessary for a line drawn between the tops of the masts to clear the curvature of the earth, they would have had to have been over 1,000 feet high. I give these results to show what satisfactory progress is being made with this system.

In America wireless telegraphy was used to report from the high seas the progress of the yachts in the international yacht race, and I think that occasion holds the record for work done in a given time, over 4,000 words being transmitted in the space of less than five hours on several different days.

Some tests were carried out for the United States Navy; but, owing to insufficient apparatus, and to the fact that all the latest improvements had not been protected in the United States at that time, it was impossible to give the authorities there such a complete demonstration as was given to the British authorities during the naval maneuvers. Messages were transmitted between the battleship *Massachusetts* and the cruiser *New York* up to a distance of 36 miles.

A few days previous to my departure from America the war in

South Africa broke out. Some of the officials of the American line suggested that, as a permanent installation existed at the Needles, Isle of Wight, it would be a great thing, if possible, to obtain the latest war news before our arrival on the *St. Paul* at Southampton. I readily consented to fit up my instruments on the *St. Paul*, and succeeded in calling up the Needles station at a distance of 66 nautical miles. By means of wireless telegraphy, all the important news was transmitted to the *St. Paul* while she was underway, steaming 20 knots, and messages were despatched to several places by passengers on board. News was collected and printed in a small paper called the *Transatlantic Times* several hours before our arrival at Southampton.

This was, I believe, the first instance of the passengers of a steamer receiving news while several miles from land, and seems to point to a not far distant prospect of passengers maintaining direct and regular communication with the land they are leaving and with the land they are approaching, by means of wireless telegraphy.

At the tardy request of the war office, we sent our Mr. Bullocke and five of our assistants to South Africa. It was the intention of the war office that the wireless telegraph should be used only at the base and on the railways, but the officers on the spot realized that it could be of any practical use only at the front. They therefore asked Mr. Bullocke whether he was willing to go to the front. As the whole of the assistants volunteered to go anywhere with Mr. Bullocke, their services were accepted, and on December 11 they moved up to the camp at De Aar. But when they arrived at De Aar, they found that no arrangements had been made to supply poles, kites, or balloons, which, as you all know, are an essential part of the apparatus, and none could be obtained on the spot. To get over the difficulty, they manufactured some kites, and in this they had the hearty assistance of two officers, viz, Major Baden-Powell and Captain Kennedy, R.E., who have often helped me in my experiments in England. (Major Baden-Powell, it will be remembered, is a brother of the gallant defender of Mafeking.)

The results which they obtained were not at first altogether satisfactory, but this is accounted for by the fact that the working was attempted without poles or proper kites, and afterwards with poles of insufficient height, while the use of the kites was very difficult, the kites being manufactured on the spot with very deficient material. The wind being so variable, it often happened that when a kite was flying at one station there was not enough wind to fly a kite at the other station with which they were attempting to communicate. It is therefore manifest that their partial failure was due to the lack of proper preparation on the part of the local military authorities, and has no bearing on the practicability and utility of the system when carried out under normal conditions.

It was reported that the difficulty of getting through from one station to another was due to the iron in the hills. If this had not been cabled from South Africa, it would hardly be credible that any one should have committed himself to such a very unscientific opinion. As a matter of fact, iron would have no greater destructive effect on these Hertzian waves than any other metal, the rays apparently getting very easily around or over such obstacles. A fleet of 30 ironclads did not affect the rays during the naval maneuvers, and during the yacht race I was able to transmit my messages with absolute success across the very high buildings of New York, the upper stories of which are iron.

However, on getting the kites up, they easily communicated from De Aar to Orange River, over a distance of some 70 miles. I am glad to say that, from later information received, they have been able to obtain poles, which although not quite high enough for long distances are sufficiently useful. We have also sent a number of Major Baden-Powell's kites, which are the only ones I have found to be of real service.

Stations have been established at Modder River, Enslin, Belmont, Orange River, and De Aar, which work well and will be invaluable in case the field telegraph line connecting these positions should be cut by the enemy.

It is also satisfactory to note that the military authorities have lately arranged to supply small balloons to my assistants for portable installations on service wagons.

While I admire the determination of Mr. Bullocke and our assistants in their endeavor to do the very best they could with most imperfect local means, I think it only right to say that if I had been on the spot myself I should have refused to open any station until the officers had provided the means for elevating the wire, which, as you know, is essential to success.

Mr. Bullocke and another of our assistants in South Africa have been transferred, with some of the apparatus, to Natal to join General Buller's forces, and it is likely that before the campaign is ended wireless telegraphy will have proved its utility in actual warfare. Two of our assistants bravely volunteered to take an installation through the Boer lines in Kimberley; but the military authority did not think fit to grant them permission, as it probably involved too great a risk.

What the bearing on the campaign would have been if working installations had been established in Ladysmith, Kimberley, and Mafeking before they were besieged, I leave military strategists to state. I am sure you will agree with me that it is much to be regretted that the system could not be got into these towns prior to the commencement of hostilities.

I find it hard to believe that the Boers possess any workable instruments. Some instruments intended for them were seized by the authorities at Cape Town. These instruments turned out to have been manufactured in Germany. Our assistants, however, found that these instruments were not workable. I need hardly add that as no apparatus has been supplied by us to anyone, the Boers cannot possibly have obtained any of our instruments.

I have spoken at great length about the things which have been accomplished. I do not like to dwell upon what may or will be done in the immediate or more distant future, but there is one thing of which I am confident, viz, that the progress made this year will greatly surpass what has been accomplished during the last 12 months; and, speaking what I believe to be sober sense, I say that by means of the wireless telegraph, telegrams will be as common and as much in daily use on the sea as at present on land.

[Mr. Marconi's experiments in transatlantic telegraphing were thus described in the New York *Herald* of Sunday, December 15, and Tuesday, December 17, 1901:

[EXTRACT FROM THE NEW YORK HERALD,
DECEMBER 15, 1901.]

ST. JOHNS, NEWFOUNDLAND, *Saturday, December 14.*
Mr. Marconi announced today that he has successfully received by
wireless telegraphy, at the station on Signal Hill, messages from
the station recently erected near the Lizard, in Cornwall, England.
These messages, Mr. Marconi said, were received on Wednesday
and Thursday afternoons. He had arranged with the Cornwall
station that the letter "S" was to be signaled at 6 o'clock in the
evening, which would be half-past 2 o'clock here, and signals were
received as arranged on Wednesday and Thursday, though no
signal came yesterday or today.

MR. MARCONI DESCRIBES THE TEST.

"I thought it advisable," said Mr. Marconi, "with the machinery
which had escaped damage at Cornwall, to see whether it was
possible to obtain signals here from England at the same time I
tried experiments with transatlantic liners.

"When the kite elevated the wire to a height of 400 feet above
Signal Hill on Wednesday a number of signals, consisting of the
letter 'S,' which signal was ordered to be sent from Cornwall, were
clearly received on Signal Hill by the receiving instruments. We
again received the signals perfectly on Thursday.

"The signals were obtained only when the kite was up to a considerable height. For some reason yesterday nothing was received,
and today we could not get the kite up on account of the weather.
It has been blowing too heavily every day for balloons, which
would be best to experiment with.

SUCCESS HAS ALTERED HIS PLANS.

"The success of these tests will alter my plans. I intend to sus-
pend further tests with kites and balloons for a short time and
erect a large station here, at a cost of $50,000, having towers, or
masts, for supporting wires. This, of course, provided there is no
governmental or other objection. This will necessitate my going

back to England at the end of next week in order to have the necessary equipments sent here, with suitable transmitting machinery and other requirements.

"By that time I hope to have the Cape Cod Station in working order again, so as to complete a regular triangular service. No doubt the success of my experiments here will cause a sensation in telegraphic circles, and many will find it difficult to believe it.

"I myself had very little doubt as to our ultimate success, but I thought it advisable not to communicate beforehand the exact scope of these tests, as I considered it would be better to assure myself of success before publishing details even of installations at Cornwall and Cape Cod, and what we hoped to accomplish by them. It is right, however, that the public should now know of the grand result of my experiments here.

"I hope in the course of a few months to have a system of direct communication across the Atlantic in working order, and it can then be easily ascertained whether the discovery is of practical use for commercial and other purposes. I have no doubt in the matter, but I am content to wait and let events prove that I am correct in my belief.

"The instruments I have at present are extremely sensitive, and I am of the opinion that in order to make the signals absolutely reliable it will be necessary to arrange for more power at the sending station in Cornwall, which I will arrange for on my return to England."

Mr. Marconi's company about a year ago decided to put up two very large stations, at a cost of $70,000 each, at Cape Cod, Massachusetts, and near the Lizard, in Cornwall, England, the object being to ascertain how much an application of a large amount of power would increase the practical distance by which it is possible to communicate by wireless telegraphy.

The stations in Cornwall and Cape Cod consisted of heavy machinery and 20 poles, 210 feet high, supporting a large number of vertical wires. The station in Cornwall was practically destroyed during a heavy gale in September, and was only partially renewed. It will not be completely repaired for another two or three months. The Cape Cod Station was also damaged recently.

ST. JOHNS, NEWFOUNDLAND, *Saturday.*
Confirm that signals were received here Thursday and Friday
direct from Cornwall, receiving wire suspended from a kite.
MARCONI.

[FROM THE NEW YORK HERALD,
DECEMBER 17, 1901.]

To the Editor of the New York Herald:
I have to confirm the dispatch of your correspondent regarding
the receipt by me here of signals direct from Cornwall. The exact
particulars are as follows:

Before leaving England I arranged for our long distance station
near the Lizard to signal me the letter "S" repeatedly for three
hours when I had advised them that I was ready to receive the
same. I cabled on Monday that all was in readiness and asked the
signal to be sent at short intervals between 3 o'clock and 6 o'clock,
Greenwich time, and to be continued each day until ordered to
stop. This time would correspond approximately with half past 11
to half past 2 here.

I received on Thursday indications of the signals at half past 12,
and with certainty and unmistakable clearness at 10 minutes after
1, quite a succession of "S" being received with distinctness. A
further number were received at 20 minutes after 2, the latter not
so good. Signals were received Friday at 28 minutes after 1 o'clock,
but not so distinct as on Thursday.

I am of the opinion that the reasons why I did not obtain continuous results, were: First, the fluctuations in the height of the
kite, which suspended the aerial wire; and second, the extreme
delicacy of my receiving instruments, which were very sensitive
and had to be adjusted repeatedly during the course of the experiments.

When a permanent station is installed here I will not be dependent upon fluctuations of the wind, and I am confident of making
the signals strong and reliable — that is, not requiring such delicate
and sensitive receiving instruments by employing much greater
power at the sending station.

I must go immediately to England to make arrangements for

employing more power at the sending station, and I trust in a very short time to establish communication between the two continents in a thoroughly reliable and commercial manner.

MARCONI.]

ST. JOHNS, NEWFOUNDLAND, *December 16, 1901.*

J. EDGAR HOOVER

Physical Science in the
Crime-Detection Laboratory

[FROM THE SMITHSONIAN REPORT FOR 1939°]

IT MAY BE *something of a surprise to find an article by J. Edgar Hoover, famous Director of the Federal Bureau of Investigation, in a science reader. But the title of the article makes clear the reason for its inclusion — it provides another convincing example of the great practical usefulness of physical discoveries originally made in the course of purely academic research. The instances cited by Mr. Hoover pertain to the use of the spectrograph, the comparison microscope, and various regions of the electromagnetic spectrum, including ultraviolet and infrared radiation and radio.*

Mr. Hoover makes it clear that the cases cited are only a few samples of the many uses of physical science in crime detection. He also points out that the marshals and sheriffs of television Westerns would have been astounded at the present-day evidence developed in crime-detection laboratories through the use of physical science.

° Revised as of December 1959 by insertion of addendum at end of article.

Dᴜʀɪɴɢ the latter part of 1937 a police department in one of the eastern states, in submitting to the Federal Bureau of Investigation for laboratory examination a pocketknife and telephone cord, advised that the telephone cord had been severed by a burglar in an effort to delay notification of the authorities of the crime, and that the pocketknife had been recovered in the possession of a suspect apprehended during the subsequent investigation. In addition to the examination of other evidence forwarded at the same time, the police department requested that an effort be made to ascertain whether the suspected pocketknife had in fact been used to cut the telephone cord.

Under the microscope there were observed on the cutting edge of the knife blade minute bronze-colored stains. These stains were far too small to permit their ready removal and identification by routine chemical analytical methods. However, a spectrographic examination of the cutting edge of the knife blade revealed the presence thereon of the two chemical elements, copper and tin, which elements were found by a similar examination of the back edge of the knife blade to be elements not a part of the blade material itself. Inasmuch as a spectrographic analysis of the telephone cord indicated that copper and tin were the principal constituents of the severed conductor, this information was immediately furnished to the contributing agency for use in its further investigation and prosecution of the matter.

During the early part of 1938 an examiner from the Bureau's technical laboratory testified relative to his findings in the matter before a court hearing the evidence against the suspect, as a result of which, together with other evidence introduced at the trial, the suspect was found guilty of the burglary and sentenced to a penitentiary for a period of from 5 to 10 years.

The above case illustrates, probably better than any other proof which might be brought forward, the profoundly important part which modern scientific methods, and more specifically the application of physical techniques, are playing in the unending war against crime. The contrast between present-day methods embodying scientific principles and those of an earlier era can be summed up no more aptly than in the amusing but pointed exclamation, "Shades of Wyatt Earp! The old boy would turn over in his grave if he could hear that," which a western officer was heard to make upon having the advantages of spectrographic examination pointed out to him.

While the spectrograph has been a familiar instrument in physical and chemical laboratories throughout the world for many years, because of its fundamental importance in these sciences, consideration of its possible application in crime-detection problems is relatively recent. Cognizant of the invaluable assistance already gained from scientific methods, and in line with its policy of exploring new methods of attack, the Federal Bureau of Investigation some time ago installed such an instrument in its technical laboratory in an effort to ascertain the extent of its application to law-enforcement work. The rapidly increasing number of instances in which it has proved of value already indicates that there is a definite place for it in this field, in spite of the fact that only the surface has been scratched in exploring its possibilities.

Although the instance cited above indicates spectrographic results to be important from an affirmative evidentiary standpoint, it should be noted that its results may be equally valuable purely from an investigative standpoint as exemplified in the following case in which an extortionist identified the proposed pay-off spot by the simple process of painting a rock white at the desired location. During the subsequent investigation, special agents of the Federal Bureau of Investigation removed small flakes of this white paint and submitted them to the Bureau's technical laboratory together with specimens of white paint recovered from the home of a suspect. A spectrographic analysis of the paint used by the extortionist indicated it to be of a zinc base type whereas a similar analysis of the suspected paint showed it to possess a titanium base, and therefore to be not identical with the paint removed from the rock, a result which could have been obtained only with difficulty, if at all, by the usual chemical procedures because of the limited amount of material available for analysis.

Although the science of physics has contributed in some manner or other to almost every branch of crime detection, it is difficult, because of the overlapping nature of the various sciences today, to

isolate and attribute specific improvements or techniques to physics alone or to any other single branch of scientific endeavor, such
improvements or techniques in most instances having been rather
the result of a gradual development in several allied fields. However, by noting the relation and application of various portions of
the electromagnetic radiant energy spectrum to specific crime detection problems it is believed that a fairly representative, even if
necessarily somewhat brief and incomplete, picture of the subject
as a whole may be presented.

Leaving the fascinating subject of spectrographic analysis which
in its broadest sense may encompass a relatively large portion of
the spectrum, and disregarding possible application of cosmic and
radioactive gamma radiation which at the present are of little more
than academic interest in relation to crime detection, there is found
at the short wavelength end of the spectrum a powerful ally to
law-enforcement work in the X-ray. Probably the most important
use to which this valuable aid is put in police work lies in its application to the examination of packages suspected of containing explosives. Each year finds its quota of persons horribly mutilated or
of homes and business establishments wrecked by such bombs, and
the problem confronting the officer who is charged with the responsibility of investigating and destroying these weapons of a
crazed mind is a very real one. Fortunately, it is now possible in
many instances through the agency of the X-ray to ascertain the
contents of a suspected package without opening or otherwise disturbing the package in any way, thereby permitting appropriate
action to be taken in the event the parcel is actually found to contain dangerous explosives.

Illustration 54, figure 1, is an X-ray photograph taken of a model
bomb showing the possibility of tracing the ignition wiring, thus
permitting the bomb to be opened harmlessly. Illustration 54, figure
2, on the other hand is an X-ray of a package received by a high Government official and suspected of containing explosives, but found
as indicated to contain only a gavel presented by an admiring constituent, much to the relief of the recipient.

Above the X-rays in the radiant energy spectrum there is found
a type of radiation known as ultraviolet light, so named, of course,
because of its relation to the violet end of the visible spectrum

1. X-ray photograph of a package containing a model bomb.

ILLUS. 54—

2. X-ray photograph of a package suspected of containing explosives but shown to contain only a gavel.

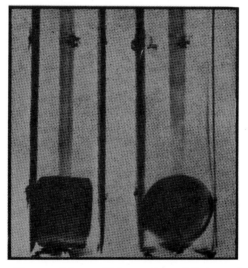

which will be discussed later. This portion of the spectrum, in addition to exhibiting in general different selective reflection and transmission characteristics from those encountered in the visible region, further possesses the ability to excite to a state of luminescence many materials which are normally nonluminous, a phenomenon which is known as fluorescence.

Both of these properties find wide application in crime-detection problems. Inasmuch as the fluorescent radiation is in general different in wavelength or color from the incipient radiation and in many instances is highly characteristic of the material illuminated, it therefore offers one method of analysis to determine the nature of unknown materials received for examination. For instance, in connection with the investigation of rape cases, it frequently becomes necessary to examine clothing for the presence of seminal stains. Advantage is taken of the fact that such stains fluoresce brilliantly under the ultraviolet light, to localize certain areas which are then subjected to specific tests for the stain in question. The time saved by virtue of such a preliminary examination is immediately obvious.

Again, drawing on the field of document examination, we find the fluoresence of certain materials permitting their use as secret inks, invisible when viewed by ordinary lighting but standing out vividly in glowing contrast when subjected to ultraviolet illumination. Thus, the ultraviolet affords a rapid and convenient method of examination of documents or other evidence suspected of carrying a secret message. A special case of this application of ultraviolet is found in the examination of evidence containing obliterated writing, that is, writing which for some reason or other has been removed by physical or chemical processes. In many such cases there remain imbedded in the surface of the document, invisible to the eye, one or more constituents of the original writing ink which when viewed under the ultraviolet light reveal the fluorescent outline of the original. Illustration 55, figure 1, is a photograph taken by the usual methods of a portion of a page from an account book belonging to the subject of a case under investigation by this Bureau. Evidence in the case indicated that the subject had represented the bank account to be much larger than it actually was. From a preliminary examination of the first entry shown in Illustration 55, figure 1, it was apparent that a number had been placed before the entry and then subsequently removed, although it was not possible to tell definitely what the number had been. When placed under the ultraviolet light, however, a "4" was seen to stand out in a faint fluorescent glow, before the original entry. This "4" is clearly visible in Illustration 55, figure 2. The evidence made available through the use of ultraviolet light in this instance was of material assistance in the subsequent prosecution and conviction of the subject.

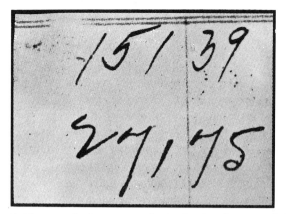

1. *Photograph of an account book, showing the removal of a figure before the 15139.*

ILLUS. 55—

2. *The same page of an account book under ultraviolet light; the removed figure is seen to be a 4.*

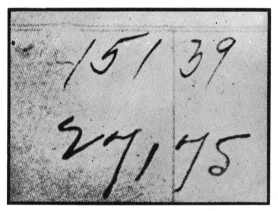

In order to utilize the selective reflection and transmission characteristics which several materials exhibit for the ultraviolet region, it is necessary to employ the action of the ultraviolet light directly on a photographic plate or other suitable recording medium. This process is readily carried out, of course, by the utilization of quartz optical systems and appropriate filters, resulting in incontrovertible evidence in those instances where the materials involved are such as to yield to this method of attack. Used to supplement each other, the two ultraviolet techniques outlined above have proved so valuable that they have become an indispensable part of many routine examinations.

Immediately above the ultraviolet portion of the spectrum, there appear in orderly sequence the visible colors ranging from violet through extreme red, and inasmuch as these colors are directly involved in the all-important process of vision, it obviously would be futile to attempt, even in a much more comprehensive discussion than space permits here, to touch upon more than a very few of the applications to crime detection. Some of these, however, are so outstanding as to demand consideration.

Foremost among these is the microscope as we know it today. With these "seven-league glasses" it becomes possible for the expert to ascertain whether the wisp of hair found clinging to the door hinge of a suspected hit-and-run automobile is identical with comparison specimens of hair removed from the head of the child found lying unconscious with a fractured skull at the edge of the road near a small southern community; whether the printed fabric found wrapped around a murdered victim's neck in another instance is identical with similar fabric found at the home of a suspect; or whether the stain appearing upon an ax recovered at the home of a suspect is only rust, as claimed by the suspect, or is in fact a stain caused by blood of human origin received when the ax was utilized in a vicious attack on one of the suspect's neighbors.

By adding polarizing elements to the microscope, the petrographer is able to examine the colored interference patterns produced by birefringent crystalline materials and thereby determine, for example, whether the soil removed from the shoes of a suspect is similar in mineral content and structure to soil taken from the area where a safe, which had been stolen from a mercantile store, had been forced open and the contents looted.

In the field of firearms identification, we find a somewhat different modification of the microscope employed. Of several problems which properly fall within the scope of this work, the principal one deals with the examination of evidence — bullets and cartridge cases — in an effort to ascertain whether they have been fired from a suspected weapon recovered during the investigation. Such an examination is based upon the existence on both bullet and cartridge case of many minute markings, arising in the case of the bullet from its passage over the microscopic imperfections present in the gun barrel, and in the case of the shell from various imperfections in the breech face, firing pin, and similar sources. It has been amply demonstrated that each weapon creates a combination of such microscopic marks which is not duplicated by any other weapon; accordingly, each weapon, in effect, places its "fingerprint" upon all projectiles or shells which are fired from it. The immediate problem thus resolves itself into a determination of whether the microscopic markings on the questioned bullet or shell coincide with similar markings upon test specimens fired by the examining expert from the suspected gun.

To meet this problem, which demands enlargement of the characteristic markings and provision for directly observing the coincidence or lack of coincidence between the sequence of the marks, the crime-detection laboratory has drawn upon the field of applied optics in creating an ingenious device known as the comparison microscope. This instrument not only furnishes the required magnification to make the minute markings distinctly visible, but in addition optically "splits" the specimens being compared in such a manner that images of opposite halves of the specimens are placed in proper juxtaposition to permit direct comparison of the marking sequence. In Illustration 56 is shown a photograph illustrating the manner in which the characteristic markings are seen to flow smoothly from one bullet into the other when both have been fired from the same weapon.

To illustrate the extreme value of this type of examination, attention is invited to a case in which a trapper in Alaska was found murdered in his cabin. Two suspects were located, each of whom was in the possession of a rifle of the type from which the fatal bullet had come. However, suspicion was directed more strongly toward one suspect than the other because of a prior criminal record which he was found to have and further because of the presence of bloodstains on his clothing. Upon receipt of the two suspected weapons in the technical laboratory of the Federal Bureau of Investigation, test specimens were fired from each and by means of the comparison microscope were compared with the fatal bullet. When this examination had been completed, it was found that the fatal bullet had been fired from the weapon belonging to the suspect toward whom the finger of suspicion had pointed less strongly, thereby completely exonerating the suspect with the prior criminal record. The bloodstains appearing upon the latter's clothing were found not to be of human origin, the suspect having previously claimed that they were caused by reindeer blood. Thus, it will be seen that the examination not only assisted very materially in the solution of the case, but even refuted circumstantial evidence tending to point to another suspect.

It is also of importance to note that the comparison microscope is not by any means limited in its application to the examination of firearms evidence. Whenever two objects of differing hardness are forcibly placed in contact, markings characteristic of the surface imperfections of one are invariably impressed upon the other. For example, a pair of bolt clippers used by a burglar to gain access to a business establishment may readily be identified as the instrument actually used, by virtue of the microscopic marks which small dents and other imperfections in its cutting edges leave upon the severed ends of the window bars.

Case after case could be cited, each with a different story to tell, illustrative of the endless manner in which applied optics in the visible region of the spectrum has yielded a welcome solution to

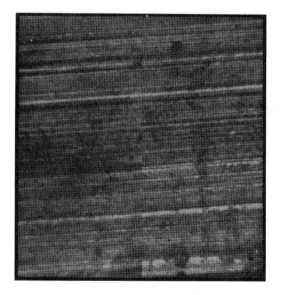

ILLUS. 56—Photograph of two bullets fired from the same gun as seen under the comparison microscope. The characteristic markings flow smoothly from one bullet into the other.

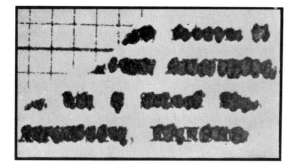

ILLUS. 57—

1. Ordinary photograph of an obliterated return address.

2. Photograph of same return address using optical filters and photographic plates sensitized to infrared radiation.

an otherwise difficult problem. However, space will not permit a more detailed discussion.

Corresponding to ultraviolet light lying beyond the short wavelength at the end of the visible spectrum, there appears above the limit of visibility at the long wavelength end, light which is known as infrared. This portion of the spectrum also has been found to possess certain characteristics which are of value to the scientific investigator; chief among these is the ability of infrared radiation to penetrate materials which are normally opaque to the unaided eye. As an example of this property, Illustration 57, figure 1, shows a photograph by ordinary process of an obliterated return address appearing upon an envelope in which an anonymous derogatory letter was mailed. It will be noted that the obliteration has been carried out by marking over the original form with ink.

Aware of the characteristics of the infrared portion of the spectrum, the examiner immediately photographed the questioned area utilizing suitable optical filters and special photographic plates sensitized to this type of radiation. Illustration 57, figure 2, shows the resulting photograph, clearly revealing the original printed return address through the overlayer of ink which now appears only as a light smudge. Here again by properly applying familiar principles of selective optical absorption, the source of the stationery employed by the anonymous writer was readily ascertained. Without the utilization of infrared photography much time and effort might have been required to accomplish the same end.

Another instance involves the examination of a leather money bag found on the person of a desperate criminal following his arrest. Other equipment in the possession of this criminal included 24 sticks of dynamite, a supply of nitroglycerin, numerous travelers checks, and a supply of weapons.

Visual examination of the money bag, as indicated in Illustration 58, figure 1, disclosed no identifying data which would be of assistance in tracing it. However, upon its receipt in the technical laboratory of the Bureau, infrared photographs clearly disclosed the name of the bank where it had originated, as shown in Illustration 58, figure 2.

Moving to the long wavelength portion of the radiant energy spectrum, the contribution of radio to law enforcement must be acknowledged. The rapidity with which radio as a means of communication has been accepted by law-enforcement agencies throughout the country is ample proof of its value to such organizations. The ability to transmit to the farthest corners of the State, pertinent information relative to a crime almost before the perpetrator has completed the act, thereby rendering it extremely difficult, if not impossible, for him to escape, is a development of the utmost importance, particularly in view of the swift modes of transportation available to the criminal of today. In addition to furnishing an unparalleled means of communication the principles of radio have been utilized to throw protecting "fields" about homes or other specific areas, permitting actuation of almost any desired type of alarm upon the entry within the protected area by an intruder.

It is again to be emphasized that the few examples given above represent only a very small number of the myriad applications through which physical science has been of assistance to law enforcement. Indeed, reviewing the results which modern scientific methods have brought to crime detection, one is constantly tempted to ask with an earlier school of thought, "What more is there to be discovered?" only to be answered with a new development, startling in its implication and promise.

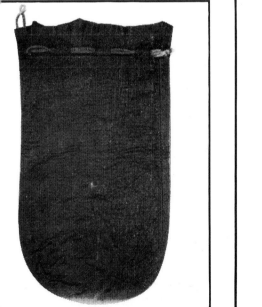 

ILLUS. 58—

1. *Money bag found on a criminal upon his arrest, containing no identifying data.*
2. *Same money bag photographed with infrared radiation, showing lettering that permitted the deciphering of the name of the bank from which it came.*

ADDENDUM, DECEMBER 1959

In reviewing the earlier article preparatory to its inclusion in the present collection, it was of interest to note that all of the scientific techniques mentioned therein have withstood the test of time and are still currently furnishing valuable assistance to the investigator. However, the growth of scientific crime detection has paralleled in its scope the almost explosive growth of science generally, so that today we find the earlier techniques supplemented by a multitude of new ones.

Automatic recording spectrophotometers in the infrared, visible, and ultraviolet portions of the spectrum are in daily operation assisting in the identification of fragments of evidence through a determination of the detailed selective absorption characteristics of the material under examination. Gamma radiation from man-made radioactive isotopes is a valuable additional source of radiographic energy, supplementing the X-ray applications cited in the original article. X-ray diffraction and X-ray fluorescence instruments automatically record the respective diffraction or fluorescence curves of a host of materials, furnishing valuable information as to the identify of the evidence under study.

Other examples, almost without limit, could be cited; however, possibly an even more striking indication of the growth of scientific crime detection may be found in comparing the volume of examinations currently being made by the FBI Laboratory against the volume of such examinations some 20 years ago. In this regard, for example, during fiscal year 1958 the FBI Laboratory made 165,462 scientific examinations of evidence as contrasted with some 5,904 examinations in fiscal year 1938. This evidence comes to the FBI Laboratory not only from our own field offices throughout the United States but also from police departments and other local law-enforcement agencies all over the nation. This certainly is a powerful testimonial to the impact of science on crime detection.

In conclusion, it may be mentioned that the final paragraph of the original article is as applicable today as it was at the time of original writing. We look forward with anticipation to the scientific developments of tomorrow.

J. EDGAR HOOVER

PAUL C. AEBERSOLD

Radioisotopes–New Keys
to Knowledge

[FROM THE SMITHSONIAN REPORT FOR 1953*]

RADIOISOTOPES *are unstable forms of the chemical elements. The arrangement of protons, neutrons, and other components of each nucleus in their atomic structures is not acceptable to nature; the nucleus will — in times ranging from millionths of a second to many trillions of years — rearrange itself to stability by emitting energy in the form of radiation. Some radioisotopes occur in nature, others are man-made. Produced in quantity only since nuclear reactors became available during World War II, these "new keys to knowledge" have opened whole vistas in scientific research and practical applications. They are ideal as tracers in biological, physiological, and chemical systems since radiation can be detected from radioisotopes in almost incredible dilution. As sources of radiation, they find hundreds of uses in gaging thicknesses, densities, and levels; in nondestructive testing; and in medical therapy and industrial radiation processing.*

The author, Dr. Paul C. Aebersold, is Director of the Office of Isotopes Development, U. S. Atomic Energy Commission, Washington, D. C. Selected to direct the AEC's first public distribution of radioisotopes in 1946, Dr. Aebersold has since held primary re-

* Revised as of January 1960.

sponsibility for Commission activities in developing and encouraging their use. He has represented the Commission as delegate to numerous international conferences on nuclear science and isotope technology. Here Dr. Aebersold presents a concise account of the discovery, present production and availability of these new tools, and their wide-ranging applications in science, medicine, agriculture, and industry.

CHRONOLOGY

THIRTY YEARS AGO the field of atomic energy as we know it today had not even been conceived; nuclear science was just getting under way. Of course, Roentgen had discovered X-rays; Becquerel had discovered radioactivity; the Curies had discovered radium and polonium; Rutherford had originated his concept of the atom with a tiny, heavy nucleus surrounded by planetary electrons; and Soddy had proved the existence of isotopes — different forms of atoms of the same element — and some 30 different naturally occurring radioactive isotopes had been identified. The fact that atoms of an ordinary stable element may differ in weight, that elements may have stable isotopes, had been determined from positive ray studies by J. J. Thompson and Aston. Also, Rutherford, working with alpha particles from radioactive sources, had observed the transmutation of nitrogen atoms to oxygen atoms.

In spite of the seemingly large volume of information that had been accumulated by 1928 on the atom and its nucleus, the real attack on the nucleus itself and an understanding of what it is made of was yet to come. Chadwick had not discovered the neutron; Anderson had not discovered the positron; Urey had not discovered deuterium; I. Joliot-Curie and her husband, F. Joliot, had not discovered that radioactivity could be induced in ordinary stable elements; E. O. Lawrence, of the University of California, had not invented the cyclotron; and nuclear fission and the uranium chain reactor were entirely beyond the realm of imagination of our most learned physicists.

Roentgen's discovery of X-rays and Becquerel's discovery of radioactivity just before the turn of the century had begun the era of modern physics. It was generally agreed by such learned nineteenth-century scholars as Kelvin, Helmholtz, Boltzman, Michelson, and Lorentz that all the great discoveries in physics had already been made and that future progress was to be looked for, not in bringing to light qualitatively new phenomena, but rather in making more exact quantitative measurements upon old phenomena. In simpler terms this meant obtaining more significant figures beyond the decimal point. As Robert Millikan said after hearing Professor Roentgen report his discovery of X-rays to the German Physical Society, ". . . we all began to see that the nineteenth century physicists had taken themselves a little too seriously, that we had not come quite as near sounding the depths of the universe, even in the matter of fundamental physical principles, as we thought we had." But no one, even as recently as 30 years ago, dreamed of the amazing developments of nuclear physics or atomic energy that have taken place since.

Radioactivity was the key that had opened up door after door in the dramatic development of nuclear science. It was the study and use of radioactivity that led to Rutherford's concept of the atom, to Soddy's concept of isotopes, to Chadwick's discovery of the neutron, to the Joliot-Curie's man-made radioactivity, and finally to Hahn's discovery of fission from which have come both the chain reaction and the nuclear reactor.

ISOTOPES

But radioactivity proved to be more than an ordinary key. It has been a master key, for it has provided us with a whole chain of "new keys." We shall concern ourselves here with only one of these "keys" — the reactor-produced radioactive isotopes. We shall consider the production, distribution, and use of these radioisotopes and look at what radioisotopes have meant to science and what they may mean to the individual.

At the risk of going backward once more, let us try to imagine what scientific tool investigators of 30 years ago might have desired most. I am thinking now not only of physicists but also of chemists, biologists, physiologists, and other types of researchers. Among the things that scientists of that day could not do but no doubt sincerely wished they could do was "to trace atoms." Think of being able to trace a certain diet element or compound through the digestive and metabolic processes of an animal or even a human being. Think of being able to find out what plants do with carbon dioxide or with fertilizer, or following the diffusion of atoms in solid metal. Scientists of 30 years ago could only dream of doing these things. Man-made radioisotopes have now made these dreams possible! Today, even undreamed of things have become routine. But the story taken from this page of science is much more dramatic than "first you can't, then you can."

DEFINITIONS

Webster reminds us that the word "isotope" comes from two Greek words, "iso" and "topos," meaning "same" and "place." The word "isotope" was chosen to describe certain atoms which, although different in weight, still occupy the same place in the periodic table of elements. Since they are atoms of the same element, they will behave alike chemically, their differences being only in physical properties. Isotopes, therefore, are like twins that look and act alike but that are different in weight. Radioactive isotopes, or radioisotopes for short, are atoms that give off radiation and disintegrate to become other kinds of atoms.

Actually, isotopes are very intimately associated with our everyday lives. They are not only to be found in the laboratory but everywhere. Isotopes are common in the elements around us here — including those in our bodies. For example, hydrogen, the simplest and one of the most abundant elements, exists naturally in two forms (Illus. 59). One is ordinary hydrogen, which has a weight of approximately one unit of atomic mass, called hydrogen 1. The other is approximately twice as heavy and is called heavy hydrogen, or hydrogen 2. We can also make a still heavier hydrogen 3.

Both hydrogen 1 and hydrogen 2 are stable; that is, they do not

WHAT AN

Isotope

IS ....

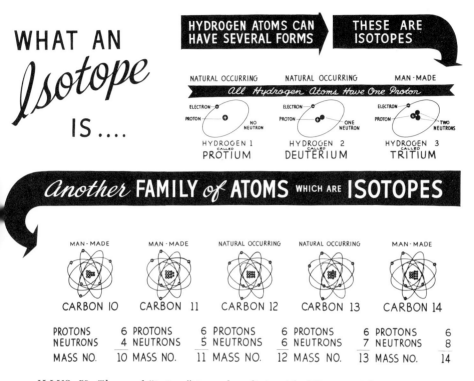

HYDROGEN ATOMS CAN HAVE SEVERAL FORMS

THESE ARE ISOTOPES

NATURAL OCCURRING   NATURAL OCCURRING   MAN-MADE

All Hydrogen Atoms Have One Proton

ELECTRON	ELECTRON	ELECTRON
PROTON	PROTON	PROTON
NO NEUTRON	ONE NEUTRON	TWO NEUTRONS
HYDROGEN 1 CALLED PROTIUM	HYDROGEN 2 CALLED DEUTERIUM	HYDROGEN 3 CALLED TRITIUM

Another FAMILY *of* ATOMS WHICH ARE ISOTOPES

MAN-MADE	MAN-MADE	NATURAL OCCURRING	NATURAL OCCURRING	MAN-MADE
CARBON 10	CARBON 11	CARBON 12	CARBON 13	CARBON 14
PROTONS 6	PROTONS 6	PROTONS 6	PROTONS 6	PROTONS 6
NEUTRONS 4	NEUTRONS 5	NEUTRONS 6	NEUTRONS 7	NEUTRONS 8
MASS NO. 10	MASS NO. 11	MASS NO. 12	MASS NO. 13	MASS NO. 14

ILLUS. 59—The word "isotope" is used to distinguish different-weight atoms of the same element. The simplest of the elements, hydrogen, has three isotopes. Two of them—hydrogen having a unit weight of 1, called protium, and hydrogen having a unit weight of 2, called deuterium—exist in all naturally occurring hydrogen in the respective concentrations of 99.985 percent and 0.015 percent. Hydrogen 3 can be made by man in the nuclear reactor although it does not occur in nature. All other elements have at least three isotopes and some have considerably more. The element xenon, for example, has 24 known isotopes. A total of more than 1,000 isotopes have been identified to date. Pictured with the isotopes of hydrogen are the isotopes of carbon.

change with time, or disintegrate, or give off radiation. Hydrogen 3, on the other hand, is radioactive and disintegrates or decays to a stable isotope of helium. In disintegrating, hydrogen 3 gives off radiation.

Six isotopes are known for the element carbon, only two of which are stable. (Carbon 15, which contains six protons and nine neutrons in its nucleus and has only a 2.3 second half life,* is not shown in Illus. 59.) Carbon 10, carbon 11, and carbon 14 are radioactive and have to be made artificially. Generally speaking, most naturally occurring isotopes are stable, whereas most radioactive isotopes have to be made. There are, however, exceptions particularly in the case of the heavy elements.

NATURALLY OCCURRING RADIOISOTOPES

The historical sequence of events leading to today's widespread availability of radioisotopes is unique. It was the naturally occurring radioelement uranium which even before the turn of the century led to the discovery of radioactivity. This subsequently led to the discovery of some 45 other naturally occurring radioisotopes, including such important isotopes as radium and radon, whose uses are familiar. Approximately 50 years later the same radioelement, uranium, led to the design and operation of the nuclear reactor, today's mass producer of man-made radioisotopes. Just as radioactivity proved the key to the development of nuclear science, uranium proved the key to the availability of radiomaterials. But we are getting ahead of our story.

In 1913 Hevesy and Paneth conducted the first tracer experiment when they used minute amounts of naturally occurring radioactive lead to study the solubilities of sparingly soluble lead salts. Later these investigators used the same naturally occurring radioactive lead to study the absorption and translocation of that element in plants. This was in 1923. Other studies of a similar nature were conducted in the years that followed, but none of them were very broad in scope. The reason was simple. There just were not any radioactive counterparts for most of the elements usually found in plant and animal systems. No naturally occurring radioisotopes for those elements existed, and no one knew how to make them. Here then was a technique that admittedly had unlimited possibilities but that could not be used because the materials to do the job were not available.

* The half life of a radioisotope is the length of time required for a given quantity to decay to one half of its initial value. If a radioisotope has a half life of two days, for example, its initial radioactivity will be reduced 50 percent in two days. In two more days the remaining activity again will be reduced 50 percent, or to 25 percent of the initial value.

MAN-MADE RADIOISOTOPES

Then came the key to a whole new era for radioactivity. In 1934 I. Joliot-Curie and her husband, F. Joliot, while bombarding light elements with alpha particles from polonium, discovered quite by accident that ordinary elements can be made to become radioactive.

The first man-made radioactive isotope produced was phosphorus 30. It was immediately shown that the path of this new isotope in chemical reactions could be followed by its radioactivity. In less than a year Hevesy was using another form of radioactive phosphorus, phosphorus 32, to study the uptake of that element in plants, but only infinitesimally small amounts of radioactive isotopes could be produced in this way.

CYCLOTRON-PRODUCED RADIOISOTOPES

Shortly thereafter a new way was found for making larger quantities of man-made radioisotopes. E. O. Lawrence and M. S. Livingston had built their first cyclotron at Berkeley in 1931. It was not long after the discovery of man-made radioactivity that the cyclotron was put to work making radioactive forms of most of the elements.

Physicists all over the world immediately became engrossed in the possibilities offered by these two developments, the invention of the cyclotron and the discovery of man-made radioactivity. By the start of World War II, 10 years later, radioactive isotopes were being made in perhaps as many as 50 cyclotrons throughout this country as well as in a number of foreign laboratories. By this time the usefulness of radioisotopes for tracing atoms was well established. At least two isotopes, radioactive iodine 131 and radioactive phosphorus 32, had also been used in medicine for the radiation treatment of certain diseases.

But there was still one catch. Cyclotron production of most radioisotopes was and still is very slow and very expensive. But most serious of all, the cyclotron can produce only limited quantities of radioisotopes. Therefore, with the exception of those laboratories which were fortunate enough to have cyclotrons, there just were not enough man-made radiomaterials to go around. And

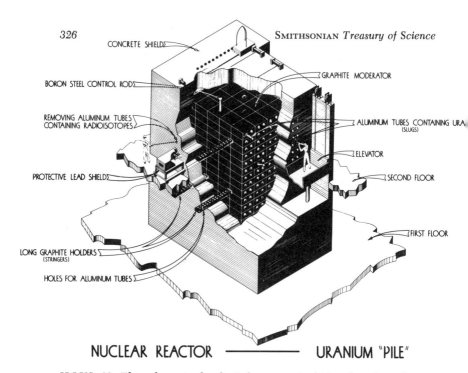

CONCRETE SHIELD

GRAPHITE MODERATOR

BORON STEEL CONTROL RODS

REMOVING ALUMINUM TUBES
CONTAINING RADIOISOTOPES

ALUMINUM TUBES CONTAINING URA
(SLUGS)

ELEVATOR

PROTECTIVE LEAD SHIELD

SECOND FLOOR

FIRST FLOOR

LONG GRAPHITE HOLDERS
(STRINGERS)

HOLES FOR ALUMINUM TUBES

NUCLEAR REACTOR ———— URANIUM "PILE"

*ILLUS. 60—This schematic sketch of the reactor is designed to show the two
principal ways in which radioisotopes are produced. The three
most important functional parts of the reactor are the uranium
slugs, the graphite moderator, and the boron steel control rods.
When a fissionable uranium 235 atom in one of the slugs is hit
by a neutron, it fissions or splits. In the fission process, 1 to 3
more neutrons are produced which, when slowed down by the
graphite moderator, are available for splitting more uranium 235
atoms. The multiplication of this process many, many times leads
to the chain reaction. Boron has a greater affinity for neutrons
than does uranium, and therefore when the boron steel control
rods are inserted into the reactor, they "soak up" a sufficient
number of neutrons to slow down the chain reaction or stop it,
depending on how far they are inserted into the reactor.*

even when a cyclotron was available, tracer studies were generally
limited to those experiments that would require only a very small
amount of the precious radiomaterial.

REACTOR-PRODUCED RADIOISOTOPES

The nuclear reactor developed during World War II makes an
excellent radioisotope production unit. Although not so wide a

variety of radioisotopes can be produced in the reactor as in the cyclotron, what is much more important, the radioisotopes can be produced in large quantity. Also, with the reactor it is possible to produce many different radioisotopes at the same time. This, of course, is not possible with the cyclotron or with other particle accelerators.

Uranium, which heralded the discovery and use of naturally occuring radioactivity, reentered the scene to make an even greater contribution in the production of man-made radioactivity or radioisotopes.

NUCLEAR REACTOR

A few facts concerning the Oak Ridge reactor, the production unit for most of the radioisotopes made in the United States today, may be of interest.

As one first sees the Oak Ridge reactor (Illus. 60) it appears to be a concrete structure 47 feet long, 38 feet high, and 32 feet deep. The concrete, however, is a 7-foot thick shield built around the reactor to protect operating personnel. The reactive portion of the reactor is a 24-foot cube built of stacks of graphite blocks through which pass some 1,200 channels containing uranium metal as fuel.

Reactor operation is based on the fissioning or splitting of uranium 235 atoms in the uranium fuel. Perhaps the only other characteristic necessary for a simple understanding of the reactor as a radioisotope production unit is the neutron flux or density. The flux of the Oak Ridge reactor is of the order of a million million neutrons passing through each square-centimeter area (about the size of a fingernail) per second.

Radioisotopes are produced in a nuclear reactor either by fissioning — that is, by splitting of uranium (Illus. 61) — or by bombarding ordinary stable elements with neutrons, the subatomic particles that keep the chain reaction going (Illus. 62). Although from the standpoint of the physics involved as well as from the standpoint of a manufacturing process, radioisotope production is a complex operation, in principle it is as simple as putting biscuits in an oven to cook (Illus. 64). Almost any element, or for that matter almost

URANIUM FISSION AND BETA CHAIN DECAY

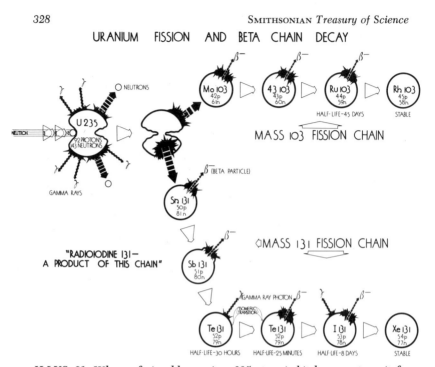

ILLUS. 61—*When a fissionable uranium 235 atom is hit by a neutron, it fissions or splits the uranium atom into two different atoms. These atomic fragments are called fission products and make up a wide variety of radioisotopes of elements from zinc, with an atomic number of 30, to gadolinium, with an atomic number of 64. After the uranium slug is removed from the reactor, the fission products are chemically separated from the uranium and plutonium and from each other. One of the most useful radioisotopes produced by this method is radioactive iodine.*

any object such as a penny or dime or a bobby pin or the phosphorus from the head of a match, can be placed in a small aluminum tube and introduced into the reactor. After neutron irradiation or bombardment for a week, a month, or perhaps longer, depending on the radioisotope being produced, the aluminum tube is taken out and the radioactive material removed. Depending on the radioisotope produced, it may or may not be chemically processed before shipping it to the user. In some instances the aluminum tube and all are shipped directly to the user after having been placed in the proper shipping container.

The production output of the reactor is phenomenal. For example,

PILE PRODUCTION OF RADIOISOTOPES

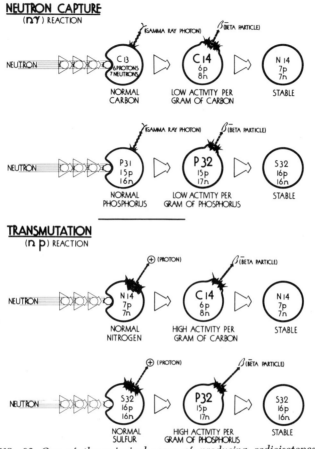

ILLUS. 62—One of the principal ways of producing radioisotopes in the
nuclear reactor is to bombard ordinary stable isotopes with neutrons, the subatomic particles formed when a uranium 235 atom
fissions. The chart shows two types of nuclear reactions which
take place when a stable isotope is bombarded with neutrons. In
the first case a neutron is absorbed and a gamma ray given off.
This has the effect of increasing the atomic weight of the target
nucleus by 1, as shown in the production of carbon 14 from
carbon 13 and in the production of phosphorus 32 from phosphorus 31. In neither instance is this a particularly good way of
producing the radioisotope since there is no way of chemically
separating the radioactive isotope from the original stable isotope.
The transmutation reaction, on the other hand, results in the production of a radioisotope of a different element than is used in
the original target. Here a chemical separation can be effected
and the resultant radioisotope made available in pure form.

ILLUS. 63—*Preparing to remove plugs from some of the 1,248 fuel-channel openings in the shield of the Oak Ridge graphite reactor, personnel stand on an elevating platform. In brackets on the wall of the elevator, in front of the two men, can be seen a horizontal bundle of 10-foot lengths of light steel poles used as "push rods." As a rod is inserted into a channel, another rod is threaded to it, increasing its length to permit traversing the length of the fuel channel.*

ILLUS. 64—*Here we see operating personnel at the Oak Ridge National Laboratory removing some material which has been irradiated in the graphite reactor. The material is in the small aluminum tube held by the extension tongs which permit the operator to maintain a "safe" distance from the radioactive material. The operator in the foreground is opening a lead-vault storage container in which the radioactive material will be kept until it is transferred to the processing and shipping facility in another building.*

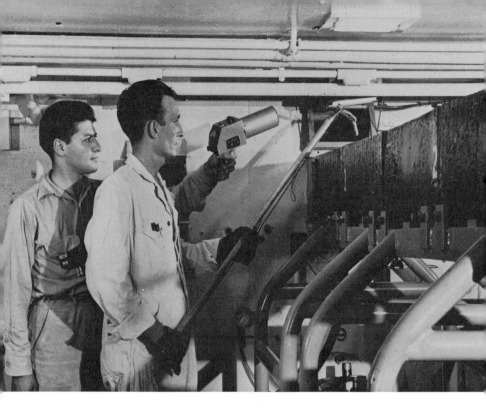

ILLUS. 65—

1. *This is a close-up view of the operation shown in Illus. 64.*
   The graphite "stringer" containing the holes in which the
   aluminum tube has been inserted for irradiation can be seen
   in the mirror above the lead "coffin" through which the
   stringer is being pulled out of the reactor. The operator at
   the left is surveying the level of radiation with a "cutie pie"
   radiation-detection instrument.

over 640,000 curies* of radioactive cobalt 60 have been shipped
from Oak Ridge in the 13 years since the distribution program began in 1946. This is equivalent in radioactivity to over one ton of
radium. Although it is difficult to estimate the current world in-

---

* The curie, which gets its name from Madame Curie, was originally the
unit of radioactivity represented by a 1 gram of radium. Today it is defined
as the quantity of any radioactive material giving 37 billion disintegrations
per second.

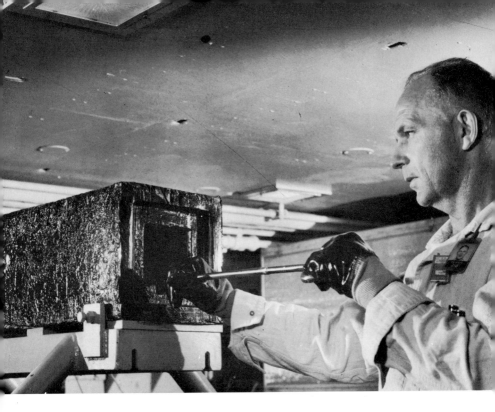

2. *This shows a close-up of the lead "coffin" through which the stringer shown in the photograph above will be pulled out of the reactor. Note that the operator wears rubber gloves to prevent the possibility of his hands becoming contaminated. Also note that he wears a film badge clipped to his collar and two pocket meters in the pocket of his coveralls to measure the amount of radiation to which he is exposed during the operation.*

ventory of refined radium, in the six years preceding the availability of reactor-produced cobalt 60 the United States imported less than one pound of radium.

Another example is the case of radioactive carbon 14, one of the most useful radioisotopes for biological tracer studies. It has been estimated that 1 millicurie of carbon 14 produced in the cyclotron would cost $1,000,000. The same quantity of reactor-produced carbon 14 can be purchased today for $13.00.

RADIOISOTOPE AVAILABILITY

Of the more than 1,200 nuclear species or isotopes that have been identified to date, some 275 are stable and over 900 are radioactive. Approximately 100 of the radioactive variety are routinely manufactured at Oak Ridge and distributed to scientists all over the world. This means that reactor-produced radioisotopes or radioactive forms of most of the known elements are now available in quantities sufficient for wide-scale use. Those available include such important radioisotopes as radiohydrogen (tritium, H 3), radiocarbon (C 14), radiophosphorus (P 32), radiosulfur (S 35), radiocalcium (Ca 45), and radioiron (Fe 55, 59). Most of these radioisotopes emit either beta radiation (high-speed electrons) or a mixture of beta and gamma rays (electromagnetic radiation like X-rays). However, the energies of radiation and the half-lives, that is, the rates with which the various radioisotopes disintegrate, vary widely.

The only radioisotope currently available under the distribution program which emits alpha radiation (nuclei of helium atoms) is polonium 210. Although this radioisotope exists in nature as one of the decay products of radium and is commercially extracted from radium wastes, it can now be obtained easier and cheaper by producing it in the reactor by the irradiation of bismuth. (Alpha-emitting plutonium is also available as a component of neutron sources.)

HOW RADIOISOTOPES ARE USED

Sources of radiation. — The first and simplest way of using radioisotopes is as sources of radiation. Most persons are familiar with the way in which radium and X-ray machines have been used to treat certain diseases and to take pictures of heavy metal castings in looking for possible cracks and flaws. Reactor-produced radioisotopes can be used in much the same way.

The principal advantage of reactor-produced radioisotopes is that, because there are a lot of them to choose from, the investigator has a much wider choice of type and energy of radiation. Also, reactor-produced radioisotopes are generally easier to handle and are much cheaper.

Tracers. — Radioisotopes or radioactive atoms are much more widely used as tracer atoms — atoms that can be traced by the radiations they emit.

Since the radioactive atoms of an element are like the ordinary nonradioactive or stable atoms of the element and behave like them chemically, they go along with them in all chemical and biochemical processes. But because of the radiations given off by the radioactive atoms, they can act as "atomic detectives." With instruments such as the geiger counter these radiations can be detected; that is, they can be made to produce impulses or signals which may be seen or heard or mechanically counted. This means that we can always locate the radioactive atoms and hence distinguish between the atoms added to a system and other atoms of the same element which were already present. The use of radioisotopes in this way is referred to as the tracer technique.

POWER OF TRACER TECHNIQUE

The tracer technique derives part of its power from its versatility. We can label and trace almost any compound or material that we care to. Sometimes radiomaterials can be used in the simple chemical form as shipped from Oak Ridge. This means as the element, as a simple salt such as the carbonate or nitrate, or as the oxide. For most biological tracer experiments, however, it is necessary to incorporate the radioisotope in some complex compound. If an investigator wants to use a radioisotope, say carbon 14, in trying to find out what happens to a sugar or an amino acid or a vitamin in a plant or animal process, he must first incorporate the radioisotope into the compound being studied. Sometimes these labeled or tagged compounds can be made by the chemist in the laboratory. Frequently, however, it is necessary to make them by biological means, that is, the radioisotope in some simple form is injected into an animal and subsequently extracted from the blood, urine, or tissues of the animal as the desired complex compound.

The tracer technique to a greater extent, however, derives its power from a combination of extreme sensitivity and unique specificity. So sensitive are the methods for measuring the radiations from radioisotopes that it is possible to detect the presence of atoms with millions to hundreds of millions times the sensitivity possible with other ordinary physical and chemical means now known. It is not difficult to detect radioisotopes that have been diluted as much as a billion or 10 billion times, while dilutions of more than a trillion are attainable (Illus. 66, fig. 1). This means that in a tracer experiment in biology it would be possible to detect one-hundred-millionth of an ounce of radioactive material after it had become distributed in an animal as large as a 1,000-pound cow. Or to put it another way, it would be possible to detect 1 ounce of radioactive material, say radioactive sugar, mixed uniformly in 100 million tons or in 2 billion 100-pound sacks of nonradioactive or ordinary sugar.

When we say that the tracer method has a unique specificity, we mean simply that radioisotopes provide scientists with the ability to follow a specific batch of atoms through a complicated system irrespective of all the chemical processes that may be going on. For example, it would be possible to trace an isotope in a soil nutrient through a plant grown on the soil, through a cow fed on the plant, and finally through a rabbit fed on milk obtained from the cow. Even though the isotope would pass through a number of complex processes, its telltale radiation would permit its positive identification throughout.

Radioactive tracer atoms have allowed us to increase our power of perception. They have permitted measurements and analyses at concentrations far below those hitherto permissible. Equally important, they have permitted us positive identification of products and processes. Their value as research tools can perhaps be best described by noting what they have meant to the field of biology.

In the seventeenth century the invention of the microscope marked the beginning of our understanding of the importance of individual cells and their relations to the whole organism. The discovery of isotopes and their applications as tracer atoms in the twentieth century has given us a tool whereby we can explore the physiology and biochemistry of organisms in the dynamic state

1. Pictured here is a typical counting setup for assaying radio-active samples in the laboratory. The cylindrical unit on the work bench at the right is a shielded container, often called a "pig," housing a geiger counter. The sample to be counted has been placed on one of the shelves in the "pig," The rectangular unit in the center is the scaler, which picks up the impulse from the counter, amplifies it, and records it on a mechanical counter. The plastic box on the left is a container to hold various absorbers which will be used in counting certain samples. The absorbers, usually aluminum sheets, are placed in the "pig" on a shelf above the sample.

ILLUS. 66—

2. Here we see the application of radioactive phosphate fertilizer. The fertilizer is prepared in the laboratory and then applied to the soil from a hopper attached to the tractor shown in the photograph. The operator in the foreground is surveying the row with a radiation-survey meter to determine the distribution of the radioactive fertilizer. Note that both of the men in the foreground are wearing dust masks to prevent possible inhalation of the radioactive fertilizer.

with even greater detail. The microscope permits examination of the structural details of individual cells. Isotopes permit examination of the chemical activities of individual batches of molecules, atoms, and ions within cells.

The isotope, particularly the reactor-produced radioactive isotope, has truly been a new key to knowledge. It is a key that has already opened up many doors. Many, many more, however, remain to be opened and can be opened by this new key.

EXAMPLES OF APPLICATIONS

Reactor-produced radioisotopes have been used, particularly as tracer atoms, in nearly every phase of the physical, chemical, and biological sciences. They have also been used extensively in many of the applied problems of medicine, agriculture, and industry. Since the distribution program began in the summer of 1946, more than 130,000 shipments of radioisotopes have been made from the principal production facilities in Oak Ridge, Tennessee, to users in every State and in almost every foreign country. Also, over 50,000 shipments are being made every year by secondary commercial suppliers in the form of specially processed radiomaterials, radioactive drugs, radiation sources, etc.

In the past 13 years, over 16,000 papers and reports dealing with isotope investigations have been published in scientific and technical journals. A number of books also have been written on the subject.

Since the number of different kinds of applications could run into the thousands, we shall try to select examples representative of a large number of applications. Also, to keep the story short, we shall stick to applications in medicine, agriculture, or industry.

MEDICINE

The largest percentage of radioisotope shipments go for use in the field of medicine. This is not only because radioisotopes are used extensively in medicine but because most medical applications use short-lived radioisotopes and therefore require repeated shipments. Radioisotopes have found valuable uses in medical research, diagnosis, and treatment.

MEDICAL RESEARCH

Radioisotopes have been used as tracer atoms in medical research to study the movement of elements and compounds in the body. For example, they have permitted investigators for the first time to measure the absorption of a specific batch of atoms of an element by a particular tissue or organ. They have shown how elements are transported within the body, how they are absorbed from the intestinal tract, and how they move across blood-vessel walls. They have even been used to measure the uptake and turnover of biochemicals within cells.

But what can isotopes tell us that cannot be determined by other methods? Let us assume that we want to find out how rapidly sodium travels through the body and at what rate it is taken into various body fluids and tissues. All we have to do it to take some table salt and irradiate it in a reactor. This gives us radioactive sodium. We can then give some of this radiosodium to a person by mouth or by vein and then follow its path through the body with a geiger counter or some other radiation instrument.

The gamma rays from the radiosodium are so penetrating that we can detect them just by holding a counter over various areas of the body. This simple procedure allows us to see when blood carrying the radioactive sodium reaches a certain part of the body. In fact, this technique is used for determining the adequacy of blood circulation to the extremities such as the arms and legs. If we want more detailed information on the movement of sodium within the body, we cannot just hold a counter outside but we have to measure the radioactivity of samples of blood, urine, sweat, and other body fluids taken at various intervals after the radiosodium is injected.

Such an experiment shows that sodium goes across the blood-vessel walls at an extremely rapid rate — back and forth at the rate of 50 pounds of salt a day. Movement of this type could not be found by other methods because we could not tell the ordinary sodium atoms on one side of the blood-vessel wall from those on

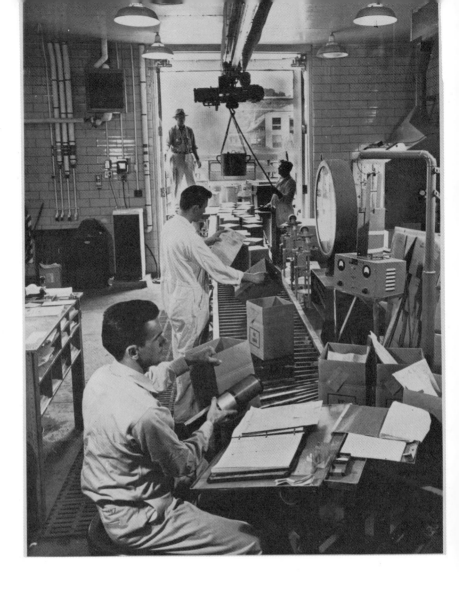

ILLUS. 67—

1. Packaging radioisotopes for shipment does not differ essentially from other industrial packaging operations. The surface of each package, however, must be monitored by sensitive radiation detection instruments (foreground) to assure that surface radiation does not exceed the extremely low prescribed levels. Larger quantities of radioisotopes, especially those that emit penetrating radiation, are packaged in heavy, thick-walled containers (background) to provide necessary shielding.

2. *Fast transportation is vital in the use of radioisotopes with short half lives. Here a commercial supplier of labeled pharmaceuticals transships its products to an air freight carrier for most rapid delivery. These radiopharmaceuticals are synthesized from the simple chemical forms of the radioisotopes supplied by Oak Ridge National Laboratory in wholesale quantities. Rigid purification and standardization are necessary for radioactive drugs to be used in medical research, diagnosis, or therapy.*

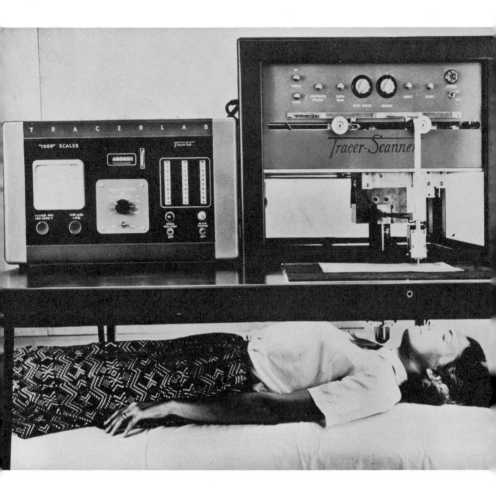

ILLUS. 68—

1. *Diagnosis of various clinical conditions has been improved by the use of radioisotope tracers. Here, thyroid function is being analyzed. The patient has drunk a solution of radioiodine which is taken up by thyroid tissue. The illustrated "scanner" passes a radiation detection instrument over the thyroid area and automatically draws a diagram indicating the distribution of the radioactive iodine. The scan gives information on thyroid disease, tumors, and cancer. Complete body scans can be made to detect the metastases of thyroid cancer.*

2. The "Gamma Garden" at Brookhaven National Laboratory, Upton, Long Island. A 2,000-curie cobalt 60 gamma source can be raised from its underground storage pit into the vertical pipe in order to irradiate the plants growing in concentric circles about it. Potted plants can be placed near the source for intense short-term irradiation, while other plants are grown in soil at various distances from the source. Radiation-induced mutations are sought for use in breeding improved vegetable, grain, fruit, and other crops. The area is fenced, and interlocks between gate and source mechanism prevent exposure of gardeners and plant scientists.

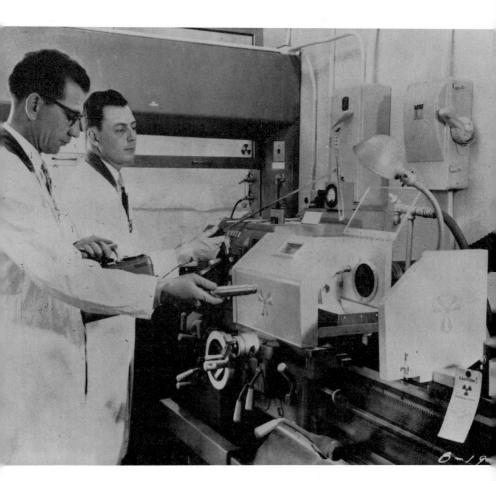

ILLUS. 69—

1. Manufacturers and operators of machine tools are using radioisotopes in extensive studies to improve machining equipment
and operations. Here an experimental tool bit, made radioactive by neutron activation in a reactor, is placed in position.
Radioactivity appearing in the cutting fluid or in the chips
will give in a few minutes a measurement of wear not otherwise obtainable except after weeks or months of operation.

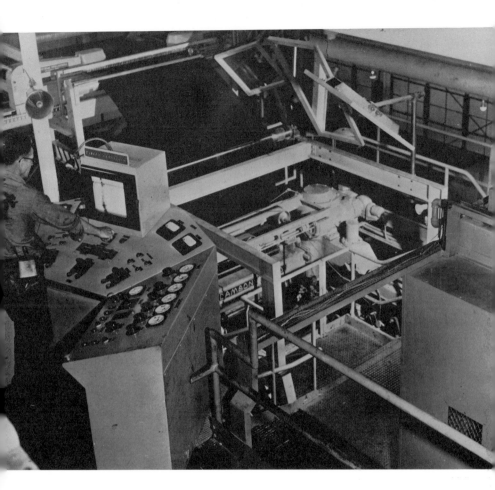

2. *Radioisotopic gages are contributing to increased mechanization in many industries. Here the thickness of rubber fabric is accurately measured by penetration of beta radiation. The radiation sources and detection instruments are mounted in the gage heads shown extending over the fabric sheet in the upper left corner of the illustration. The operator has an instantaneous record of thickness variations on the strip chart recorder and can adjust roller separation and other process variables without leaving his station.*

ILLUS. 70—

1. *A pipewall thickness gage being used to measure scaling on the inside of a pipe carrying petroleum products. Gamma radiation from a radium or radioisotope source at the far end of the gage penetrates the pipe wall and scale and is detected in the hand-held base. This device also is commonly used to measure internal erosion and corrosion and, in trouble shooting, to detect obstructions in piping.*

2. *Intense radiation from large quantities of radioisotopes may find extensive applications in industry just as it has in medicine and agriculture. Here, the effects of intense radiation from spent reactor fuel elements on potatoes and canned milk (background) is being investigated. Besides food preservation, radiation can initiate chemical reactions, polymerize a wide range of materials, sterilize medical and hospital supplies, and provide the fuel for electric power sources for satellites and remote weather stations.*

the other side. However, by putting labeled sodium atoms on one side we can observe the rate at which the labeled sodium atoms appear on the other, and thus find the rate of transfer of sodium.

Similar experiments using isotopes of hydrogen to label water molecules show that water passes back and forth across the blood-vessel walls at the rate of about 20 barrels a day.

The most rapid transfer of sodium in the body is by circulation of the blood. Only about 15 seconds are required for the sodium to go from one arm through the heart, through the lungs, and into the other arm. It was found that in 60 additional seconds the sodium had diffused out into the tissues and had been excreted from the sweat glands on the opposite arm.

But radioisotope studies have called our attention to much more amazing facts on the day-to-day operation of our bodies. Medical men used to think of the human body as an engine that takes in food, air, and water mainly as fuel to keep running on. Only a small part of the intake was thought to go for replacement of engine wear. Investigations with isotopes have demonstrated that the body instead is much more like a very fluid military regiment which may retain its size, form, and composition even though the individuals in it are continually changing: joining up, being transferred from post to post, promoted, or demoted; acting as reserves; and finally departing after varying lengths of service.

Tracer studies show that the atomic turnover in our bodies is quite rapid and quite complete. For example, in a week or two half of the sodium atoms that are now in our bodies will be replaced by other sodium atoms. The case is similar for hydrogen and phosphorus. Even half of the carbon atoms will be replaced in a month or two. And so the story goes for nearly all the elements. Indeed, it has been shown that in a year approximately 98 percent of the atoms in us now will be replaced by other atoms that we take in in our air, food, and drink.

Instead of just tracing atoms of an element in the body, radioisotopes are used for the much more complicated job of tracing complex compounds and molecules and even parts of molecules. Such studies have permitted investigators in physiology to develop an entirely new technique for studying body metabolism, that is, the details of biochemical reactions by which foods and other materials are taken into the body, used, and finally broken down and eliminated. In such studies they have been used to label and trace through complex body processes a wide variety of important materials such as amino acids, proteins, vitamins, hormones, antibodies, viruses, and cancer-producing agents (Illus. 71).

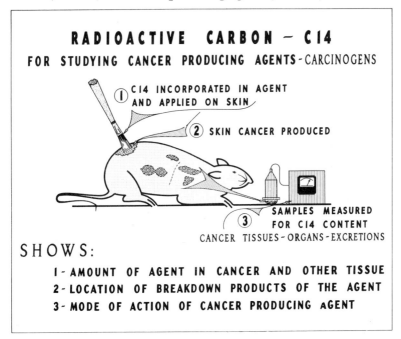

RADIOACTIVE CARBON — C14

FOR STUDYING CANCER PRODUCING AGENTS - CARCINOGENS

① C14 INCORPORATED IN AGENT AND APPLIED ON SKIN

② SKIN CANCER PRODUCED

③ SAMPLES MEASURED FOR C14 CONTENT

CANCER TISSUES - ORGANS - EXCRETIONS

SHOWS:

1 - AMOUNT OF AGENT IN CANCER AND OTHER TISSUE
2 - LOCATION OF BREAKDOWN PRODUCTS OF THE AGENT
3 - MODE OF ACTION OF CANCER PRODUCING AGENT

ILLUS. 71—

A typical case would be that of studying the biological fate of a labeled amino acid. The compound is synthesized using a radioisotope such as radioactive carbon or radioactive sulfur. It can then be fed to rats or other animals. After the labeled compound has entered into the body's reactions, the animal is sacrificed. Analysis of radioactivity in various tissues such as the spleen, liver, and kidney indicates where the radioactive atoms have become located. In addition, biochemical analysis indicates the chemical form in which the radioisotope now exists. Some of the radioisotope will be found in protein material, some in uncombined amino acids, and some in breakdown products of the amino acids.

In this way the investigator determines what happened to the originally ingested amino acid and what its role is in the body.

Such experiments clearly prove that our body processes are continually breaking down and building up organic molecules. The breaking-down process or degradation of complex molecules releases the energy which is necessary for proper functioning of our bodies. It also furnishes some of the less complex components of our tissue. A fine balance is maintained between the degradation to obtain energy and the synthesis to make new organic molecules for our body's needs.

Radioisotopes are thus providing us with information not only on how we "tick" when healthy but on what goes wrong in disease. By comparing the behavior of isotope-labeled compounds in normal animals with their behavior in animals having diseases such as cirrhosis of the liver or cancer, investigators are able to look for differences which may give valuable leads as to the cause and cure of the disease.

Another goal of this type of investigation would be to use the behavior of the labeled compound for diagnosing such diseases.

MEDICAL DIAGNOSIS

In medical diagnosis radioisotopes have been used to determine blood volumes; blood circulation to the extremities; pumping efficiency of the heart; thyroid-gland activity; and the location of brain tumors.

Radioisotopes have been used by many large hospitals and medical centers for measuring the volume of blood in patients, especially those scheduled for surgery. In this particular diagnostic test a portion of the blood, the serum albumin, is labeled with a known concentration of radioiodine and then injected into the patient. After the blood has had a chance to circulate throughout the body, another blood sample is taken and the concentration redetermined. The amount of dilution that has taken place is a measure of the total volume of blood in the patient. Even wounded United Nations troops in Korea were tested for loss of blood by radioisotope blood-volume determinations. These same troops also benefited from better methods of using blood preservatives and plasma substitutes developed through tracer studies.

The most widely used diagnostic test, however, is the radio-iodine test for thyroid activity. The test is also simple. Radioactive iodine in the compound, sodium iodide, is given to the patient by mouth. It appears that the patient is simply drinking a glass of water.

Practically all iodine, which is absorbed in the body, is taken up by the thyroid gland. This is because of the gland's production of an iodine-containing hormone caled thyroxine. If the gland is overactive (hyperthyroidism), its production of thyroxine is large and accordingly its ability to take up iodine is large. Underactivity of the gland (hypothyroidism) produces the opposite effect.

The radioactive iodine will also go to the thyroid, but since it gives off penetrating gamma rays, its rate of uptake in the gland may be determined by using a geiger counter or other radiation detector placed over the neck outside the gland. Comparison with a normal uptake rate indicates whether the gland is overactive or underactive. This particular test is now being used routinely by hundreds of hospitals and physicians all over the world.

One thing that makes radioisotopes such a useful diagnostic aid is that only extremely small harmless amounts of the radiomaterial are required. This means that we should see a much wider diagnostic use of radiosotopes in the future.

MEDICAL THERAPY

Radioisotopes have also been used in medical therapy for treating such things as hyperthyroidism (overactive thyroid), cancer, polycythemia vera (overproduction of red cells), leukemia (overproduction of white cells), and lesions of the eye and skin.

Some applications are like those of radium and X-rays; a diseased tissue or organ is exposed to radiation from a source placed either inside or outside the body. When the source is located outside the body, the treatment is known as "teletherapy." Teletherapy devices contain large quantities of radioactive cobalt — up to 2,000 curies or more — and thus give off a penetrating beam of gamma rays which can be used to treat deep-seated lesions, such as cancer of the lung. The beam is as penetrating as that from a 2- to 3-million volt X-ray machine. The radiocobalt unit, besides being cheaper to buy and operate, offers a number of medical advantages. Great flexibility is possible in irradiating tumors of different shapes. Rotational teletherapy, diagrammed in Illustration 72, permits the gamma beam to play continuously on the tumor while, because the source rotates about the patient, minimizing the radiation dose to the skin and other organs. Almost 200 teletherapy machines have been installed in hospitals and clinics throughout the country.

The same radioactive cobalt in much smaller quantities has been used, again like radium, for treating cancer of easily accessible areas of the body like the cheek and lip. Radium is usually used as "seeds" or "needles." Although it is widely employed it is expensive and cannot be easily adapted to a wide variety of uses. The use of cobalt, on the other hand, can be made very flexible. For example, radioactive-cobalt wire can be inserted into small-diameter nylon tubing and sewed into the tissue to be treated.

ROTATIONAL TELETHERAPY
USING
Co 60 GAMMA RAYS
(FRANCIS DELAFIELD HOSPITAL – NYC)

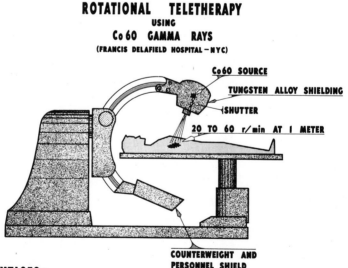

Co 60 SOURCE

TUNGSTEN ALLOY SHIELDING

SHUTTER

20 TO 60 r/min AT 1 METER

COUNTERWEIGHT AND
PERSONNEL SHIELD

ADVANTAGES:

1 – EFFECTIVE DOSE AT DEEP-SEATED TUMOR – SMALL DOSE AT SURFACE
2 – ALLOWS SELECTION OF IRRADIATION PATTERNS
3 – ROTATION AND SHUTTER REMOTELY CONTROLLED

ILLUS. 72—

The more unique type of treatment possible with radioisotopes is based on giving the radiomaterial to the patient by vein or mouth and depending on body processes to locate the radioactivity in the desired tissue or organ. For example, radioactive iodine is used in treating hyperthyroidism in the same way that it is used to diagnose hyperthyroidism, except that much larger quantities of the radiomaterial are used. Indeed, radioactive iodine is becoming the treatment of choice in an increasing number of medical centers both in the United States and abroad for hyperthyroidism. It has been reported that in about 90 percent of the cases treated, hyperthyroidism is controlled in 2 to 4 months by one or two treatments; 10 percent of the patients may require a third treatment. Similarly, radioactive phosphorus is considered the treatment of choice of many physicians in treating polycythemia vera and has been found to offer some relief in certain cases of chronic leukemia.

Neither the physical-placement nor biochemical-placement type of radioisotope treatment, however, should be regarded as a "permanent" cure. Both are mainly measures to control the disease and prolong the comfortable and useful life of the patient.

AGRICULTURE

Many of the complex and difficult problems in agriculture, like those in medical research, have to do with the fundamental processes of growth. What minerals and organic nutrients do plants need? How do plant roots pick them up and how are they utilized? What are the innermost workings of photosynthesis, the little-understood process of nature that accounts for all the world's food and most of its fuel?

In some respects the agricultural problems confronting us today are even bigger than the medical problems and certainly more critical. Advances in medicine tend to lengthen man's life and hence we have more people to feed, clothe, and house. Also, our birth rate is staying at the high level it reached after World War II.

Carroll A. Hochwalt, vice president of the Monsanto Chemical Co., sized up the situation recently in a paper before a meeting of the American Association for the Advancement of Science in St.

Louis. As he pointed out, if we keep populating our nation at the present rate, by 1975 we shall have at least 25 per cent more people to feed and clothe. It will take 15 billion more eggs a year; 20 million more hogs; and another 10 billion quarts of milk just to keep our people eating as well as they are today. And this is only part of the story, for this includes only the United States. Even today many people in other areas of the world are badly undernourished.

The problem becomes even more serious when we consider the waste that is taking place. For example, it has been estimated that insects alone destroy as much as 4 billion dollars worth of crops annually. Plant diseases destroy another 4 billion dollars worth. But what is more amazing is the costly damage that we can attribute to weeds. It is almost beyond belief to realize that by choking out crops, clogging irrigation ditches, and poisoning farm animals, weeds cost the farmer 5 billion dollars each year.

Thus, we must find ways to increase the world's productivity not only because we have found ways to increase the world's health and because our world population is increasing at a rapid rate, but also because so many factors are working against us.

Radioisotopes are helping to provide some of the answers. They have, for example, become an extremely useful tool in studying the efficient use of fertilizers. Since food productivity is dependent to a large extent on soil fertility, the replenishment of depleted and overworked soils with fertilizers is a major problem.

One of the most important group of fertilizers, the phosphate fertilizers, can be readily studied with radioactive phosphorus (Illus. 66, fig. 2). Here, as in so many other tracer studies, the radioisotope technique is used primarily because it provides the means for following a specific batch of atoms. The radioactive phosphorus is incorporated in the fertilizer which is added to the soil being studied. Later, radioactivity analyses of the plant show what parts of the plant have taken up the radioactive atoms and hence the fertilizer. Chemical analyses of the plant indicate the total amount of phosphorus coming from the fertilizer plus that coming from the ordinary phosphorus previously present in the soil.

From such studies investigators can determine not only how much phosphorus is taken up by a plant and where it came from but also the efficiency of the fertilizer, the best type of fertilizer to use, and the most desirable place to put the fertilizer with reference to the location of the plant. The U. S. Department of Agriculture, working with various State agricultural experiment stations, is conducting extensive programs of such tests on numerous crops, such as alfalfa, cotton, corn, rice, peanuts, sugarcane, peaches, pineapples, cantaloupes, and others.

The most fundamental of all tracer experiments, however, is the use of radioactive carbon and other isotopes in man's effort to learn the secret of photosynthesis. Chemical studies have shown that plants combine water and carbon dioxide in the presence of sunlight to form sugars and starches, but the details of how the synthesis takes place are still unknown. By tagging with radioactive carbon 14 the carbon dioxide fed to plants and studying intermediate products formed during this complicated synthesis, investigators are beginning to achieve a more detailed understanding of the photosynthetic process.

Radioisotopes have also been used to supply new knowledge on reactions between various soil elements, on insecticides and weed killers, and on various types of blight and other plant diseases. Similarly, radioisotope investigations have helped scientists to understand better the problems concerned with nutrition and diseases of livestock and the production of milk and eggs.

The existence in foods of potentially hazardous residues from insecticides, weed killers, defoliants, growth regulators, veterinary drugs, fumigants, food additives, and other agricultural and food processing chemicals is of considerable public concern. The ability of radioisotopes to trace materials through complicated biological systems may contribute to solution of the processor's problems in meeting public health standards.

Developments in plant genetics have been particularly rapid since the availability of radioisotopes provided intense radiation sources. When exposed to sufficiently high levels of radiation, plants develop mutations in the seeds and growing parts. These mutations provide differences which the plant breeder can use to produce new and improved forms of plants. Mutation breeding techniques have produced plants having more food value and higher yield, better adaptation to adverse soil conditions, higher resistance to disease or drought, better suitability for mechanical harvesting, and improved selling properties such as richer color or firmer texture. Over 60 different crop plants are being studied and improved in this way.

The most striking example of a practical application of intense radiation to an agricultural problem has been the eradication of the screwworm fly from Florida and the southeastern States. The screwworm, which is so named because the larva resembles a wood screw, is a serious livestock pest which lays eggs in cuts and scratches of cattle. The resulting grubs cause debilitating sores, which if not treated can cause death. It has been eliminated by rearing the larvae on a beef and blood medium and exposing them to cobalt 60 gamma radiation at a critical period in their growth. This produced sexually sterilized, but otherwise normal, adults. When the adults were released, matings with the wild population led to sterile eggs. Continued for several generations, this reduced the screwworm population to zero. Over 2.75 billion screwworm flies were reared, irradiated and released over a 75,000 square mile area in this eradication campaign.

Within the inherent limitations of mating habits and extent of migration, this "sterile male" technique may also be developed for use against other pests such as the cotton boll weevil, sugarcane borer, Oriental fruit fly, and the Mediterranean fruit fly. Sterilization control of mosquitoes carrying yellow fever and malaria and, in Africa, the tsetse fly, are in early stages of investigation.

INDUSTRY

As in the fields of medicine and agriculture, radioisotopes may be used in industry as tracer atoms to measure the transfer of materials by physical and physical-chemical means and to follow the mechanisms of industrial chemical processes. Also, a variety of ways have been found for employing radioisotopes as sources of radiation, especially in the control of certain manufacturing operations.

An example of an industrial tracer application is the radioisotope method of measuring wear or friction. Several companies are using this method for studying wear in engines. A piston ring or some other motor part is sent to Oak Ridge, made radioactive in the nuclear reactor, and then returned for replacement in the engine. The motor with its radioactive piston rings is then run. As the rings wear, some of the radioactive atoms will get into the oil. Periodic sampling and radioactivity analysis of the oil lubricant will show just how much the ring is wearing away by friction.

Another example of tracer application in industry is their use in following the flow of oils through pipelines. It is common practice to use the same pipeline to transport a wide variety of crude or refined oils. The location of the boundary between the two oils must be known in order to route different oils to different takeoff points and terminals along the line. The radioisotope method is based on injecting into the line a small amount of radioactive material just at the boundary as a product is changed. Geiger counters detect and record the passage of radioactivity in this boundary at various points along the line. Clean separation of the different oils means a large saving in money. One company is routinely using this method of boundary marking in a pipeline running from Salt Lake City, Utah, to Pasco, Wash. — a distance of more than 550 miles. The same company has said that the new method means a saving of hundreds of barrels per day of oils that would have an average retail value of about $10 a barrel.

As tracers in industrial research, radioisotopes have also been used to test the efficiency of washing machines, to follow the movement of preservatives in telephone poles, to study the action of detergents, to investigate the mechanisms of such industrial processes as vulcanization and polymerization, to study the synthetic production of gasoline (Illus. 73), to investigate the raising of bread, and to help solve a host of other industrial problems.

Other than as tracers, the simplest type of radioisotope application depends merely on measuring the change in intensity from a stationary radioactive source when something is placed between it and the detecting instrument. This change is usually measured by a counter, as in the radioactive thickness gage or liquid-level gage. Sometimes, however, as in radiography, a photographic film is used as the radiation detector. Instead of an instrument recording we get a photographic picture of the change in radiation intensity.

Radiographic testing is probably the oldest industrial application of radioactivity and one of the simplest ways of using a radio-

CONTROL OF CATALYST FLOW RATE
USING
RADIOACTIVE BEADS

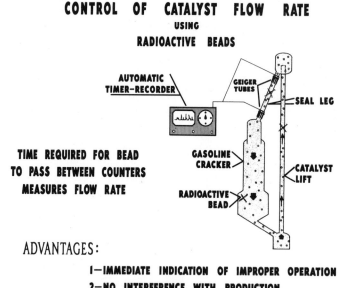

AUTOMATIC
TIMER-RECORDER

GEIGER
TUBES

SEAL LEG

TIME REQUIRED FOR BEAD
TO PASS BETWEEN COUNTERS
MEASURES FLOW RATE

GASOLINE
CRACKER

CATALYST
LIFT

RADIOACTIVE
BEAD

ADVANTAGES:

1—IMMEDIATE INDICATION OF IMPROPER OPERATION

2—NO INTERFERENCE WITH PRODUCTION

ILLUS. 73—   3—POSSIBLE AUTOMATIC ADJUSTMENT OF FLOW RATE

isotope as a stationary source of radiation. The test is carried out by placing the radioactive source on one side of a weld or casting and a photographic film on the other side. A darkening of the developed film indicates the location of any flaws or cracks since more radiation penetrates through these places and causes greater exposure to the film.

Naturally occurring radium and radon used to be the only radioisotopes available for this kind of application. Today, however, more and more industries are using radioactive cobalt instead. Radiocobalt is more readily available and easier to handle than radium. It can also be obtained in greater radiation strength, in any desired shape and size, and is much cheaper.

Another stationary-source type of application is the so-called radioactive thickness gage. In the simplest type of gage, a radioactive source which emits beta rays, that is, high-speed electrons, is placed on one side of the material whose thickness is to be measured and a radiation instrument on the other side. The amount of radiation which penetrates through the material decreases with the thickness of the material, that is, the thicker the material the less radiation gets through and vice versa. The radiation meters used in these gages are designed to read in thickness values.

Radioactive thickness gages are now being sold by numerous commercial manufacturers. Approximately 6,000 have been installed by all types of industry. They are very sensitive to small differences in thickness and give very reproducible results. Another big advantage is that the gage makes no mechanical contact with the material being measured. This means that the gage can be used without stopping or cutting the rolling sheet and without danger of tearing or marking the sheet. Still another advantage is that the gage can be made to control automatically the settings of the rollers rolling out the sheet.

Radioactive thickness gages have been used to measure the thickness of paper, rubber, plastic, glass, and steel sheets. Firms using them have been able to meet more exacting specifications and as a result have been able to cut down on the amount of reject material.

In summing up the industrial applications of isotopic gages, we should mention the radioactive liquid-level gage used in measuring the level of molten metal in a cupola and the radioactive density gage used in measuring the water content of mountain snowpacks in remote areas and the silt and mud content of water in front of power dams.

The great versatility of radioisotopes in solving industrial problems, increasing assembly line efficiency, and developing new products is accompanied by considerable savings to industry and to the consumer. The National Industrial Conference Board has recently published a report, "Radioisotopes in Industry," which is not only a census of radioisotope uses throughout industry, but gives details of the benefits and savings derived from numerous specific applications.

Although the total benefits that radioisotopes are conferring on American industry are difficult to estimate, the Conference Board found that 523 companies for which information was available had average annual savings in labor, raw materials, research time, and reduced scrap and other benefits of $100,000 each.

THE FUTURE OF RADIOISOTOPES

We can certainly expect a much wider use of radioisotopes in the future. They are being produced in sufficient quantities to make them available to everybody who has a need for them and who knows how to use them. They are becoming recognized by scientists everywhere as a valuable and necessary tool. Old uses, like the radioiodine treatment of hyperthyroidism and the radioisotope gaging of thicknesses, are becoming routine procedure in thousands of institutions. New uses keep appearing on the scene. Manufacturers are continually improving the design and performance of radiation detection instruments and handling devices. Better techniques are being developed for getting more out of the sensitivity and precise labeling possibilities of the isotope method. The Atomic Energy Commission, through its Isotope Development Program, is developing basic radioisotope technology and attempting to accelerate the over-all applications of isotopes in the public interest.

There is little doubt that radioisotopes are one of the most valuable research and industrial tools ever developed. Yet not nearly as many chemists or biologists or engineers use isotopes as could profitably do so. We need more people trained in the use of isotopes — people who can apply this new tool to tomorrow's problems in medicine, science, and technology — more "isotopologists." But the need goes further than this. A rapidly expanding atomic-energy problem, for instance, needs many more young scientists and engineers who know and want to work with radioactivity. Our whole national security and national welfare today are more dependent than ever on advancements in science. The need for technically trained people has never been greater. The opportunities have never been greater.

We have hardly scratched the possibilities of scientific achievement. I have no doubt that someone 20 years hence will tell us of things which even now are beyond our remotest dreams. I hope, however, that I may be able to point to some of these developments of the future and say that they were made possible in part by isotopes — by what we now call new keys to knowledge.

REFERENCE

SPECIAL SOURCES OF INFORMATION ON ISOTOPES, January 1960. Available from Office of Isotopes Development, U. S. Atomic Energy Commission, Washington 25, D. C. No charge.

HANS E. SUESS

The Abundance of the
Chemical Elements

[FROM THE SMITHSONIAN REPORT FOR 1958]

WHEREAS *the previous article on the production and uses of radio-isotopes lies on the nebulous borderline between physics and chemistry, the following discussion of the relative abundance of the chemical elements bridges the narrow gap between chemistry and geology. Our earth, the other planets, the stars and galaxies, all are composed of the same chemical elements, although in varying proportions. The relative abundance of the elements here on earth is one field of study in the science of geochemistry.*

The author, Dr. Hans E. Suess, formerly research associate at Hamburg University in Germany and later chemist with the U.S. Geological Survey, is now professor of geochemistry at the University of California, La Jolla. Dr. Suess discusses three lines of attack on the problem of the distribution of chemical elements throughout the universe: spectral analysis of the sun and stars, chemical analysis of the meteorites that have been found on the surface of the earth, and the isotopic composition of the elements. He concludes with a review of the latest theories regarding the origin of the chemical elements.

E VERYBODY KNOWS that gold is a very rare element and iron is very abundant on the surface of the earth. Elements like magnesium, silicon, oxygen, or aluminum represent the major constituents of the earth's crust and its rocks, whereas others like gallium, platinum, thallium, and uranium are present only in rare minerals or in the form of minor impurities. Just how much more abundant one element is relative to another is a question dealt with in the field of geochemistry.

The first attempt to answer this question in a quantitative way was made by F. W. Clarke and H. S. Washington during the last decades of the 19th century. Numerous rock analyses were compared by these authors and an average figure for the occurrence of each element in terrestrial rocks was given. In 1889 Clarke said that he attempted to represent the relative abundances of the elements obtained in this way by a curve, taking their atomic weight for one set of ordinates. He had hoped that some sort of periodicity might become evident, but no such regularity appeared. During the following 50 years the work of geochemists led to an understanding of the distribution of the elements between various types of rocks, but it could not yet be explained why some elements were more abundant than others.

Another basic question that could not be answered at the time that Clarke and Washington began their studies was whether the earth was unique in its chemical composition compared to other heavenly bodies. Did other planets, the sun, and the stars have an entirely different composition or was the composition of the earth's crust representative in a general way of the material of which the universe is composed? Three lines of new scientific evidence enable us now to interpret geochemical data and answer all these questions in a satisfactory way. These are: spectral analysis of the sun and stars, chemical analysis of meteorites, and the isotopic composition of the elements.

THE COMPOSITION OF THE SUN AND STARS

Spectral analysis of the light of stars and distant nebulae is undoubtedly the most direct way to determine the relative abundances of the elements in the universe as a whole. The intensity of
the absorption lines, the so-called Fraunhofer lines, in the spectrum depends on the concentration of the atoms causing the absorption. In general it is not difficult to identify the element that
causes an observed absorption line. In order to calculate the correlation of line intensity with atomic concentration, a number of
physical properties of the absorbing atoms and the thermodynamic
state of the absorbing stellar matter have to be known in detail.

Unfortunately, the experimental determinations of these properties are not yet complete and one has to rely in many cases on
theoretical calculations which often give only crude approximations. Furthermore, various other quantities such as optical depth
of the layer in which the absorption occurs, thermal velocity of the
absorbing atoms, their macroscopic turbulent motion, and other
characteristics have to be known before the exact functional dependence of line intensity and atomic concentration can be calculated.

The first abundance data based on spectral analyses were obtained by Miss Payn in 1925 and by Russel in 1929. Since then the
work of these authors has been improved and extended by many
investigators, and it was found that the chemical composition of
the universe is indeed remarkably uniform, although the most
recent investigations indicate definite systematic variations in the
composition of stars, depending on their age and their position in
the galaxies.

The most important result of the astronomical investigations is
the discovery that hydrogen is by far the most abundant element
in the universe. Next to hydrogen in abundance is helium. In the
sun helium constitutes about one-fourth of the atoms. All the other
elements make up only about 1 percent of the sun's total mass.
The most prominent of these other elements are carbon, nitrogen,
oxygen, and neon. Among the metals sodium, magnesium, aluminum, calcium, and iron are the most abundant ones.

COMPOSITION OF METEORITES

Another set of empirical abundance data can be derived from chemical analysis of meteorites. It is generally assumed that meteoritic matter has undergone less chemical fractionation than any terrestrial material found on the surface of the earth since the time is was formed from solar material. The main type of fractionation recognizable in meteorites is that of a separation of the elements into three chemical phases: a metal phase, a sulfide phase, and a silicate phase. Iron meteorites consist of metal and small amounts of sulfide only. Other meteorites are composed entirely of silicate.

A large fraction of meteorites, primarily the so-called chrondrites, contain all three phases in remarkably constant proportions. It is generally believed that the chrondrites contain all the condensable, nonvolatile components of solar matter in approximately primeval proportion. In any case it seems unlikely that chemically similar elements were separated from each other when the meteorites formed from a gas cloud because of the incompleteness of the separation of the three main phases.

Harold C. Urey compared the mean densities of meteorites with those of the terrestrial planets and the moon and concluded that average chrondrites and the moon probably contain the same ratio of metal to silicate, whereas the earth and the terrestrial planets contain relatively more metal. During the formation of the terrestrial planets a fraction of the silicate originally present escaped condensation. The much lower densities of the outer planets, Jupiter, Saturn, Uranus, Neptune, and Pluto, show that these planets have retained most of the volatile substances, a large part of the hydrogen and helium, the oxygen as water, nitrogen as ammonia, and carbon as methane.

Clearly, chemical analysis of meteorites cannot tell us anything about the solar abundances of the rare gases and of elements that form such highly volatile compounds. The concentration of many other elements in meteorites, however, shows a surprising agreement with the results of astronomical data. The relative amounts of elements such as sodium, aluminum, silicon, potassium, or calcium are found to be the same in the sun and in meteorites within the limits of errors of the analytical methods. Some values for heavier elements, for example strontium and barium, are also in perfect agreement.

True differences undoubtedly exist in the case of the lightest elements, particularly for lithium, beryllium, and boron. The concentrations of these elements on the surface of the sun are much smaller than those expected from the data on meteorites. The abundance of lithium relative to silicon on the sun is less than one-hundredth of that in meteorites. Beryllium and boron may be almost completely absent.

The deficiency of these elements on the sun is now understood as a consequence of thermonuclear reactions in the sun's interior. These reactions use up these elements as well as the heavy hydrogen isotope, deuterium. At the high temperatures of the sun's interior these elements react with protons and form either helium or heavier nuclear species. The nature of these reactions is now known in detail. It is also known that the isotopes of carbon and nitrogen participate in nuclear reactions which lead to the transmutation of hydrogen into helium. The sun and the stars derive their energy from this transmutation.

THE ISOTOPIC COMPOSITION OF THE ELEMENTS

The nuclei of the atoms are composed of neutrons and protons. Nuclei containing the same number of protons are called isotopes; they belong to the same chemical element and in general cannot be separated from one another by natural chemical processes. Most elements are composed of more than one isotope. The isotopic composition of all the elements is known with great accuracy.

For most elements, this composition is absolutely constant. It is the same in all terrestrial material and in meteorites. Small variations have only been observed for light elements as a consequence of minute differences in the chemical properties due to the difference in mass. Variations also occur if one or more isotopes of an element are produced by radioactive decay as in the case of lead. Otherwise we have reason to assume that the isotopic composition of the elements is basically a universal quantity valid for our solar system and for many stars.

If one plots the logarithm of the percentage of each isotope in a given element against the mass number (the number of neutrons plus protons) of the isotope, very peculiar figures are obtained, as shown in Illustration 74, taking several elements as examples. It was impossible for a long time to interpret these figures and to explain them in a quantitative way. Many scientists have been fascinated by their mysterious appearance in the same way that men have been fascinated by the mysterious features of the constellations in the night sky for the past thousands of years.

Certain rules have been recognized governing the isotopic composition of the elements, as for example the rule of Harkins which states that isotopes with an odd mass number are on the average less abundant than their even-mass-numbered neighbors. Another remarkable observation can be expressed in the following way: the geometry of the figures obtained by plotting the logarithms of the isotope abundances of a given element against their mass number, as shown in Illustration 75, is similar for neighboring elements with even atomic number. The character of the figures changes in general only gradually with atomic number.

However, in regions where the nuclei contain certain numbers of neutrons, an abrupt change occurs. These numbers of neutrons, the so-called magic numbers, signify nuclear shell closures. The prominent magic numbers are: 8, 20, 28, 50, 82, and 126. The irregularities that occur beyond barium may be interpreted on this basis, since we are dealing with isotopes of a "magic number" of 82. Furthermore, one can see that nuclear species containing just such a number of neutrons are in general exceptionally abundant (Illus. 76).

These facts indicate that the abundance of nuclear species is determined by nuclear properties. The individual abundances of nuclear species should therefore form a coherent system of some kind; they should depend in a similar fashion on the number of protons and the number of neutrons in a nucleus.

We know the relative abundance of nuclei containing the same number of protons (isotopes) with great precision from mass-

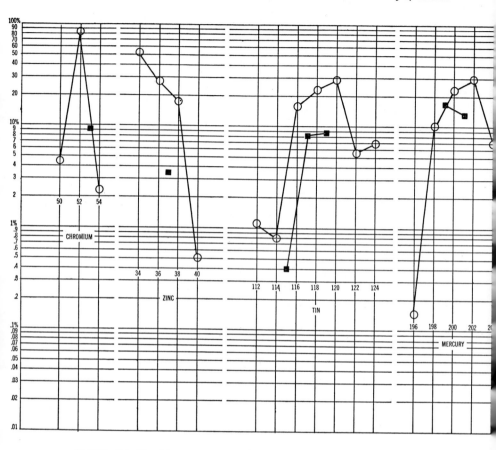

ILLUS. 74—*Graphic presentation of isotopic composition of some elements. Circles denote even-mass-numbered isotopes; squares, odd-mass-numbered isotopes.*

spectroscopic measurements, and can expect that all the abundances of the nuclear species should in some way be connected with these data. This indeed can be shown to be the case.

It is possible to modify within the limits of the error of the analytical data the values for the abundances of the elements in meteorites in such a way that the abundances of the individual nuclear species as a function of their mass number form regular smooth lines for the odd-mass-numbered isotopes. A similar smooth line is obtained with these modified abundance values, if one adds up at each mass number the abundance values of even-mass-numbered species with the same mass number (isobars). The isotopic composition of adjacent elements with even atomic number (graphically represented as in Illus. 75) then fit together like pieces of a jigsaw puzzle (see Illus. 76).

Careful estimates, weighing the possible errors in the empirical abundance data of the elements, were made by H. C. Urey and the author. They led to an abundance distribution as shown in Illustration 76 and in table 1.*

THE ORIGIN OF THE ELEMENTS

When in 1889 Clarke was looking for regularities in the relative abundances of the elements, he expected to find some connection with the periodic table. Spectral analysis of the stars and chemical analysis of the meteorites together with determinations of the isotopic composition of the elements made it possible more than 40 years later to discern certain types of regularities, but these regularities followed different laws from those of the atomic structure and had nothing to do with the periodic table. An entirely new aspect began to reveal itself, promising to lead far deeper into the fundamental fields of science than Clarke had expected.

We have seen that solar abundances of the elements reflect properties of the atomic nucleus. The matter surrounding us repre-

* Suess, H. E., and Urey, H. C., *Rev. Mod. Phys.*, vol. 28, p. 53, 1956, and *Encyclopedia of Physics*, vol. 51, p. 296, Heidelberg, 1958. The values given in table 1 are the ones given in the later article. Further necessary revisions especially for the heavy elements thallium, lead, and bismuth are indicated by more recent analyses.

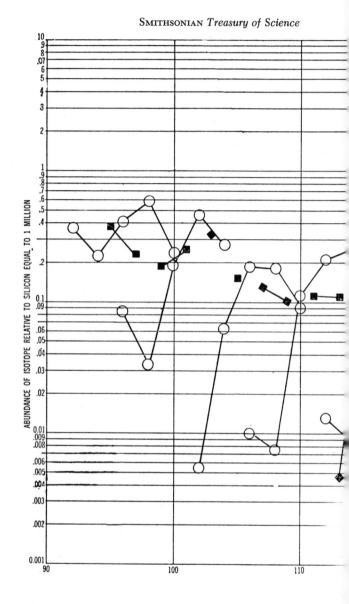

ILLUS. 75—*Abundances of nuclear species. Circles, even-mass-numbered isotopes. Squares, odd-mass-numbered isotopes. The points for isotopes of each element, even and odd separately, are connected by lines.*

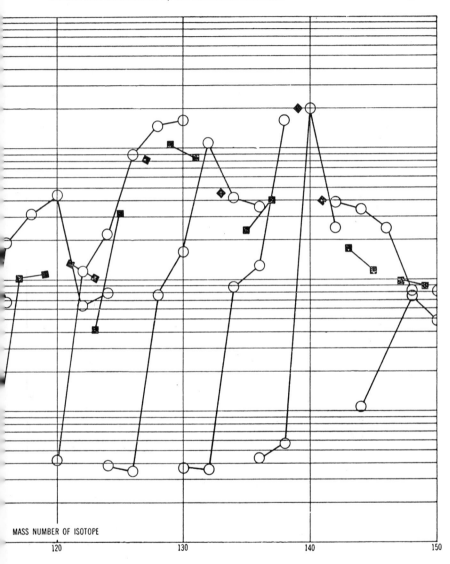

MASS NUMBER OF ISOTOPE

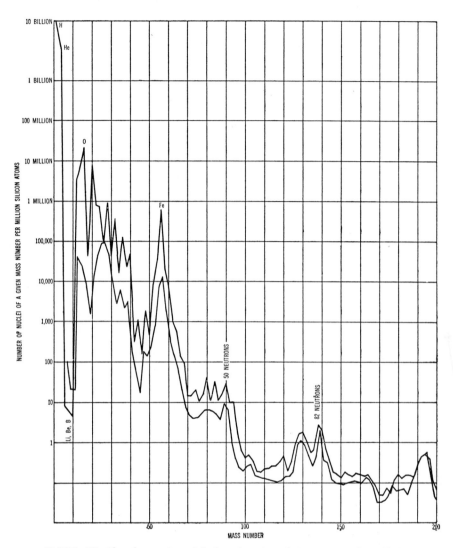

ILLUS. 76—*Abundance of nuclei plotted against their mass number. The upper line refers to nuclei with even, the lower line to those with
odd, mass number.*

sents the ashes of cosmic nuclear reactions. These reactions took
place some 6 billion years ago at a time before our sun and the
planets existed. They led to the formation of many radioactive nuclear species which subsequently decayed into the stable isotopes
of the existing elements. Only a few rare radioactive species such
as the isotopes of uranium, thorium, and potassium 40 are still

TABLE 1.—*Abundances of the elements in the primeval gas cloud from which earth and the meteorites formed*

[The number of atoms of each element per million atoms of silicon is given in the table]

Atomic No.	Element	Atoms	Atomic No.	Element	Atoms
1	Hydrogen	30 billion.	44	Ruthenium	1.49.
2	Helium	4 billion.	45	Rhodium	0.214.
3	Lithium	100.	46	Palladium	0.675.
4	Beryllium	20.	47	Silver	0.26.
5	Boron	24.	48	Cadmium	0.89.
6	Carbon	10 million.	49	Indium	0.11.
7	Nitrogen	3 million.	50	Tin	1.33.
8	Oxygen	30 million.	51	Antimony	0.246.
9	Fluorine	1,600.	52	Tellurium	4.67.
10	Neon	8.6 million.	53	Iodine	0.80.
11	Sodium	43,800.	54	Xenon	4.0.
12	Magnesium	912,000.	55	Cesium	0.456.
13	Aluminum	94,800.	56	Barium	3.66.
14	Silicon	1 million.	57	Lanthanum	2.00.
15	Phosphorous	10,000.	58	Cerium	2.26.
16	Sulphur	375,000.	59	Praseodymium	0.40.
17	Chlorine	8,850.	60	Neodymium	1.44.
18	Argon	150,000.	61	Promethium	0.
19	Potassium	3,160.	62	Samarium	0.664.
20	Calcium	49,000.	63	Europium	0.19.
21	Scandium	28	64	Gadolinium	0.684.
22	Titanium	2,440.	65	Terbium	0.096.
23	Vanadium	220.	66	Dysprosium	0.556.
24	Chromium	7,800.	67	Holmium	0.118.
25	Manganese	6,850.	68	Erbium	0.316.
26	Iron	600,000.	69	Thulium	0.032.
27	Cobalt	1,800.	70	Ytterbium	0.220.
28	Nickel	27,400.	71	Lutetium	0.050.
29	Copper	212.	72	Hafnium	0.438.
30	Zinc	486.	73	Tantalum	0.065.
31	Gallium	11.4.	74	Tungsten	0.49.
32	Germanium	50.5.	75	Rhenium	0.135.
33	Arsenic	4.	76	Osmium	1.00.
34	Selenium	67.6.	77	Iridium	0.821.
35	Bromine	13.4.	78	Platinum	1.625.
36	Krypton	51.3.	79	Gold	0.145.
37	Rubidium	6.5.	80	Mercury	0.017.
38	Strontium	18.9.	81	Thallium	0.1.
39	Yttrium	8.9.	82	Lead	0.5.
40	Zirconium	54.5.	83	Bismuth	0.1.
41	Niobium	1.0.	90	Thorium	0.02.
42	Molybdenum	2.42.	92	Uranium	0.006.
43	Technetium	0.			

present today like smoldering sparks that survived from the time of the original nuclear fire.

For many years scientists have tried to explain the mechanism of the nuclear reactions that led to the formation of nuclear species and their abundance distribution. Our detailed knowledge of nuclear abundances serves now as a firm basis for such considerations. Many theories have been advanced, none of which could account for all the empirical facts, even in a crude way. All the past theories had in common the assumption that the matter surrounding us was created by one and the same nuclear process. The existence of radioactive nuclei and their abundance lead to the conclusion that this process must have taken place some 5 to 7 billion years ago.

The earlier theories of the origin of the elements can be divided into two groups: equilibrium theories and nonequilibrium theories. In the equilibrium theories it is assumed that the existing abundance distribution corresponds approximately to the equilibrium concentrations of the nuclear species at a certain temperature and pressure at which they were "frozen in." This assumption requires a correlation of abundances with the total binding energies of the nuclei. Such correlation seems indeed to exist, but only within certain relatively narrow ranges of mass numbers. The thermodynamic parameters, however, cannot be adjusted in such a way that the over-all abundance distribution would correspond to that of a thermodynamic equilibrium. It was therefore assumed that equilibrium considerations cannot be regarded as a useful way of obtaining reasonable approximations.

In the nonequilibrium theories it is hopefully assumed that a relatively simple type of kinetic process has led to the empirical abundance distribution. Two such theories have been attracting wide interest: the neutron buildup theory, proposed in 1948 by George Gamow, and the polyneutron fission theory by Mayer and Teller. According to the neutron buildup theory the heavier nuclei were formed by the addition of neutrons to very light nuclei and by subsequent beta decay into stable nuclear species.

Many features, in particular the smoothness of the abundance lines (Illus. 76) at higher mass numbers, show conclusively that such processes have indeed taken place. However, this theory cannot explain the abundance of the lighter elements, the excessive abundance of iron, and the existence of the light isotopes of many heavier elements. Similarly, the polyneutron fission theory predicts certain features in the abundance distribution but fails to approximate the over-all trend of the abundance data as a function of mass number. The theory leads to abundances of the heavy elements which are many thousand times too high.

These and many other attempts have finally convinced scientists that it is impossible to explain the abundances of the elements and their isotopes as a product of one particular type of nuclear reaction. A group of scientists at the California Institute of Technology* has found a surprisingly simple way out of this dilemma by considering solar and planetary matter as a mixture of the product of different types of nuclear reactions, in particular such reactions as can plausibly be assumed to occur in the interior of stars.

Occasionally astronomers observe the sudden appearance of a bright new star, a so-called nova. The brightest of them, the supernovae, occur in our galaxies about once every 500 years. The supernovae, however, are bright enough to be observable in distant galaxies almost every year. The energy produced in a supernova outburst is equivalent to that of a hydrogen bomb of a size several times that of the sun. The debris of the stellar explosion is thrown out into space.

One interesting observation points to a true similarity between man-made hydrogen bombs and supernova explosions. The astronomer Baade observed that the light intensity of some supernovae decreases in a regular way within 56 days to just one-half of its value. The debris from explosions of hydrogen bombs was found to contain the heavy isotope californium 254. This isotope has a natural fission half-life of just 56 days. The possibility has been widely discussed recently that the light emitted by the gas cloud resulting from the explosion of a supernova is essentially supplied by energy from the breakup of californium 254 nuclei.

If this hypothesis is true, then occurrence of such a transuranium element as californium in supernovae proves that neutron buildup of heavy elements takes place during the explosion, necessarily leading to the formation of all nuclear species predicted by the neutron buildup theory.

* Burbridge, E. M., Burbridge, G. R., Fowler, W. A., and Hoyle, F., *Rev. Mod. Phys.*, vol. 29, p. 547, 1957. See also Cameron, A. G. W., *Astrophys. Journ.*, vol. 130, pp. 429, 452, 1959.

There is a variety of other possibilities that can lead to the explosion of a star. Helium, continuously produced from hydrogen in most stars, can react at the high pressures of a stellar interior to form carbon 12, oxygen 16, and heavier elements. When the buildup of nuclei reaches iron, the star can become unstable and expel a large fraction of its mass into outer space. The debris of such stars will contain large amounts of iron. Other types of stellar explosions will result in the formation of the light elements preferentially. Certain types of stars have been observed to eject matter continuously. Various mechanisms of nuclear synthesis proposed in earlier theories may be realized in the interior of different types of stars. In this way it becomes understandable that these theories were capable of predicting the relative abundances of nucleids of a certain type and of a certain mass range, but always failed to account for all the empirical facts.

The question of whether one can accept the hypothesis that the elements have formed in stars depends largely on quantitative considerations of the absolute amounts that can be produced in such a way during a reasonable time interval, and the amount necessary to explain the observed composition of the stars of our galaxies. One can estimate that at present only about one-half of the mass of our galaxies is concentrated in stars. The other half is present in the form of interstellar gas and dust.

It can be assumed that about 7 billion years ago our galaxies had the form of a huge gas mass of pure hydrogen. Out of this gas mass, large hydrogen stars condensed. In their interior hydrogen was converted into helium and into heavier elements. The rate of such processes in large stars is greater than in small ones, so that the large stars become unstable relatively quickly. The matter they ejected contained heavier elements. New generations of stars accumulated continuously from interstellar matter. They contained increasing amounts of heavier elements. Our sun, the solar system, and the earth were formed about 4.5 billion years ago. New astronomical evidence indicates that stars younger than our sun contain a larger percentage of heavier elements.

To many scientists this picture seems now acceptable. Many details are still unknown or questionable and will have to be evaluated in close collaboration between astronomers, nuclear physicists, and geochemists. In this connection the abundances of the elements lithium, beryllium, and boron may become particularly interesting, because these elements can form only under very special conditions. They are easily destroyed at high stellar temperatures.

Our picture of the origin of the elements cannot be correlated in its present stage with the fundamental question whether the universe as a whole is eternal or has been created at a defined time. The present attempts by F. Hoyle and others to recognize nuclear genesis as part of a consistent cosmological model are not quite convincing. We can expect fascinating developments of our knowledge in these fields of science.